SOCIAL STATISTICS

Hubert M. Blalock, Jr.

Associate Professor of Sociology
Yale University

McGRAW-HILL BOOK COMPANY, INC.

New York   Toronto   London   1960

SOCIAL STATISTICS

VI

05750

THE MAPLE PRESS COMPANY, YORK, PA.

To

ANN, SUSIE,
AND KATIE

PREFACE

This text is written primarily for those students of sociology, both advanced undergraduates and graduate students, who actually intend to engage in social research. Since the vast majority of students in the social sciences lack a background in college mathematics, this text has been written so as to avoid mathematical derivations in so far as possible. A quick review of certain algebraic principles listed in Appendix 1 should therefore be sufficient preparation for the average student. But although it is not necessary in a first course in statistics to stress mathematical derivations, the author is convinced that certain basic and fundamental ideas underlying the principles of statistical inference must be thoroughly understood if one is to obtain more than a mere "cookbook" knowledge of statistics. For this reason, you will find a relatively heavy emphasis on the underlying logic of statistical inference, including a chapter on probability, with relatively less attention being given to some of the more or less routine topics ordinarily discussed in elementary texts.

One of the most difficult problems encountered in the teaching of applied statistics is that of motivating students, both in enabling them to overcome their fears of mathematics and in learning to apply statistics to their own field of interest. It is for the latter reason that the author has not attempted to cover a wide range of applications but has selected examples of primary interest to sociologists. To some extent, examples have also been chosen from disciplines which border on sociology: fields such as social psychology, social work, and political behavior. In most instances each new topic has been illustrated by a single example, under the assumption that most students will lose track of the basic line of thought if too many examples are used to illustrate the same point. Additional examples are therefore given in the form of exercises at the end of each chapter. In general, the author has tried to strike a reasonable compromise between the desirability of stating basic principles as clearly and concisely as possible and the necessity of repeating some of the more difficult ideas each time a new topic is discussed. In so far as possible, new ideas have been introduced gradually and, equally important, an effort has been made to relate each new topic to those which have preceded it. In so doing, the major goal has been to give an appreciation of the basic similarities underlying many of the most commonly used tests and measures.

Since this text is not primarily intended for the average undergraduate who does not actually expect to use statistics in his own research, the author has not covered descriptive statistics in exhaustive detail but has placed a much greater emphasis on inductive statistics. It is also assumed that most students using this text will already have been exposed to at least one course in research methods. Therefore, no attempt has been made to discuss such topics as the construction of interview schedules, reliability and validity, experimental design, coding and tabulating, or various types of scaling techniques or index construction. Most of these topics are far too complex to be discussed at all adequately in a general text on statistics. Nor is the present text intended as a general reference work treating all of the statistical techniques currently in use in the social sciences. Instead, an effort has been made to cover certain of the most important and basic statistical techniques with sufficient thoroughness that, once these have been understood, the student will be able to consult more specialized sources with some degree of confidence and understanding.

The book is divided into three parts. Part I is intended as an introduction which will enable the student to place statistics in a larger perspective and which may serve to point out a few of the major problems encountered in relating theory, measurement, and statistics. Some of the descriptive measures and computing routines which will be needed in later work are taken up in Part II. The normal curve is also discussed in this section. Part III deals with some of the basic concepts of inductive statistics: the nature of statistical inference, probability, significance tests, confidence intervals, types I and II errors, and power functions. The problem of controlling for relevant variables is discussed first in Chap. 15 and again in Chaps. 16, 19, and 20. The importance of measures of association, as contrasted with significance tests, is stressed in Chap. 15 as well as later chapters, and attention is given to the basic problem of making causal inferences from correlational data (Chap. 19). A number of nonparametric procedures are treated in Chap. 14 and subsequent chapters, and in Chaps. 19 to 21 are discussed various multivariate techniques. A major emphasis running throughout the text is upon the limitations and possible misuses of statistics as well as its various applications.

Included in the text are a number of sections, paragraphs, and exercises which are either conceptually difficult or which presuppose that the student is reasonably familiar with topics ordinarily covered in courses on research methods. These portions of the text have been marked with an asterisk (*) and may be skimmed on first reading or omitted entirely. Instructors using the text for a one-semester course may wish to indicate that students should omit these materials.

A number of persons have contributed, either directly or indirectly, to the writing of this text. I would especially like to thank those students and colleagues at the University of Michigan who have read and suggested improvements in various earlier drafts of the book. To Richard T. LaPiere, Sanford Dornbusch, Robert Ellis, Santo Camilleri, and Theodore Anderson my appreciation for reading and criticizing the entire manuscript. For proofing, typing, and checking computations I would like to thank Ann Blalock, Diane Etzel, Ann Laux, and Doris Slesinger. My thanks also to Daniel O. Price who deserves the major credit for stimulating my interest in statistics.

I am indebted to Professor Sir Ronald A. Fisher, Cambridge, to Dr. Frank Yates, Rothamsted, and to Messrs. Oliver and Boyd Ltd., Edinburgh, for permission to reprint Tables No. III, IV, and V from their book *Statistical Tables for Biological, Agricultural and Medical Research*. I am equally grateful to those other publishers and authors, acknowledged in the appropriate places, who have kindly given their permission to make use of various tables and computing forms.

Hubert M. Blalock, Jr.

CONTENTS

Part I

INTRODUCTION

Chapter 1

INTRODUCTION: PURPOSES AND LIMITATIONS OF STATISTICS

The field of statistics has widespread applications as indicated by the fact that statistics courses are offered in such dissimilar subjects as dentistry and sociology, business administration and zoology, and public health and education. In spite of this fact, there are many misconceptions concerning the nature of this rapidly developing discipline. The layman's conception of statistics is apt to be very different from that of the professional statistician. A statistician is sometimes thought of as a person who manipulates numbers in order to prove his point. On the other hand, some students of sociology or other social sciences have tended to worship the statistician as someone who, with the aid of his magical computing machine, can make almost any study "scientific." Possibly because of the awe many persons have for anything with a hint of mathematics, students often find it difficult to approach a course in statistics with other than mixed feelings. Although they may be terrified at the prospect of working with numbers, they may also come to expect too much of a discipline which appears so formidable. Before jumping into the subject too quickly and thereby losing perspective, let us first ask ourselves just what statistics is and what it can and cannot do.

It is perhaps easiest to begin by stating what statistics is not. Statistics first of all is not a method by which one can prove almost anything he wants to prove. In fact, we shall find statisticians very carefully laying down rules of the game to ensure that interpretations do not go beyond the limits of the data. There is nothing inherent in statistical methods to prevent the careless or intellectually dishonest individual from drawing his own conclusions in spite of the data, however, and one of the most important functions of an introductory course in statistics is to place the student on guard against possible misuses of this tool.

Statistics is not simply a collection of facts. If it were, there would hardly be much point in studying the subject. Nor is statistics a substitute for abstract theoretical thinking or for careful examination of exceptional cases. In some of the older textbooks on research methods one used to find lengthy discussions on the relative merits of the case study method versus the statistical method. It is now clearly recognized that statistical methods are in no sense "opposed" to the qualitative analysis of case studies but that the two approaches are complementary. It is not even true that statistics is applicable only when there are a large number of cases or that it cannot be used in exploratory studies. Finally, statistics is not a substitute for measurement or the careful construction of an interview schedule or other instrument of data collection. This last point will receive further attention toward the end of this chapter and in Chap. 2.

Having indicated what statistics is not, can we say definitely what it is? Unfortunately, persons who call themselves statisticians seem to disagree somewhat as to exactly what is covered under the general heading of statistics. Taking a pragmatic approach to the problem, we shall say that statistics has two very broad functions and that anything not fulfilling these functions is not part of statistics. The first of these functions is description, the summarizing of information in such a manner as to make it more usable. The second function is induction, or the making of generalizations about some population on the basis of a sample drawn from this population. Each of these functions will be discussed in turn.

1.1. Functions of Statistics

Descriptive Statistics. Quite frequently in social research a person will find himself in the position of having so much data that he cannot adequately absorb all of his information. He may have collected 200 questionnaires and be in the embarrassing position of having to ask, "What do I do with it all?" With so much information it would be exceedingly difficult for any but the most photographic minds to grasp intuitively what is in the data. The information must somehow or other be boiled down to a point at which the researcher can see what is in it; it must be summarized. By computing measures such as percentages, means, standard deviations, and correlation coefficients it may be possible to reduce the data to manageable proportions. In summarizing data by substituting a very few measures for many numbers, certain information is inevitably lost, and, more serious, it is very possible to obtain results which are misleading unless cautiously interpreted. Therefore, the limitations of each summarizing measure must be clearly indicated.

Inductive Statistics. Statistics would be a fairly simple subject if attention were confined to descriptive measures. Perhaps a far more important function of statistics, and certainly the one which will occupy most of our attention in this text, is that of induction or inferring properties of a population on the basis of known sample results.   Statistical inference, as the process is called, involves much more complex reasoning than does descriptive statistics, but when properly used and understood becomes a very important tool in the development of a scientific discipline.   Inductive statistics is based directly on probability theory, a branch of mathematics.   We thus have a purely deductive discipline providing a rational basis for inductive reasoning.   To the writer's knowledge there is no other rational basis for induction.   This general point will be discussed in more detail in Chap. 8.

There are several practical reasons why it is often necessary to attempt to generalize on the basis of limited information.   The most obvious is the time-cost factor.   It would be wholly impractical, if not prohibitively costly, to ask every voter how he intended to vote in order to predict a national election.   Nor can the ordinary researcher afford to tap every resident of a large city in order to study prejudice, social mobility, or any other phenomenon.   He first decides upon the exact nature of the group about which he wishes to generalize (the population).   For example, he may select all citizens of voting age or all white males over eighteen residing within the city limits of Detroit.   He then usually draws a sample consisting of a relatively small proportion of these people, being primarily interested, however, not in this particular sample but in the larger population from which the sample was drawn.   For example, he may find that within his particular sample of 200 white males there is a negative relationship between education and prejudice.   Recognizing that had another set of 200 individuals been sampled the results might have been quite different, he would nevertheless like to make certain inferences as to the nature of the relationship had the entire population of adult white males in Detroit been studied.

Another reason for generalizing on the basis of limited information is that it may be impossible to make use of the entire population simply because the population is infinite or not easily defined.   In replicating an experiment in the natural or social sciences the goal always seems to be some kind of generalization which it is hoped will apply "under similar circumstances."   Or a social scientist may have collected data on all of the cases available to him.   For example, he may have used all 50 states as his units of analysis in studying internal migration.   Nevertheless, he may want to generalize about migration under "similar" conditions.   In each of these instances the situation calls for inductive statistics.

At this point you may ask a question of the following sort: "If statistics is so important, why is it that sciences such as physics and chemistry have been able to get along so well without the extensive use of statistical techniques? Is there anything different about these sciences?" Quite obviously there is. Some of the natural sciences have developed for centuries without the use of inductive statistics. But this seems to be primarily a matter of good fortune or, to give these scientists credit for their own efforts, a relatively satisfactory control over disturbing elements in the environment. As will become apparent in later chapters, to the degree that carefully controlled laboratory conditions prevail there is less practical need for statistical techniques. In this sense statistics is a poor man's substitute for contrived laboratory experiments in which all important relevant variables have been controlled. It should be emphasized, however, that many of the same statistical principles apply to laboratory experiments in physics, to somewhat less precise agricultural experiments, and to social surveys. For example, if an experiment in physics has been replicated 37 times with similar results, it is nevertheless conceivable that subsequent trials will yield different outcomes. The scientist must therefore generalize on the basis of a limited number of experiments, and the inferences he makes are essentially statistical in nature. Also, the problem of measurement error can be conceived in statistical terms. No matter how precise the measuring instrument, the scientist never obtains exactly the same results with each replication. He may attribute these differences either to measurement error or to disturbing effects of uncontrolled variables. Statistics becomes especially necessary whenever there is so much variation from one replication to the next that differences cannot be ignored or attributed to measurement error. Basically, then, statistical inference underlies all scientific generalizations, although the need for statistical training and the use of sophisticated statistical techniques vary considerably from one field to another.

1.2. The Place of Statistics in the Research Process

The importance of statistics in the research process is sometimes exaggerated by the emphasis given to it in graduate curricula. Statistics proper does not include measurement problems such as the construction of indices or the scoring of items on a questionnaire. Rather, statistics involves a manipulation of numbers under the assumption that certain requirements have been met in the measurement procedure. Actually, statistical considerations enter only into the analysis stage of the research process, after all data have been collected, and near the beginning when initial plans for analysis are made and when a sample is to be drawn.

While the above statement to the effect that statistics enters only into the analysis and sampling stages of the research process may be technically correct, it is very likely to be misleading unless qualified. It certainly does *not* mean that a social scientist can plan and carry out his entire research without any knowledge of statistics and then dump the whole project into the lap of a statistician saying, "Now I've done my job. You analyze it." If he did this the results would probably be disappointing if not completely useless. Quite obviously, problems that will be encountered in analysis have to be anticipated in every stage of the research process, and in this sense statistical considerations may be involved throughout. A highly sophisticated statistical analysis can rarely if ever compensate for a poorly conceived project or a poorly constructed data-collection instrument, however. This last point deserves special note. It means that statistics may be an aid to, but never a substitute for, good sound thinking. From the standpoint of the social scientist it is merely a tool.

1.3. A Word of Advice

Some students experience a degree of fear ranging from mild apprehension to an extreme mental block whenever they see a number or mathematical equation. If you happen to belong to this category, you should especially try to set aside any notion you may have to the effect that "statistics is something I know I'll never be able to understand." The level of mathematics required in this text is such that several years of high school algebra plus a quick review of a few elementary algebraic operations given in Appendix 1 should be ample preparation. It must be remembered, however, that mathematics and statistics texts cannot be expected to read like novels. Material is usually presented in a highly condensed form. Therefore careful rereading and an active rather than passive orientation to the material presented will be required. For this reason, there is no substitute for daily preparation and the working of practice problems found at the end of each chapter.

REFERENCES

1. Hagood, M. J., and D. O. Price: *Statistics for Sociologists*, Henry Holt and Company, Inc., New York, 1952, chaps. 1 and 2.
2. Tippett, L. H. C.: *Statistics*, Oxford University Press, New York, 1943.
3. Walker, H. M.: *Mathematics Essential for Elementary Statistics*, Henry Holt and Company, Inc., New York, 1951.
4. Wallis, W. A., and H. V. Roberts: *Statistics: A New Approach*, Free Press, Glencoe, Ill., 1956, chaps. 1–3.

Chapter 2

THEORY, MEASUREMENT, AND MATHEMATICS

The purpose of this chapter is to outline the relationships among theoretical propositions, empirical hypotheses, measurement, and mathematical models. Many of the problems dealt with in this chapter are not usually discussed in connection with courses in statistics, partly because of the regrettable tendency to compartmentalize courses under the headings of "theory," "research methods," and "statistics." This often means that the nature of the interrelations among these areas becomes obscured. In order to place statistics in its proper perspective it will be helpful to give at least some attention to the relationships between theoretical propositions and research hypotheses and also to those between research hypotheses and mathematical models.

One commonly hears statements to the effect that it is the purpose of research to test hypotheses developed theoretically and that statistical methods enable us to make such tests. It must be realized, however, that the processes involved in getting from theory to actual research hypotheses and from these hypotheses to probability statements of the kind used in statistical inference are by no means direct. In both cases certain decisions have to be made, decisions which may lead to considerable controversy. Let us first examine the nature of those decisions required in developing testable hypotheses from theoretical propositions.

*2.1. Theory and Hypotheses: Operational Definitions

The moment we begin to design a research project the aim of which is to test a proposition of the sort which may appear in a theoretical work, it becomes very evident that a number of things must be done before the

* An asterisk preceding a section, paragraph, or exercise indicates that the material involved either is conceptually difficult or deals with subjects which are likely to be unfamiliar to students with limited backgrounds in research methodology. These materials can safely be omitted or skimmed by the beginning student. An asterisk preceding a section heading indicates that the entire section may be omitted if desired.

test can be made. As a concrete example let us take the proposition "The higher a person's social status the lower his prejudice toward Negroes." Suppose "social status" has been defined as one's position relative to others in the status hierarchy and "prejudice" as an underlying tendency to discriminate against a minority or as a negative attitude based on prejudgment. Although you may prefer to substitute other definitions of these two concepts, you will undoubtedly discover that no matter what definitions you choose it will not be possible to use them directly to enable you to decide exactly what Jones's status or prejudice level may be.

The reason for this is that most ordinary definitions are theoretical rather than operational definitions. In a theoretical definition a concept is defined in terms of other concepts which supposedly are already understood. In the ideal model of the completely deductive system, certain concepts would be taken as undefined (primitive), and all other concepts would be defined in terms of these. In Euclidian geometry, for example, the concepts *point* and *line* may be taken as undefined. The notions of *angle, triangle,* or *rectangle* can then be defined in terms of these primitive concepts. Although the choice of undefined concepts is to a certain extent arbitrary, the fact that there must always be some primitive concepts is a reflection of the necessity of defining theoretical concepts in terms of each other.

Operational definitions, on the other hand, are definitions which actually spell out the procedures used in measurement ([6], pp. 58 to 65). An operational definition of "length" would indicate exactly how the length of a body is to be measured. An example of an operational definition of prejudice would include a test such as the Bogardus social-distance scale or, perhaps, a 24-item list of anti-Negro stereotypes, together with detailed instructions for collecting the data, scoring the items, and so forth. Warner's index of status characteristics (ISC) and the Chapin living room scale are examples of procedures used in developing operational definitions of social status. Since all measurement involves classification as a minimal requirement, an operational definition can be considered to be a detailed set of instructions enabling one to classify individuals unambiguously. The notion of reliability is thus built into this conception of the operational definition. The definition should be sufficiently precise that all persons using the procedure will achieve the same results. The theoretical definitions of prejudice and social status given above would not directly permit this to be done.

We are thus arguing that two different kinds of definitions are used in any science. Several alternative ways of viewing the relationship between theory and research lead to essentially the same conclusion. Northrop refers to what we have called theoretical definitions as "concepts by postulation" and to operational definitions as "concepts by intuition" [7]. We have used a terminology which seems to imply that there are two distinct ways of defining the "same" concept, whereas Northrop chooses to refer to two different kinds of concepts. Others prefer to think in terms of indices rather than operational definitions. The concept *index* usually implies that the procedure used gives only an imperfect indicator of some underlying variable which is not directly measurable. According to this perspective, then, there is both an underlying variable and an indicator of this variable. Regardless of the perspective one prefers, it is necessary to understand the nature of the linkage between the two kinds of definitions, concepts, or variables. We may ask whether or not there is any purely *logical* method of associating the two kinds of definitions. An alternative way of phrasing the question would be to ask if there is any logical way of determining whether a given operational definition (or index) "really" measures the theoretically defined concept or variable. The answer to both questions seems to be in the negative.

Northrop essentially argues that there is no method of associating the two kinds of concepts or definitions except by convention or common agreement. Persons simply agree that a given operational definition should be used as a measure of a certain concept if the operations seem reasonable on the basis of the theoretical definition. Presumably, if several operational definitions are possible, those operations will be selected which seem most appropriate and at the same time most reliable. "Appropriateness" must inevitably be judged on the basis of one's understanding of the theoretical definition. The term *face validity* is sometimes used to refer to the appropriateness of the index or operational definition ([9], p. 165). Ideally, as Bridgman points out, operations and theoretical definitions should be associated on a one-to-one basis ([2], pp. 23 ff.). In other words, if we change the operation we should use a new concept. Such an ideal is perhaps an unrealistic one for the social sciences in their present stage of development, however. Its application would undoubtedly lead either to a rigidity capable of stifling further methodological advances or to a proliferation of theoretical concepts [1].

What can be done then? We can admit the possibility of having a number of different operations or indices associated with each theoretical concept. But then we may run into a common difficulty: these procedures may yield different results. One procedure for measuring prejudice may lead to results which indicate that our "hypothesis" has been confirmed. In another case a different procedure may lead to the opposite conclusion. In a sense this is the way progress is made, provided it does not lead to endless bickering about which of the procedures is "really" measuring prejudice (the essence of which is presumed understood.) In order to avoid confusion it is important to realize that *the actual test is made in terms of the concepts as operationally defined. Propositions involving concepts defined theoretically are therefore not directly testable.* Thus, if there are two distinct operational definitions of prejudice there will be two distinct hypotheses being tested.

It has been admitted that it may be desirable to have more than one operation associated with any given theoretical concept, and it has been pointed out that such operations may lead to different results. We are now in a position to give a working, pragmatic criterion for an empirically satisfactory theoretical definition of a concept. Let us imagine that we have a concept defined theoretically and several operational definitions which might possibly be associated with this theoretical definition. On the basis of this latter definition, most scientists in the field will probably agree that certain of the operations should be eliminated as not tapping what is implied in the theoretical definition. For example, they may decide that items referring to delinquent tendencies or musical tastes should not be used to measure prejudice. But there may be several operations which have more or less equal status in the opinion of these judges. In other words, on the basis of the theoretical definition, experts may not be able to agree that one operational procedure should be selected in preference to the others. We may then say that *to the extent that these several procedures yield different results* (under similar circumstances), *the theoretical definition is unsatisfactory* in the sense that it is probably in need of revision or clarification. For example, the concept *prejudice* may have been defined in such a manner that it is too vague. Perhaps it will be found necessary to distinguish between several kinds or dimensions of prejudice and to associate different operations with each. In a manner such as this—whether it is explicitly recognized or not—the research process may be used to help clarify theoretical concepts.

There thus seem to be two distinct languages linked by a kind of dictionary, arrived at by consensus, which enables one to associate concepts in the one language with those in the other. Scientists think in the theoretical language and make tests in the operational language. It is not necessary to associate operations with all concepts in the theoretical language. It is important to realize, however, that concepts which have not been operationally defined should not ordinarily be permitted to appear in statements purporting to be testable hypotheses. If this occurs, the questions raised by the "hypotheses" will usually be operationally meaningless and may lead to endless debate.

2.2. Level of Measurement: Nominal, Ordinal, and Interval Scales

We have just seen that the process of going from theoretically defined concepts to operationally defined concepts is by no means direct. Certain decisions have to be made in associating one type of concept with the other.   Likewise, the process of selecting the appropriate mathematical or statistical model to be used with a given research technique or operational procedure also involves a number of important decisions.   It might be thought that once a phenomenon had been measured the choice of a mathematical system would be a routine one.   This all depends on what one means by the word *measure*.   If we use the term to refer only to those types of measurement ordinarily used in a science such as physics (e.g., the measurement of length, time, or mass), there is little or no problem in the choice of a mathematical system.   But if we broaden the concept of measurement to include certain less precise procedures ordinarily used in the social sciences, as will be done in this text, the whole problem becomes more complex.   We can then distinguish between several levels of measurement, and we shall find different statistical models appropriate to each.[1]

Nominal Scales.   The basic and most simple operation in any science is that of classification.   In classifying we attempt to sort elements with respect to a certain characteristic, making decisions about which elements are most similar and which most different.   Our aim is to sort them into categories which are as homogeneous as possible as compared with differences between categories.   If the classification is a useful one, the categories will also be found to be homogeneous with respect to *other* variables [8].   For example, we sort persons according to religion (Methodists, Presbyterians, Catholics, etc.) and then see if religion is related to prejudice or political conservatism.   We might find that Presbyterians tend to be more conservative than Catholics, the Presbyterians having uniformly high scores as compared with the Catholics. Had individuals been sorted as to hair color, a perfectly proper criterion for classification, probably no significant differences would have been found among hair-color classes with respect to other variables studied. In other words, differences *among* hair-color classes would have been slight as compared with differences *within* each category. Thus, classification is fundamental to any science.   All other levels of measurement, no matter how precise, basically involve classification as a minimal operation.

We therefore can consider classification to be the lowest level of measurement as the term is used in its broadest sense.   We arbitrarily give names to the categories as convenient tags, with no assumptions about relationships between categories.   For example, we place Presbyterians and Catholics in distinct categories, but we do not imply that one is "greater than" or "better than" the other.   As long as the categories are exhaustive (include all cases) and nonoverlapping or mutually

[1] For further discussions of these different levels of measurement see [4], [5], [10], and [11].

exclusive (no case in more than one category), we have the minimal conditions necessary for the application of statistical procedures. The term *nominal scale* has been used to refer to this simplest level of measurement.   Formally, nominal scales possess the properties of symmetry and transitivity.   By symmetry we mean that a relation holding between A and B also holds between B and A.   By transitivity we mean that if $A = B$ and $B = C$, then $A = C$.   Put together, this simply means that if A is in the same (different) class as B, B is in the same (different) class as A and that if A and B are in the same class and B and C in the same class, then A and C must be in the same class.

It should be pointed out that numbers may be arbitrarily associated with each category, but this fact in no way justifies the use of the usual arithmetic operations on these numbers.   The function of numbers in this case is exactly the same as that of names, i.e., the labeling of categories.   It would obviously make absolutely no sense to add social security numbers or room numbers in a hotel.   Although we would never be tempted to carry out such a ridiculous operation, there are other instances in social science research where the absurdity is by no means as obvious.   Thus although numerical values may arbitrarily be assigned to various categories, the use of certain of the more common mathematical operations (addition, subtraction, multiplication, and division) requires also that certain *methodological* operations be carried out in the classification procedure.   We shall have occasion shortly to see what the nature of these operations must be.

Ordinal Scales. It is frequently possible to order categories with respect to the degree to which they possess a certain characteristic, and yet we may not be able to say exactly how much they possess.   We thus imagine a single continuum along which individuals may be ordered. Perhaps we can rank individuals so precisely that no two are located at the same point on the continuum.   Usually, however, there will be a number of ties.   In such instances, we are unable to distinguish between certain of the individuals and we have lumped them together into a single category.   We are able to say, however, that these individuals all have higher scores than certain other individuals.   Thus we may classify families according to socioeconomic status: "upper," "upper-middle," "lower-middle," and "lower."   We might even have only two categories, "upper" and "lower."

The kind of measurement we are discussing is obviously at a somewhat higher level than that used in obtaining a nominal scale since we are able not only to group individuals into separate categories, but to order the categories as well.   We refer to this level of measurement as an "ordinal scale."   In addition to having the symmetrical properties of the nominal scale, an ordinal scale is asymmetrical in the sense that certain special relationships may hold between A and B which do *not* hold for B and A. For example, the relationship "greater than" ($>$) is asymmetric in that if $A > B$ it cannot be true that $B > A$. Transitivity still holds: if $A > B$ and $B > C$ then $A > C$. It is these properties, of course, which enable us to place A, B, C, . . . along a single continuum.

It is important to recognize that an ordinal level of measurement does not supply any information about the *magnitude* of the differences between elements. We know only that A is greater than B but cannot say how much greater. Nor can we say that the difference between A and B is less than that between C and D.[2] We therefore cannot add or subtract distances except in a very restricted sense. For example, if we had the following relationships

we can say that the distance

$$\overline{AD} = \overline{AB} + \overline{BC} + \overline{CD}$$

but we cannot attempt to compare the distances $\overline{AB}$ and $\overline{CD}$. In other words, when we translate order relations into mathematical operations, we cannot, in general, use the usual operations of addition, subtraction, multiplication, and division. We can, however, use the operations "greater than" and "less than" if these prove useful.

Interval and Ratio Scales. In the narrow sense of the word, the term *measurement* may be used to refer to instances in which we are able not only to rank objects with respect to the degree to which they possess a certain characteristic but also to indicate the exact distances between them. If this is possible we can obtain what is referred to as an *interval scale*. It should be readily apparent that an interval-scale level of measurement requires the establishment of some sort of a physical unit of measurement which can be agreed upon as a common standard and which is replicable, i.e., can be applied over and over again with the same results. Length is measured in terms of feet or meters, time in seconds, temperature in degrees Fahrenheit or centigrade, weight in pounds or grams, and income in dollars. On the other hand, there are no such units of intelligence, authoritarianism, or prestige which can be agreed upon by all social scientists and which can be assumed to be constant from one situation to the next. Given a unit of measurement, it is possible to say that the difference between two scores is twenty units or that one difference is twice as large as a second. This means that it is possible to add or subtract scores in an analogous manner to the way we can add weights

---

[2] The term *ordered-metric* has been used to refer to scales in which it is possible to rank the size of *differences* between elements. See [5].

on a balance or subtract 6 inches from a board by sawing it in two ([3], pages 296 to 298). Similarly, we can add the incomes of husband and wife whereas it makes no sense to add their IQ scores.

If it is also possible to locate an absolute or nonarbitrary zero point on the scale, we have a somewhat higher level of measurement referred to as a *ratio scale*. In this case we are able to compare scores by taking their ratios. For example, we can say that one score is twice as high as another. Had the zero point been arbitrary, such as in the case of the centigrade or Fahrenheit scales, this would not have been legitimate. Thus we do not say that 70°F is twice as hot as 35°F although we can say that the *difference* between these temperatures is the same as that between 105°F and 70°F. In practically all instances known to the writer this distinction between interval and ratio scales is purely academic, however, as it is extremely difficult to find a legitimate interval scale which is not also a ratio scale. This is due to the fact that if the size of the unit is established it is practically always possible to conceive of zero units, even though we may never be able to find a body with no length or mass or to obtain a temperature of absolute zero. Thus in practically all instances where a unit is available it will be legitimate to use all of the ordinary operations of arithmetic, including square roots, powers, and logarithms.

*Certain important questions arise concerning the legitimacy of using interval scales in the case of a number of sociological and social psychological variables. Unfortunately, it will be impossible to discuss these questions in detail in a general text such as this although some can be mentioned briefly. It is sometimes argued that a variable such as income, if measured in dollars, is not really an interval scale since a difference of $1,000 will have different psychological meanings depending on whether the difference is between incomes of $2,000 and $3,000 or between incomes of $30,000 and $31,000. This argument, it seems, confuses the issue. What is actually being said here is that income as measured in dollars and "psychological income" (assuming this could be measured in terms of some unit) are not related in a straight-line or linear fashion. This is a question of fact which is irrelevant to the question of whether or not there is a legitimate unit of measurement.

*Another question can be raised as to whether or not it is possible to attain an interval scale in the area of attitude measurement. Several attempts have been made to approximate this goal. In the Thurstone method of equal-appearing intervals, judges are asked to sort items into a number of piles which are equally far apart along the attitude continuum ([9], pages 359 to 365). It is reasoned essentially that if there is a high degree of consensus among the judges an interval scale can legitimately be used. This process, it is argued, is similar in essence to that used in other disciplines to obtain interval scales. The argument seems to be a legitimate one provided there actually is a high degree of consensus among judges and provided judges are given a large number of piles into which they can sort the items. For example, if they were forced to place items into one of three or four piles we would expect a high degree of consensus simply due to the crudity of the measuring instrument. There would be such a wide range of variability within each pile that one could hardly claim that the items in the various piles were equal distances apart. Even assuming perfect agreement and maximal freedom in sorting the items into piles, Thurstone's method still presents difficulties in conceptualizing the unit concerned. It becomes necessary to postulate that it is the existence of such a unit which makes agreement among judges possible. It seems safe to say that at this point in the development of attitude measurement most techniques yield very poor approximations to interval scales. Many probably should not even be considered to give legitimate ordinal scales. The implications of this for statistical analysis will become apparent as we proceed.

2.3. Measurement and Statistics

We have seen that there are several distinct levels of measurement, each with its own properties. It should be noted that these various levels of measurement themselves form a cumulative scale. An ordinal scale possesses all the properties of a nominal scale plus ordinality. An interval scale has all the qualities of both nominal and ordinal scales plus a unit of measurement, and a ratio scale represents the highest level since it has not only a unit of measurement but an absolute zero as well. The cumulative nature of these scales means that it is always legitimate to drop back one or more levels of measurement in analyzing our data. If we have an interval scale we also have an ordinal scale and can make use of this fact in our statistical analysis. Sometimes this will be necessary when statistical techniques are either unavailable or otherwise unsatisfactory in handling the variable as an interval scale. We lose information in doing so, however. Thus if we know that Jones has an income of $11,000 and Smith an income of $6,000 and if we make use only of the fact that Jones has the higher of the two incomes, we in effect throw away the information that the difference in incomes is $5,000. Therefore in general we shall find it to our advantage to make use of the highest level of measurement that can legitimately be assumed.

What can be said of the reverse process of going up the scale of measurement from, say, an ordinal to an interval scale? We are often tempted to do so since we would then be able to make use of more powerful statistical techniques. It is even quite possible that we may do so without being at all aware of exactly what has occurred. It is important to realize that there is nothing in the statistical or mathematical procedures we ultimately use which will enable us to check upon the legitimacy of our research methods. *The use of a particular mathematical model presupposes that a certain level of measurement has been attained.* The responsibility rests squarely on the shoulders of the researcher to determine whether or not his operational procedures permit the use of certain mathematical operations. He must first make a decision as to the appropriate level of measurement, and this in turn will determine the appropriate mathematical system. In other words, a particular mathematical model can be associated with a certain level of measurement according to the considerations discussed in the previous section. The common arithmetic operations, for example, can ordinarily be used only with interval and ratio scales.

*Again, we are faced with a problem of translating from the one language to the other. The operational language involves certain physical operations such as the use of a unit of measurement. The mathematical language involves a completely abstract set of symbols and mathematical operations and is useful not only because it is precise and highly developed, but also because its abstract nature permits its application to a variety of empirical problems. Mathematics makes use of deductive reasoning in which one goes from a set of definitions, assumptions, and rules of operation to a set of conclusions by means of purely logical reasoning. Mathematics per se tells us nothing new about reality since all of the conclusions are built into the original definitions, assumptions, and rules and are not determined empirically. These mathematical conclusions then have to be translated back into the operational and theoretical languages if they are to be useful to the scientist [4].

We are arguing, then, that it is not legitimate to make use of a mathematical system involving the operations of addition or subtraction when this is not warranted by the method of measurement. Although the meaning of this fact will not become fully apparent until we actually begin using the various scales of measurement, we are in effect saying that we cannot legitimately travel up the measurement hierarchy unless the measurement process itself has been improved. No mathematical manipulations can make this possible. How do we decide what level of measurement is legitimate, then? Unfortunately the problem is not quite so simple as might be assumed. A few brief examples should be sufficient to warn you of the complexity of the problem.

*To illustrate one such problem, it is necessary to distinguish ordinal and interval scales from the *partially ordered scale* resulting from the combination of two or more ordinal (or interval) scales into a single index. It is frequently the case in sociology and other social sciences that what first appears to be a simple ordinal (interval) scale is in reality a combination of several ordinal (interval) scales, the result being that one cannot obtain an unambiguous ranking of individuals unless he is willing to make some further decisions. Let us take the example of socioeconomic status. Usually, we determine a person's status by examining a number of distinct criteria such as income, occupation, education, family background, or area of residence. If A has a higher rank than B on each of these criteria, then clearly A can be rated higher as to general status. But what if A has the higher income but B the more prominent family name? Which has the higher general status? We have several alternatives. The first is to drop the notion of general status and to think in terms of separate dimensions of status, each of which may admit of an ordinal level of measurement. We then end up with not one but a number of ordinal scales, and it becomes an empirical question as to how highly intercorrelated the different dimensions may be. Of course if there is a perfect relationship among all dimensions, the question becomes an academic one since A will be higher than B on all dimensions if he is higher on any one dimension. In practice, of course, this never happens.

*Our second alternative is to try to "force" an ordinal scale on the data by making some decisions about the relative weightings of each dimension and the equivalences involved. For example, if we can assume that a year's extra education is equivalent to \$1,338.49 in extra income, we can then translate educational units into income units and arrive at a unidimensional scale. Obviously, the problem of translating family background or area of residence into income is even more complicated. The method of measurement we are discussing here involves a type of index construction. Suffice it to say that such index construction usually involves arbitrary decisions about relative weighting. If the weighting system can be justified, an ordinal scale can be used; if it cannot, then one is in real doubt about whether or not individuals can legitimately be rank-ordered.

*One commonly used method of obtaining an ordinal scale is to make use of one or more judges to rank-order individuals according to some criterion such as power or prestige. Let us assume for simplicity that there is only one judge and that he has been forced to rank-order individuals according to their "social standing" in the community. Assuming the person cooperates, the method used assures us of obtaining an ordinal scale *regardless* of how individuals actually compare in the eyes of the judge. It is quite possible that had some other method been used, an ordinal scale would not have been obtained. Had a paired-comparisons technique been used in which judgments were made between every pair combination, the judge might have rated Smith higher than Brown, Brown over Jones, but Jones over Smith, thus violating the transitivity property of ordinal scales. The researcher is now faced with a choice.

He can reach the conclusion that there is a partially ordered scale of some kind.   Or he may consider the judge to be inconsistent or "in error." As Coombs points out, this problem of what to call measurement error is a basic dilemma faced by the social scientist ([5], pages 485 to 488).   Generally speaking, he may assume a high level of measurement and conceive of deviations of the above sort as measurement errors or he may drop down to a lower level of measurement.

*The same dilemma may be illustrated in the case of Guttman scaling. In the perfect Guttman scale, items have a cumulative property which justifies the assumption of an ordinal scale [12].   Items may be arranged from least to most extreme so that the exact response pattern of an individual can be reproduced from his total score.   For example, if there are five arithmetic problems ranging from least to most difficult, a person who solves the most difficult problem correctly will also be able to solve the others.   If he gets three correct, he will solve the three easiest ones and miss the last two.   In a perfect social-distance scale, prejudice items may be arranged according to the degree of intimacy of contact with the minority.   A white person willing to marry a Negro will obviously be willing to live on the same street with one; if he will accept him as a neighbor, he will be willing to ride on a bus next to one.   Thus we can say in the case of the perfect Guttman scale that a person endorsing four items will have endorsed exactly the same items as a person with a score of three, *plus one more*.   If the scale were only partially ordered, it would be possible to say that A is in some respects more prejudiced than B but in other respects less so since the two individuals have endorsed different sets of items.

*Seldom if ever do we attain a perfect Guttman scale in practice, however.   There are always certain persons whose response patterns deviate from the ideal.   The question then arises as to whether or not to call these persons in error.   Are they actually inconsistent because they may accept a Negro as a neighbor but refuse to ride on a bus next to him?   Perhaps.   But then again, perhaps not.   Unless the researcher is willing to *assume* that he has a legitimate ordinal scale he cannot claim the individual to be in error.   If the number of "errors" is quite large we begin to suspect our scale.   On the other hand, we are usually willing to tolerate a relatively small number of errors.   It is this principle which is behind the decision to accept the Guttman scale as an ordinal scale if the number of errors, as measured by the coefficient of reproducibility, is quite small.   One should be well aware of the fact that his decision is somewhat arbitrary, however, and that ultimately he will be faced with the problem of what to call error.

*These examples should be sufficient to indicate that it is often not a simple matter to decide what type of scale can legitimately be used. Ideally, one should make use of a data-gathering technique which permits the lowest levels of measurement, if these are all the data will yield, rather than using techniques which force a scale on the data. Thus, the method of paired comparisons will produce an ordinal scale only if the judge is in fact actually able to rank the individuals. On the other hand, if he is required to place them in a definite rank order, he will have to do so whether he believes this can be achieved legitimately or not. Having used this latter method of data collection and being unable to demonstrate empirically that individuals can be ordered without doing an injustice to data, one then has to *assume* a single continuum.

In order to emphasize that any given statistical technique presupposes a specific level of measurement, we shall develop the habit of always indicating the level of measurement required for each procedure. It used to be the practice to go ahead with statistical techniques requiring high levels of measurement, commonly interval scales, under the assumption that no major violence was being done to the data. The present practice tends in the other direction and for very good reasons. Mathematical statisticians have been well aware of the requirements of the various statistical models, but social scientists in their efforts to be "scientific" and to use the most powerful mathematical techniques available have often failed to recognize the assumptions required of their measurement techniques. One of the dangers of "cookbook" statistics is precisely this tendency to make use of statistical techniques that have been improperly understood. It is impossible to overemphasize the important point that *in using any statistical technique one must be aware of the underlying assumptions that must be made*. It is for this reason that one of the first questions one needs to ask of his data concerns the level of measurement he can legitimately assume.

At this point, our discussion of the different levels of measurement may not be too meaningful. A quick glance through the remainder of the text should be helpful in indicating that the distinction between nominal, ordinal, and interval scales will be extremely useful. After you have had occasion to become familiar with some of the various statistical procedures available, it will be helpful to reread this chapter. In fact, a number of periodic reviews will probably be necessary before the picture becomes really clear.

GLOSSARY

You should develop the habit of explaining in your own words the meanings of important concepts. New concepts introduced in this chapter are:

> Interval scale
> Nominal scale
> *Operational definition
> Ordinal scale
> Ratio scale

REFERENCES

1. Adler, F.: "Operational Definitions in Sociology," *American Journal of Sociology*, vol. 52, pp. 438–444, March, 1947.

2. Bridgman, P. W.: *The Logic of Modern Physics*, The Macmillan Company, New York, 1938, pp. 1–39.

3. Cohen, M. R., and E. Nagel: *An Introduction to Logic and Scientific Method*, Harcourt, Brace and Company, Inc., New York, 1934, chaps. 12 and 15.

4. Coombs, C. H., H. Raiffa, and R. M. Thrall: "Some Views on Mathematical Models and Measurement Theory," *Psychological Review*, vol. 61, pp. 132–144, March, 1954.

5. Coombs, C. H.: "Theory and Methods of Social Measurement," in L. Festinger and D. Katz (eds.), *Research Methods in the Behavioral Sciences*, The Dryden Press, Inc., New York, 1953, pp. 471–535.

6. Lundberg, G. A.: *Foundations of Sociology*, The Macmillan Company, New York, 1939, chaps. 1 and 2.

7. Northrop, F. S. C.: *The Logic of the Sciences and the Humanities*, The Macmillan Company, New York, 1947, chaps. 5–7.

8. Radcliffe-Brown, A. R.: *A Natural Science of Society*, Free Press, Glencoe, Ill., 1957, pp. 28–42.

9. Selltiz, C., M. Jahoda, M. Deutsch, and S. W. Cook: *Research Methods in Social Relations*, Henry Holt and Company, Inc., New York, 1959, chaps. 5 and 10.

10. Senders, V. L.: *Measurement and Statistics*, Oxford University Press, New York, 1958, chap. 2.

11. Stevens, S. S.: "Mathematics, Measurement, and Psychophysics," in S. S. Stevens (ed.), *Handbook of Experimental Psychology*, John Wiley & Sons, Inc., New York, 1951, pp. 1–49.

12. Stouffer, S. A., et al.: *Measurement and Prediction*, Princeton University Press, Princeton, N.J., 1950, chaps. 1 and 3.

Part II

DESCRIPTIVE STATISTICS

Chapter 3

NOMINAL SCALES: PROPORTIONS, PERCENTAGES, AND RATIOS

It is a much simpler matter to summarize data involving nominal scales than is the case when interval scales are used. The basic arithmetic operation is that of counting the number of cases within each category and then noting their relative sizes. A given group may consist of 36 males and 24 females, or 25 Protestants, 20 Catholics, and 15 Jews. In order to make comparisons with other groups, however, it is necessary to take the number of cases in the two groups into consideration. The measures to be discussed in the present chapter permit comparisons among several groups by essentially standardizing for size. At least two of these measures, proportions and percentages, are undoubtedly already familiar.

3.1. Proportions

In order to make use of proportions we must assume that the method of classification has been such that categories are mutually exclusive and exhaustive. In other words, any given individual has been placed in one and only one category. For sake of simplicity, let us take a nominal scale consisting of four categories with N_1, N_2, N_3, and N_4 cases respectively. Let the total number of cases be N. The proportion of cases in any given category is defined as the number in the category divided by the total number of cases. Therefore the proportion of individuals in the first category is given by the quantity N_1/N, and the proportions in the remaining categories are N_2/N, N_3/N, and N_4/N respectively. Obviously, the value of a proportion cannot be greater than unity. Since

$$N_1 + N_2 + N_3 + N_4 = N$$

we have

$$\frac{N_1}{N} + \frac{N_2}{N} + \frac{N_3}{N} + \frac{N_4}{N} = \frac{N}{N} = 1$$

Thus if we add the proportions of cases in all (mutually exclusive) categories, the result is unity.   This is an important property of proportions and can easily be generalized to any number of categories.

Let us illustrate the use of proportions with the data given in Table 3.1.

Table 3.1. Numbers of Delinquents and Nondelinquents in Two
Hypothetical Communities

Subjects	Community 1	Community 2
Delinquents		
First offenders	58	68
Repeaters	43	137
Nondelinquents	481	1081
Total	582	1286

It is rather difficult to tell which community has the larger relative number of delinquents because of their different sizes.   Expressing the data in terms of proportions enables us to make a direct comparison, however.   The proportion of first offenders in community 1 is $58/582$ or .100; the comparable figure for the second community is 68/1,286 or .053. Other proportions can be computed in a similar fashion and the results summarized in tabular form (Table 3.2).   From this table we see that the relative numbers of delinquents are quite similar for the two communities but that the second community contains a substantially lower proportion of first offenders and a higher proportion of repeaters.

Table 3.2. Proportions of Delinquents and Nondelinquents in Two
Hypothetical Communities

Subjects	Community 1	Community 2
Delinquents		
First offenders	.100	.053
Repeaters	.074	.107
Nondelinquents	.826	.841
Total	1.000	1.001

The sum of the proportions in community 2 is not exactly unity because of rounding errors.   Sometimes it is desirable to present the data in such a manner that the sums are exactly equal to 1.000.   This may require adjustment of some of the category proportions, and by convention we usually modify the figures for those categories having the largest proportions of cases.[1]   The argument in favor of this procedure is that a change in the last decimal place in a larger proportion is relatively less significant

[1] Exactly the same procedure can be used in the case of percentages.

than the same change in a smaller figure. Thus the proportion of non-delinquents in community 2 could be changed to .840 so that the resulting sum is unity.

Table 3.2 involves proportions of the total number of cases in each community. Suppose, however, that interest was mainly centered on the delinquents and we wanted to know the proportion of repeaters *among the delinquents*. The total number of delinquents in the two communities are 101 and 205 respectively. Therefore, among the delinquents the proportions of repeaters are $\frac{43}{101}$ or .426 and $\frac{137}{205}$ or .668. At first glance these figures may give a slightly different impression from the first set of proportions. We would especially want to be on guard against concluding that the second sample is "more delinquent" than the first. This last set of proportions, of course, tells us absolutely nothing about the relative numbers of nondelinquents in the two samples. Obviously there is no substitute for a careful reading of the tables. It is a good idea to develop the habit of always determining the categories which are being included in the total number of cases used in the denominator of the proportion. You should always ask, "*Of what* is this a proportion?" The answer should be clear from the context.

3.2. Percentages

Percentages can be obtained from proportions by simply multiplying by 100. The word *per cent* means *per hundred*. Therefore in using percentages we are standardizing for size by calculating the number of individuals that would be in a given category if the total number of cases were 100 and if the proportion in each category remained unchanged. Since proportions must add to unity it is obvious that percentages will sum to 100 unless the categories are not mutually exclusive or exhaustive.

Percentages are much more frequently used in reporting results than are proportions. The figures in Table 3.2 could just as well have been expressed in terms of percentages. Rather than make use of these same data let us take another table which can be used to illustrate several new points. Suppose there are three family service agencies having a distribution of cases as indicated in Table 3.3.

As is customary, percentages have been given to the nearest decimal and adjustments made in the last digits so that totals are exactly 100.0. Here there are a sufficient number of cases for each agency to justify the computation of percentages. It would have been misleading to give percentages had the number of cases been much smaller, however. Suppose agency C had handled only 25 cases in all. If there had been four unwed mothers and seven engaged couples, the percentages in these categories would have been 16 per cent and 28 per cent respectively.

Since many persons are accustomed to looking only at percentages and not at the actual number of cases involved, the impression that there were many more engaged couples than unwed mothers could easily be conveyed. As will be seen when we come to inductive statistics, a difference between four and seven cases could very possibly be due to the operation of chance factors. The use of percentages and proportions usually implies considerably more stability of numbers. For this reason two rules of thumb are important: (1) *always report the number of cases along with percentages or proportions,* and (2) *never compute a percentage*

Table 3.3. Numbers and Percentage Distributions of Cases Handled by Three Hypothetical Family Service Agencies

Type of case	Agency A		Agency B		Agency C		Total	
	No.	%	No.	%	No.	%	No.	%
Married couples	63	47.3	88	45.5	41	36.6	192	43.8
Divorced persons	19	14.3	37	19.2	26	23.2	82	18.7
Engaged couples	27	20.3	20	10.4	15	13.4	62	14.2
Unwed mothers	13	9.8	32	16.6	21	18.8	66	15.1
Other	11	8.3	16	8.3	9	8.0	36	8.2
Total	133	100.0	193	100.0	112	100.0	438	100.0

unless the number of cases on which the percentage is based is in the neighborhood of 50 or more. If the number of cases is very small it would be preferable to give the actual number in each category rather than percentages. For example, we would simply state that agency C handled four unwed mothers and seven engaged couples.

Now look at the total column which gives the breakdown of percentages for all three agencies. These figures were obtained by adding the number of cases of each type and also the total number of cases handled by the three agencies. An N of 438 was then used as a base in computing total percentages. Suppose, however, that the number of cases had not been given to us in the body of the table but had been presented as in Table 3.4. There might be some temptation to obtain the total percentages by taking a straightforward arithmetic mean of the three percentages in each row. Such a procedure would not take into consideration the fact that the agencies handled different numbers of cases; it would be justified only if the numbers of cases were in fact identical. The correct procedure would be to weight each percentage by the proper number of cases. One way to do this would be to work backwards to obtain the actual number of cases in each cell. This could be accomplished by multiplying the total number of cases handled by the agency by the *proportion* in a given category. For example, (133)(.473) = 63.

Notice that the percentages as given in Tables 3.3 and 3.4 are designed to answer certain questions but not others. They enable us to examine each agency separately and see the breakdown of cases handled. They also permit comparison of agencies with respect to type of cases handled. For example, agencies B and C handled relatively more unwed mothers

Table 3.4. Percentage Distributions of Cases Handled by Three Hypothetical Family Service Agencies, with Percentages Computed Down the Table

Type of case	Agency A (N = 133), %	Agency B (N = 193), %	Agency C (N = 112), %
Married couples	47.3	45.5	36.6
Divorced persons	14.3	19.2	23.2
Engaged couples	20.3	10.4	13.4
Unwed mothers	9.8	16.6	18.8
Other	8.3	8.3	8.0
Total	100.0	100.0	100.0

and divorced persons than did agency A. Suppose, however, that we had been primarily interested in cases of a given type and in the relative numbers handled by each agency. For example, we might wish to know the percentage of all married couples who went to agency B. It would be more helpful in this instance to compute percentages across the table. We could take the total number of married couples and determine what percentages of this category were handled by agencies A, B, and C respectively. Percentages would then add to 100 across the table, but not down, and the results would be summarized as in Table 3.5.

Table 3.5. Percentage Distributions of Cases Handled by Three Hypothetical Family Service Agencies, with Percentages Computed Across the Table

Type of case	Agency A (N = 133), %	Agency B (N = 193), %	Agency C (N = 112), %	Total (N = 438), %
Married couples (N = 192)	32.8	45.8	21.4	100.0
Divorced persons (N = 82)	23.2	45.1	31.7	100.0
Engaged couples (N = 62)	43.5	32.3	24.2	100.0
Unwed mothers (N = 66)	19.7	48.5	31.8	100.0
Other (N = 36)	—*	—*	—*	—*

* Percentages not computed where base is less than 50.

Percentages can thus be computed in either direction. A table should therefore always be examined carefully in order to determine exactly how the percentages have been computed.

3.3. Ratios

The ratio of one number A to another number B is defined as A divided by B. Here the key term is the word "to." Whatever quantity precedes this word is placed in the numerator while the quantity following it becomes the denominator. Suppose that there are 365 Republicans, 420 Democrats, and 130 Independents registered as voters in a local election. Then the ratio of Republicans *to* Democrats is $365/420$; the ratio of Republicans and Democrats *to* Independents is $(365 + 420)/130$. Notice that unlike a proportion, a ratio can take on a value greater than unity. We also see that the expression preceding or following the word "to" can consist of several separate quantities (e.g., Republicans and Democrats). Usually a ratio is reduced to its simplest form by canceling common factors in the numerator and denominator. Thus the ratio of Democrats to Independents would be written as $42/13$ or equivalently as $42:13$. Sometimes it is desirable to express a ratio in terms of a denominator of unity. For example, the ratio of Democrats to Independents might be written as 3.23 to 1.

Proportions obviously represent a special type of ratio in which the denominator is the total number of cases and the numerator a certain fraction of this number. Ordinarily the term *ratio* is used to refer to instances in which the A and B represent separate and distinct categories, however. We might obtain the ratio of delinquents to nondelinquents or of married couples to engaged couples. It is evident that with four or five categories, the number of possible ratios which could be computed is quite large. Therefore, unless interest is centered primarily on one or several pairs of categories it will usually be more economical and less confusing to the reader to make use of percentages or proportions. Notice that if there are only two categories it will be possible to compute a proportion directly from a ratio or vice versa. For example, if we know that the ratio of males to females is $3:2$, then out of every five persons there must be an average of three males and two females. Therefore the proportion of males is $3/5$ or .6.

Ratios can be expressed in terms of any base which happens to be convenient. The base of a ratio is indicated by the magnitude of the denominator. For instance sex ratios are conventionally given in terms of the number of males per 100 females. A sex ratio of 94 would therefore indicate slightly fewer males than females, whereas a sex ratio of 108 would mean a preponderance of males. Bases involving large numbers such as 1,000 or 100,000 are often used in computing *rates*, another type of ratio, whenever the use of proportions or percentages might result in small decimal values. Birth rates, for example, are usually given in terms of the number of live births per 1,000 females of childbearing age. Murder rates may be given in terms of the number of murders per 100,000 population.

Rates of increase are another common type of ratio. In computing such a rate we take the actual increase during the period divided by the size at the *beginning* of the period. Thus if the population of a city increases from 50,000 to 65,000 between 1940 and 1950, the rate of increase for the decade would be

$$\frac{65{,}000 - 50{,}000}{50{,}000} = .30$$

or 30 per cent. In the case of rates of increase, percentages may obviously go well over 100 per cent and will be negative if the city has actually decreased in size.

GLOSSARY

Percentage
Proportion
Rate
Ratio

EXERCISES

1. Suppose you are given the following table showing the relationship between church attendance and class standing at a certain university:

Church attendance	Class standing				Total
	Freshmen	Sophomores	Juniors	Seniors	
Regular attenders	83	71	82	59	295
Irregular attenders	31	44	61	78	214
Total	114	115	143	137	509

 a. What is the percentage of regular attenders in the total sample?
 b. What is the ratio of freshmen to seniors?
 c. Among the regular attenders, what is the ratio of underclassmen (freshmen and sophomores) to upperclassmen?
 d. What is the proportion of irregular attenders who are seniors? The proportion of seniors who are irregular attenders?
 e. Are there relatively more irregular attenders among freshmen and sophomores than among juniors and seniors? Express results in terms of percentages.
 f. Summarize the data in several sentences.

2. A social psychologist studying the relationship between industrial productivity and type of group leadership obtains the following data indicating the productivity levels of individuals within each of three types of leadership groups:

| Productivity | Group-leadership type | | | Total |
	Democratic	Laissez-faire	Authoritarian	
High	37	36	13	86
Medium	26	12	71	109
Low	24	20	29	73
Total	87	68	113	268

a. In which direction would you prefer to compute percentages? Why?

b. Compute these percentages and summarize the data briefly.

c. What is the ratio of high to low producers in each of the three groups? For these particular data, would these three ratios adequately summarize the data? Explain.

3. If the ratio of whites to nonwhites in a particular community is $\frac{8}{5}$, what is the proportion of nonwhites? Suppose the ratio of whites to Negroes were $\frac{8}{5}$. Could you obtain the proportion of Negroes in the same manner? Why or why not?

4. If a city had a population of 153,468 in 1940 and of 176,118 in 1950, what was the rate of growth (expressed as a percentage) between 1940 and 1950?

5. If there are 12,160 males and 11,913 females in a certain county, what is the sex ratio (expressed in terms of the number of males per 100 females)?

REFERENCES

1. Dornbusch, S. M., and C. F. Schmid: *A Primer of Social Statistics*, McGraw-Hill Book Company, Inc., New York, 1955, chap. 7.

2. Hagood, M. J., and D. O. Price: *Statistics for Sociologists*, Henry Holt and Company, Inc., New York, 1952, chap. 7.

Chapter 4

INTERVAL SCALES: FREQUENCY
DISTRIBUTIONS AND GRAPHIC PRESENTATION

In the present chapter our concern will be with methods of summarizing data which are very similar to those discussed in the previous chapter. We shall group the interval-scale data into categories, order these categories, and then make use of these groupings to give an over-all picture of the distribution of cases. In so doing, we can boil down information about a very large number of cases into a simple form which will enable a reader to picture the way the cases are distributed. Later we shall find that by grouping our data we can also simplify considerably certain computations. In the following two chapters we shall be concerned with methods of summarizing data in a more compact manner so that they may be described by several numbers representing measures of typicality and degree of homogeneity.

4.1. Frequency Distributions: Grouping the Data

In the previous chapter we encountered few if any major decisions in summarizing our data. This was due to the fact that, presumably, the classes were already determined and all that was necessary was to count the number of cases in each class and then standardize for the number of cases in the total sample by computing a proportion, percentage, or ratio. If interval-scale data are to be summarized in a similar manner, however, an initial decision must be made as to the categories that will be used. Since the data will ordinarily be distributed in a continuous fashion, with few or no large gaps between adjacent scores, the classification scheme may be quite arbitrary. It will be necessary to decide how many categories to use and where to establish the cutting points. Unfortunately, there are no simple rules for accomplishing this since the decision will depend on the purposes served by the classification. Let us take up a specific example in order to illustrate the nature of the problem. Suppose the numbers given below represent the percentage of eligible voters voting in a school board election for 93 census tracts within a particular city.

39.2%	11.6%	36.3%	26.3%	37.1%	15.3%	27.3%	23.5%	13.3%
28.1	26.3	27.1	35.1	23.0	26.1	31.0	36.3	27.3
22.8	33.4	25.6	21.6	46.8	7.1	16.8	26.9	46.6
44.3	58.1	33.1	13.4	27.8	33.4	22.1	42.7	33.0
36.3	20.7	9.3	26.3	29.9	39.4	5.3	24.3	17.8
18.2	37.1	21.6	17.5	12.3	23.6	37.2	37.1	25.1
27.1	28.8	27.8	33.6	26.5	28.3	26.9	24.8	41.0
33.6	19.3	43.7	28.2	19.9	83.6	47.1	4.8	9.7
39.5	32.3	22.4	15.1	26.3	26.1	29.2	14.3	14.6
21.6	37.9	37.1	24.9	10.0	20.7	11.8	22.9	36.0
46.1	21.5	13.3						

Raw data presented in this manner are almost useless in giving the reader a clear picture of what is taking place. This will be especially true if the number of cases is very large. Suppose we wanted to compare this community and another with respect to voting turnout. A quick glance at the data indicates that most tracts had between 20 and 40 per cent turnout, but that there was one with an extremely high record. But it is indeed difficult to get a clear mental picture of the total distribution.

Number and Size of Intervals. In order to visualize this total distribution we shall find it helpful to classify similar scores within the same category. We are immediately confronted with a problem, however. How many intervals should be used in grouping these data? How big should they be? Obviously, there is no point in using intervals with peculiar widths or limits. Thus we would probably select intervals of width 5, 10, or 20 rather than those of width 4.16. Also our end points, or class limits as they are usually called, would ordinarily involve round numbers such as 5.0 or 10.0. If we are in doubt about the intervals ultimately to be used, it is a good idea to tally the scores using a large number of rather narrow intervals. The reason is obvious; having used narrow intervals we can always later combine cases into wider intervals. But if we have started with a small number of more crude categories we cannot subdivide unless we go through the counting operation all over again. Therefore, we might decide to classify the data into intervals of width 5 per cent as in Table 4.1.

Examining the frequencies in each category we see that the picture presented is a rather jagged or uneven one. Probably we can account for the variations between adjacent categories in terms of chance fluctuations. Had there been more cases we would have expected a smoother distribution. The reasoning behind this intuitive judgment will become more apparent in later chapters. Suffice it to say that empirically it always

Table 4.1. Frequency Distribution, with Data Grouped into Intervals of 5 Per Cent

Interval	Frequency, f	Interval	Frequency, f
0.0– 4.9	1	45.0–49.9	4
5.0– 9.9	4	50.0–54.9	0
10.0–14.9	9	55.0–59.9	1
15.0–19.9	8	60.0–64.9	0
20.0–24.9	16	65.0–69.9	0
25.0–29.9	23	70.0–74.9	0
30.0–34.9	8	75.0–79.9	0
35.0–39.9	14	80.0–84.9	1
40.0–44.9	4		93

seems to happen this way.   Given our particular N of 93 tracts, however, the best we can do to obtain a smoother-looking distribution is to make use of a smaller number of wider intervals.   Using intervals of width 10 we obtain Table 4.2.

Table 4.2. Frequency Distribution, with Data Grouped into Intervals of 10 Per Cent

Interval	Frequency, f
0.0– 9.9	5
10.0–19.9	17
20.0–29.9	39
30.0–39.9	22
40.0–49.9	8
50.0–59.9	1
60.0–69.9	0
70.0–79.9	0
80.0–89.9	1
	93

If we had used still wider intervals, say of width 20, the picture would have been as shown in Table 4.3.   Here, we are beginning to obscure

Table 4.3. Frequency Distribution, with Data Grouped into Intervals of 20 Per Cent

Interval	Frequency, f
0.0–19.9	22
20.0–39.9	61
40.0–59.9	9
60.0–79.9	0
80.0–99.9	1
	93

most of our original information.   We know only that about two-thirds of the cases lie between 20.0 and 39.9, but by looking at the data in this last form we cannot say much about where the bulk of the cases are within this very large interval.   Clearly, we have to compromise between using so many intervals that the picture remains too detailed or irregular and using so few categories that too much information is lost.   Incidentally, we see that in summarizing interval-scale data *some important information is practically always lost.*   On the other hand, to report all the information is to present so much detail as to confuse rather than enlighten.

Although mathematical formulas have been given which may serve as guides to the number of intervals to use, such formulas often give the impression of exactness where the best decision is usually that based on common sense and a knowledge of the use to which the frequency table will be put.   Regardless of the number of cases or smoothness of the frequency distribution, it is wise to follow the rule of thumb that an interval should be no wider than the amount of difference between values that can safely be ignored.   A $5 difference between house prices is insignificant, but not so for the prices of shirts.   Therefore, an interval should contain cases whose actual values can for practical purposes be considered alike.

Another problem presents itself with the above data.   What about the single tract with 83.6 per cent turnout?   Using intervals of width 10 leaves several empty classes with this single tract off to itself, so to speak. Of course this is essentially what must be done if the data are to be summarized accurately.   This tract *is* unique.   On the other hand it may be desirable under some circumstances to shorten the table.   If percentages could go well above 100 and if there were several extremes strung out over 10 or more intervals, we should be posed with a more difficult decision.   Several alternatives present themselves.   First, we may use intervals of *different widths*, permitting the extreme intervals to be much wider than the others.   Thus we might use a single interval 50.0 to 89.9 which would include the largest two scores.   In so doing, we of course lose information since we now have much less precise an indication of the scores of the two extreme cases.

Secondly, we might use an *open interval* to take care of the extreme cases.   The last category might then read, "50 per cent or more."   Here, we retain even less information about the data although in this particular example we happen to know that percentages cannot run over 100.   Had the data involved income and had the last interval been "$20,000 and over," the reader would have had absolutely no way of guessing from the table alone what the highest incomes might have been.   It should be noted, however, that under some circumstances it may not be at all important what these highest incomes happen to be.   In this case the simplifications introduced by using open intervals may outweigh the disadvantages.   With distributions having a small number of very extreme scores there may be no satisfactory alternative.   If one wishes to indicate the incomes of the most wealthy citizens without distorting his table he may find it easier to do so in his textual presentation. As we shall see in the following chapters, open intervals should not be used if the primary purpose of grouping data is to simplify *computations* rather than to *display* the data in a meaningful way.

True Limits. You may have noticed that in indicating the intervals, the class limits have been stated in such a way that there is no overlap between classes. In fact, there is a slight gap between them. Limits are usually stated in this manner in order to avoid ambiguity for the reader. Had they been stated as 10 to 20, 20 to 30, etc., the question would have arisen as to what we do with a score that is exactly 20.0. Actually there will always be ambiguities no matter how the intervals are stated, as can be seen if we ask what would be done with a case that is between 19.9 and 20.0. We of course notice that there are no such cases, but a little thought will convince us that this is due to the fact that the data have been *rounded* to the nearest tenth of a per cent. We therefore have to ask the following question: "Which cases actually belong in a particular interval, given the fact that data have been rounded?" We see immediately that the *true* class limits are not the same as the *stated* limits. If we had followed conventional rounding rules, a tract with a percentage turnout slightly over 19.95 would have been rounded up to 20.0 and placed in the interval 20.0 to 29.9. Had the percentage been ever so slightly below 19.95 we would have rounded the score down to 19.9 and placed the tract in the next lower category. Therefore the true limits actually used run as follows:

$$0.0 - 9.95$$
$$9.95-19.95$$
$$19.95-29.95$$
$$\text{etc.}$$

Ignoring the first interval, we see that by using the true limits each interval is exactly of width 10.0 (rather than 9.9) and that the upper limit of one interval exactly coincides with the lower limit of the following interval.[1] Had a score been exactly 9.95000 we would have followed the conventional procedure and rounded up since the digit immediately preceding the last five is odd.[2] We can therefore assign every case

[1] Where the lowest interval involves zero and where values cannot be negative (as with percentages), we still consider all intervals to be of equal width, imagining that the lower limit of the first interval is actually −.05 and that scores have been rounded up to 0.00.

[2] Notice that in the case of the intervals we have been using there would be a very slight bias since cases exactly between intervals would always be placed in the higher category. For most practical purposes such a bias can be ignored.

unambiguously to the proper interval.   Notice that if rounding has been to the *nearest* figure, as is usually the case, the true limits will always involve splitting the difference between the stated limits of adjacent intervals.   For example, if we split the difference between 19.9 and 20.0 we get 19.95.   The convention is to report figures in such a manner as to indicate the degree of accuracy in measurement, e.g., 10.45 indicates accuracy to two decimal places, 10.450 to three, and 10.4 to one.   Measurement accuracy should therefore be reported in the stated intervals so that the reader can ascertain the true limits if he wishes to make use of these limits in his computations.   For example, if limits are stated to be 10.00 to 19.99 we know that measurement is accurate to two decimal places, that rounding has been to the nearest $\frac{1}{100}$ of 1 per cent, and that therefore the true limits run from 9.995 to 19.995.   Had limits been given as 10 to 19, true limits would of course have been 9.5 to 19.5.

In a few instances, such as age *last* birthday, data may not have been rounded in the conventional way.   If we ask ourselves which interval any given case really belongs in, however, the answer should always be apparent.   Since a person who will be aged 20 tomorrow lists his age as 19 today, it is clear that an interval stated as 15 to 19 has as its true limits the values 15 and 20.   Although we may appear to be splitting hairs in distinguishing true limits from stated limits, we shall see in the following chapters that true limits must be used in computations even though they are not usually explicitly given when data are presented in the form of a frequency distribution.

Discrete and Continuous Data.   The data we have been using are *continuous* in the sense that any value might theoretically have been obtained for a percentage provided that measurement accuracy were sufficiently precise and that tracts were very large.   Thus, the value 17.4531 per cent is as possible as 17.0000 per cent.   Certain other kinds of data are *discrete* in that not all values are possible.   A woman may have exactly 0, 1, 2, or even 17 children, but she cannot have 2.31 children.   Income and city size are theoretically discrete variables in that it is impossible to earn $3,219.5618 or for a city to have a population of 43,635.7 people.   Because of the limitations of any measuring instrument and the consequent necessity of rounding at some point, empirical data always come in discrete form, but in many cases we are at least able to imagine a continuous distribution which could be obtained by the perfect measuring instrument.   As we shall see in the chapter on the normal curve, mathematicians often have to develop theoretical distributions which assume a continuous variable.

In some cases, such as income or city size, it is not too difficult to imagine that data are continuous even though actually there are very small units (pennies, persons) which cannot be subdivided.   But what

about the number of children in a family?   Here we would seem to be
doing grave injustice to the data to assume continuity.   In presenting
data in a frequency distribution we would obviously not be so foolish as
to use intervals running from 0.5 to 2.4 or 2.5 to 4.4 children.   We would
simply list intervals as 0 to 2, 3 to 4, etc., and there would be no ambiguity
concerning the gaps between intervals.   For some computations, however, it will be necessary, for pragmatic reasons, to treat the data as
continuous and to spread discrete scores over small intervals.   As
peculiar as it may seem, we may have to consider mothers with one child
as ranging in number of children from 0.5 to 1.5.   For most purposes we
shall get essentially the same results as would be obtained by keeping the
data in discrete form.   A compromise with reality in this and other
instances may be necessary in order to fit the models set up by the
mathematician.   Provided we realize what we are doing, little or no
confusion will result.

4.2. Cumulative Frequency Distributions

For some purposes it is desirable to present data in a somewhat different
form.   Instead of giving the number of cases in each interval we may
indicate the number of scores which are less than (or greater than) a

Table 4.4. Cumulative-frequency Distributions

Cumulating up			Cumulating down		
Number of cases below	Cumulative frequency, F	Per cent	Number of cases above	Cumulative frequency, F	Per cent
0.0	0	0.0	0.0	93	100.0
9.95	5	5.4	9.95	88	94.6
19.95	22	23.7	19.95	71	76.3
29.95	61	65.6	29.95	32	34.4
39.95	83	89.2	39.95	10	10.8
49.95	91	97.8	49.95	2	2.2
59.95	92	98.9	59.95	1	1.1
69.95	92	98.9	69.95	1	1.1
79.95	92	98.9	79.95	1	1.1
89.95	93	100.0	89.95	0	0.0

given value.   In the case of the data we have been using there are
obviously no tracts having less than zero turnout, there are five with less
than 9.95 per cent, 22 with less than 19.95 per cent, and all 93 have less
than 89.95 per cent turnout.   We can thus represent the data in a
cumulative fashion as indicated in Table 4.4.   Notice that we can
cumulate downward as well as upward by asking how many cases are

above a certain value.   Cumulative frequencies are usually indicated by using a capital *F* rather than the lower case letter.   If we wish, we can convert actual frequencies into percentages.   We shall have occasion to make use of cumulative distributions in Chap. 5 when computing medians and again in Chap. 14.

4.3. Graphic Presentation: Histograms, Frequency Polygons, and Ogives

There are always some persons who hesitate to read tables and who obtain a better understanding of materials if these are presented in graphic or visual form.   One of the simplest and most useful ways of

Fig. 4.1. Histogram with equal intervals.

presenting data so that differences among frequencies readily stand out is to make use of figures which have areas or heights proportional to the frequencies in each category.   For example, a bar can be used to represent each category, the height of the bar indicating its relative size.   If the scale is nominal, the actual ordering of bars will be irrelevant.   For ordinal and interval scales, the bars can be arranged in their proper order, giving a good visual indication of the frequency distribution.   The resulting figure is referred to as a *histogram*.   Either the absolute frequencies or the proportion of cases in each interval may be indicated along the ordinate as in Fig. 4.1.

It should be noted that if *heights* of bars are taken to be proportional to frequencies in each class interval, the visual picture can be very misleading unless all intervals are closed and of equal width.   Suppose, for example, that one of the middle intervals had been of width 20 instead of 10.   We would therefore find a larger number of cases in the interval and the result would be as in Fig. 4.2.   Obviously, if we wish to obtain a histogram which represents the data more faithfully, we should make the bar only half as high since we have doubled the width and have on the average included twice as many cases in the wider interval as would be in either of the two intervals of regular size.   This would give us a histogram (see Fig. 4.3) much more similar to the one originally obtained.   A little thought will convince you that if we were to think in terms of areas rather than heights we could more readily handle data involving unequal

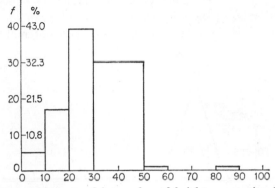

Fig. 4.2. Histogram with unequal intervals and heights proportional to frequencies.

Fig. 4.3. Histogram with unequal intervals and areas proportional to frequencies.

intervals.   In other words, we let the *areas* of the rectangles be proportional to the number of cases.   In the important special case where all intervals are of equal width, the heights will of course also be proportional to the frequencies.   If the width of each rectangle is taken to be one unit and if heights are represented as proportions, the total area under the histogram will be unity.   Thus

$$1(\tfrac{5}{93}) + 1(\tfrac{17}{93}) + 1(\tfrac{39}{93}) + \cdots + 1(\tfrac{1}{93}) = 1$$

When we take up the normal curve in Chap. 7 we shall find it necessary to deal with areas rather than heights, and it will be convenient to take the total area under the histogram to be unity.

Another very similar way of presenting a frequency distribution graphically is by means of the *frequency polygon*. To obtain a frequency polygon we simply connect the mid-points of the tops of each rectangle with straight lines and then blot out the rectangles as in Fig. 4.4. Note that the end points of the frequency polygon have been placed on the base line (horizontal axis) at the mid-points of the intervals on either side of the two extreme intervals. Ordinarily we would not make use of both

Fig. 4.4. Frequency polygon.

types of figures, but by superimposing the frequency polygon on the histogram we see that the area under the two figures must be identical. This is true because for every small triangle which lies within the frequency polygon but outside the histogram there is an identical triangle beneath the histogram but above the frequency polygon. Thus we can also take the area under a frequency polygon to be unity. Notice, however, that we have merely connected a number of points with straight lines. The points themselves may represent the number of cases in each interval, but we should be careful not to infer that there are a given number of cases at any other single point along the continuum. For example, we should *not* infer that there are approximately 28 cases with scores of exactly 20.

Frequency polygons can also be used to represent cumulative frequency distributions. The resulting figure is referred to as an *ogive*. Along the ordinate or Y axis we can indicate frequencies or percentages. We place scores of the interval-scale variable along the X axis (abscissa) as before, with the understanding that the frequencies represented indicate the number of cases which are *less than* the value on the X axis. For example, in Fig. 4.5 we see that approximately 75 per cent of the scores are less than 34. Ogives can therefore be used as a graphic method of determining the number of cases below or above a certain value. Obviously, the form of the ogive must be such that it is either always increasing or always decreasing depending on whether one is cumulating up or down. The curve will be horizontal in those intervals which are empty. If the frequency distribution is of the type given by our data, with the largest number of cases in those intervals near the center of the distribution, the

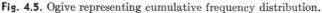

Fig. 4.5. Ogive representing cumulative frequency distribution.

ogive will be *S*-shaped, with the steepest slope in the vicinity of those intervals containing the largest number of cases.

GLOSSARY

Continuous and discrete data
Cumulative distribution
Frequency distribution
Frequency polygon
Histogram
Ogive
True limits

EXERCISES

1. Suppose the following represent the annual incomes of a sample of community residents:

$ 2,760	$3,850	$ 3,340	$ 3,890	$ 2,860
4,340	4,360	4,350	11,740	4,350
5,210	2,140	2,610	3,560	7,310
3,410	3,330	8,190	2,740	3,550
4,570	7,810	4,250	7,110	4,210
9,300	5,340	3,460	10,300	5,490
3,320	2,970	19,310	4,440	2,110
1,790	4,140	2,670	3,370	23,400
4,560	3,000	3,100	5,170	3,760
3,800	1,610	5,130	3,160	4,170
13,460	4,570	1,710	2,800	6,170
5,210	1,940	4,320	3,180	2,350
2,690	2,780	9,830	4,240	8,340

   a. Construct a frequency distribution and cumulative distribution.
   b. What are the true limits?
   c. Draw a histogram, frequency polygon, and ogive.

2. In a survey of visiting patterns among close friends and relatives, 81 respondents are asked to indicate the number of such friends and relatives with whom they ordinarily visit at least once every month. The results are as follows (figures indicating actual number of persons usually visited):

3	5	2	3	3	4	1	8	4
2	4	2	5	3	3	3	0	3
5	6	4	3	2	2	6	3	5
4	14	3	5	6	3	4	2	4
9	4	1	4	2	4	3	5	0
4	3	5	7	3	5	6	2	2
5	4	2	3	6	1	3	16	5
3	11	4	5	19	4	5	2	2
4	3	14	5	2	1	4	3	4

   a. Construct a frequency distribution and cumulative distribution.
   b. Justify as well as you can your choice of intervals.
   c. Draw a histogram, frequency polygon, and ogive.

3. Indicate the true limits in each of the following:

   a. 1,000–1,900   *c.* 1.000–1.999
       2,000–2,900   2.000–2.999
   b. 1,000–1,999   *d.* .010–.019
       2,000–2,999   .020–.029

What have you assumed about the method of rounding in each of the above?

REFERENCES

1. Dornbusch, S. M., and C. F. Schmid: *A Primer of Social Statistics*, McGraw-Hill Book Company, Inc., New York, 1955, chaps. 2 and 3.

2. Hagood, M. J., and D. O. Price: *Statistics for Sociologists*, Henry Holt and Company, Inc., New York, 1952, chaps. 4 and 5.

3. Wallis, W. A., and H. V. Roberts: *Statistics: A New Approach*, Free Press, Glencoe, Ill., 1956, chap. 6.

Chapter 5

INTERVAL SCALES: MEASURES OF CENTRAL TENDENCY

We have seen that nominal scales can easily be summarized in terms of percentages, proportions, or ratios and that these summarizing measures are essentially interchangeable. In other words, a single kind of measure is sufficient to describe the data. In the case of interval scales, we have seen that the data may be described by means of a frequency distribution. We can also make use of several distinct types of measures, the most important of which are measures of typicality or "central tendency" and measures of heterogeneity or dispersion. In each case we shall find that there are a number of distinct measures from which to choose, each measure having somewhat different properties, advantages, and disadvantages. Summarizing interval scales is therefore somewhat less straightforward than was the case with nominal scales. The present chapter is concerned with measures of typicality; in the following chapter we shall discuss measures of dispersion. Taken together, these two types of measures will ordinarily be adequate for describing interval-scale data.

The layman's conception of the term *average* is likely to be rather vague or ambiguous. In fact, he may not realize that there are several distinct measures of typicality and that under some circumstances these measures may yield very different results. The fact that it is possible to obtain such different measures of central tendency means that it is necessary to understand the advantages and disadvantages of each measure. It is also important to learn the circumstances under which each is appropriate. Why does the Census Bureau report median incomes rather than mean incomes? Would it make sense to tell the layman that the "average" family has 2.3 children and lives in a 4.8 room house? Under what circumstances will it make little difference which measure is used? These are some of the numerous questions that can be raised about the kind of average we should compute.

5.1. The Arithmetic Mean

There are two important measures of central tendency used in socio-logical research, the arithmetic mean (hereafter referred to simply as the mean) and the median. The mean is by far the more common of the two and is defined as the sum of the scores divided by the total number of cases involved. The symbol $\bar{X}$ is conventionally used to indicate the mean, although occasionally the letter M may be used. The formula for the arithmetic mean is therefore

$$\bar{X} = \frac{X_1 + X_2 + \cdots + X_N}{N} = \frac{\sum_{i=1}^{N} X_i}{N} \tag{5.1}$$

where X_1 represents the score of the first individual, X_2 that of the second, and X_i that of the general individual.[1] If there are no ambiguities we may drop the subscripts and write simply

$$\bar{X} = \frac{\Sigma X}{N}$$

where it is understood that all quantities are being summed.

The mean has the algebraic property that the sum of the deviations of each score from the mean will always be zero. Symbolically, this property can be expressed by the equation

$$\sum_{i=1}^{N} (X_i - \bar{X}) = 0$$

This fact should not be at all surprising when we realize how the mean has been defined. The proof is simple. Since we have a sum of numbers each of which is actually a difference, we can break the above expression into the difference of two sums. Thus

$$\sum_{i=1}^{N} (X_i - \bar{X}) = \sum_{i=1}^{N} X_i - \sum_{i=1}^{N} \bar{X}$$

But since $\bar{X}$ is a constant we have

$$\sum_{i=1}^{N} \bar{X} = N\bar{X} = N \frac{\sum_{i=1}^{N} X_i}{N} = \sum_{i=1}^{N} X_i$$

and we see immediately that the difference is zero.

[1] For a discussion of the summation notation see Appendix 1.

The above property can be used to simplify the computation of the mean. For example, suppose we wish to compute a mean from the numbers 72, 81, 86, 69, and 57. Adding and dividing by five we get an $\bar{X}$ of 73.0. Subtracting this mean from each of the figures and then adding, we verify that the resulting sum is zero.

X	$X - 73$	$X - 70$
72	−1	2
81	8	11
86	13	16
69	−4	−1
57	−16	−13
	0	15

Suppose, however, that we had guessed a mean of 70 and then had subtracted this guessed mean from each of the figures. The resulting sum is not zero, but we notice that each of the new differences is three units larger (in the positive direction) than the original differences. We thus see that we guessed a mean which is three too small. If we now add a correction factor of three to our guessed mean we obtain the correct mean. In actual practice we would not compare the two sets of differences in this manner. We notice, however, that the sum of the second set of differences is +15. Since there are five scores, this indicates that on the average we were below the true mean by $15/5$ or 3.0 units. As can easily be verified, had we guessed a value which was too high, the resulting sum of the differences would have been negative and we would have had to subtract from the guessed mean in order to obtain the correct figure. If $\bar{X}'$ represents the guessed mean, we may write a formula for the mean in terms of the guessed mean and a correction factor

$$\bar{X} = \bar{X}' + \frac{\sum_{i=1}^{N} (X_i - \bar{X}')}{N} \tag{5.2}$$

or, in words,

$$\text{True mean} = \text{guessed mean} + \frac{\text{sum of deviations from guessed mean}}{\text{number of cases}}$$

In order to verify the correctness of this formula, we expand the right-hand side, getting

$$\bar{X}' + \frac{\sum_{i=1}^{N}(X_i - \bar{X}')}{N} = \bar{X}' + \frac{\sum_{i=1}^{N} X_i}{N} - \frac{\sum_{i=1}^{N} \bar{X}'}{N}$$

$$= \bar{X}' + \frac{\sum_{i=1}^{N} X_i}{N} - \frac{N\bar{X}'}{N}$$

$$= \frac{\sum_{i=1}^{N} X_i}{N} = \bar{X}$$

Although we seem to have gone to a lot of trouble computing $\bar{X}$ in a roundabout manner, it is sometimes possible by this method to save considerable work when desk calculators are not available.　Making use of a guessed mean ordinarily reduces the size of the numbers to be added. The closer the guessed mean to the correct value, the smaller in magnitude will be the resulting differences.　This principle will be especially useful when we take up the computation of means from grouped data.

A second property of the mean can be stated as follows: The sum of the *squared* deviations of each score from the mean is less than the sum of the squared deviations about any other number.　In other words

$$\sum_{i=1}^{N}(X_i - \bar{X})^2 = \text{minimum}$$

The proof of this property requires calculus, but a few numerical examples will demonstrate its validity.　For the numbers given above, the squared deviations from the mean of 73 are 1, 64, 169, 16, and 256 respectively. The resulting sum is therefore 506.　If squared deviations had been computed about 70 instead, the result would have been

$$4 + 121 + 256 + 1 + 169 = 551$$

The quantity $\sum_{i=1}^{N}(X_i - \bar{X})^2$ will appear in much of our later work as a measure of the total variation or heterogeneity.　This second "least-squares" property of the mean is of greater theoretical significance than the first and will be considered again in subsequent chapters.

5.2. The Median

We sometimes want to locate the position of the middle case when data have been ranked from high to low. Or we may divide a group of students into percentiles by locating the individuals who have exactly 10 per cent of the class below them, exactly 32 per cent below them, etc. Measures of this sort are often referred to as *positional measures* since they locate the position of some typical (or atypical) case relative to those of other individuals. The median is perhaps the most important of such positional measures. We define the median as a number which has the property of having the same number of scores with smaller values as there are with larger values. Ordinarily, the median thus divides the scores in half. If the number of cases is odd, the median will simply be the score of the middle case. If N is even there will be no middle case and, in fact, any number between the values of the two middle cases will have the property of dividing the scores into two equal groups. Thus the median is ambiguously defined if N is even. By convention we take as the unique value of the median the arithmetic mean of the two middle cases. If we had the numbers 72, 81, 86, 69, and 57 the median would be 72 (as compared with a mean of 73). Had there been a sixth score, say 55, the two middle scores would be 69 and 72 and we would take as the median $(69 + 72)/2$ or 70.5. If the two middle cases happen to have the same score, the median will of course be that score itself. Notice that if N is odd the middle case will be the $(N + 1)/2$nd case. When the number of cases is even the median will be halfway between the $N/2$nd and the $(N/2 + 1)$st case. Thus if $N = 251$ the median will be the score of the 126th case; if $N = 106$ we take a value halfway between the scores of the fifty-third and fifty-fourth cases. These formulas will ordinarily be helpful when N is fairly large.

We have seen that the mean has the properties

$$\sum_{i=1}^{N} (X_i - \bar{X}) = 0$$

and

$$\sum_{i=1}^{N} (X_i - \bar{X})^2 = \text{minimum}$$

The reason that the first property holds is essentially that when the mean is subtracted from each score the values of the resulting differences are such that the negative scores exactly balance the positive ones. But suppose we had ignored the signs altogether and considered all differences as positive? It can be shown that had the *median* been subtracted from each score, the sign of the difference ignored, and the results summed, we would have obtained a sum which would be less than the comparable figure for any other measure of central tendency. In symbols

$$\sum_{i=1}^{N} |X_i - \text{Md}| = \text{minimum}$$

where Md stands for the median and the bars around the expression $(X_i - \text{Md})$ indicate that the positive (or "absolute") value of each difference is to be used. Although this property of the median is perhaps of some interest, it does not seem to have any direct applications of sociological significance.

5.3. Computation of Mean and Median from Grouped Data

Long Method for Computing Mean.   When the number of cases becomes large the computation of the mean or median may become quite tedious unless certain modifications are made in our procedures. The task of ranking several hundred scores would be especially troublesome since desk calculators would be of no real help. Whenever the number of cases becomes large, therefore, it will usually be much more efficient to group the data into categories and to compute the mean or median from the resulting frequency distribution. Sometimes, of course, we find data already given us in grouped form, and it will be either impossible or impractical to go back to the original data for purposes of computation. Census data are usually given in grouped form, for example. We would know only that there are a certain number of persons aged 0 to 4 or 5 to 9, but the exact age of each individual would be unknown.

As we shall see below, the use of data in grouped form may simplify one's work considerably.   On the other hand, we inevitably lose information when grouping data into categories.   We may know only that there are 17 persons having incomes between $2,000 and $2,900, but we do not know exactly how they are distributed within this interval. In order to compute either a mean or a median from such grouped data we have to make some simplifying assumptions about the location of individuals within each category.   In the case of the mean we shall treat all cases as though they were concentrated at the mid-points of their respective intervals.   In computing the median we imagine cases to be spread at equal distances within each interval.   These simplifications will of course lead to certain inaccuracies. We would not expect to get exactly the same results as those obtained from the raw data.   On the other hand, if the number of cases is large the distortions introduced will usually be very minor and well worth the saving of time.   Obviously, the narrower the intervals the less information we have lost and the greater the accuracy. For example, if we know that there are 17 cases between $2,000 and $2,900 and 26 cases between $3,000 and $3,900, we can obtain more accurate results by imagining the 17 cases to be at the mid-point of the first interval and the 26 persons to be at the mid-point of the second than if we were to place all 43 scores at the mid-point of the larger interval, $2,000 to $3,900. These simplifications are most likely to lead to errors in the case of extreme intervals since the scores in these intervals may be skewed toward the center of the total distribution. Thus if there are 17 cases in the lowest interval, most of these scores may be in the upper half of the interval. However, if the number of individuals in these intervals is quite small, as is usually the case, the distortion introduced is likely to be insignificant.

In computing the mean from grouped data we therefore treat all cases as though they were located at the mid-points of their respective intervals. If we preferred, we could take them as spread at equal distances through-out the interval, but, as can easily be verified, this would lead to the same results since the mean score within each interval would be exactly at the mid-point of the interval. Since all cases within each interval are treated as having the same value, we can multiply the number of cases in the interval by their common value instead of adding the scores separately. For example, if we have placed 26 cases at the value 3,450, the product $26 \times 3,450$ will be equal to the sum of 26 separate scores of 3,450. If we do this for all intervals, sum the products, and divide by the total number of cases we obtain the arithmetic mean. The formula for the mean then becomes

$$\bar{X} = \frac{\sum_{i=1}^{k} f_i m_i}{N} \tag{5.3}$$

where f_i = number of cases in ith category
$\quad m_i$ = mid-point of ith category
$\quad k$ = number of categories
The example worked in Table 5.1 should make the process clear.

In Table 5.1 all intervals are of equal width. This is not essential as long as the correct mid-points are used. It is necessary, however, to make use of closed intervals. Suppose the last interval had been $7,000 and above. What would we use as the mid-point? We have absolutely no basis on which to judge unless we can go back to the original data. Sometimes it is feasible to do this since extreme categories often contain relatively few cases. In such instances it usually makes more sense to use the actual mean of the cases in the extreme category rather than the mid-point of some wider interval. In instances where it is impossible to go back to the original data it will be necessary to make an enlightened guess as to a reasonable value for the mid-point. It is therefore clearly to our advantage to use closed intervals whenever a mean is to be computed. As we shall see in the next chapter, this is also true in computing the standard deviation, the most commonly used measure of dispersion.

Table 5.1. Computation of Mean from Grouped Data, Using Long Method

Stated limits	True limits	Mid-points (m_i)	f_i	$f_i m_i$
$2,000–2,900	$1,950–2,950	$2,450	17	$ 41,650
3,000–3,900	2,950–3,950	3,450	26	89,700
4,000–4,900	3,950–4,950	4,450	38	169,100
5,000–5,900	4,950–5,950	5,450	51	277,950
6,000–6,900	5,950–6,950	6,450	36	232,200
7,000–7,900	6,950–7,950	7,450	21	156,450
Totals			189	$967,050

$$\bar{X} = \frac{\sum_{i=1}^{k} f_i m_i}{N} = \frac{967,050}{189} = \$5,117$$

Short Method for Computing Mean. The above method will usually involve the multiplication of fairly large numbers (e.g., $2,450 \times 17$) unless the mid-points turn out to be simple numbers. With a modern desk calculator such products can easily be computed and accumulated. But if computations must be made by hand there is a much simpler method of computing the mean from grouped data. This so-called "short method" seems, at first glance, to involve more work than the "longer" one, but once it has been mastered it will prove much the simpler of the two. Basically, the short method involves guessing a mean and thereby making use of smaller numbers in the multiplication process. A correction factor is then added to the guessed mean as before.

In order to simplify our computations let us take as our guessed mean a mid-point of one of the intervals. In the above example we can see by inspection that the mean will be somewhat less than $5,450, the mid-point of the fourth interval. The advantage of using a mid-point as our guessed mean is obvious. All of the other scores will then be a certain number of intervals away from the guessed mean since each score is taken to be at one or another of the mid-points. If we now subtract the guessed mean from each score we will obtain differences of exactly $1,000, $2,000, or $3,000 in either direction. We then multiply these *differences* by the appropriate frequencies to obtain the correction factor to be added to the guessed mean. In other words, there will be 17 cases which have scores which are exactly $3,000 less than the guessed mean; there will be 26 cases with a difference of $2,000, etc. If we make use of a column d_i representing the difference between actual scores and the *guessed* mean we can modify (5.2) and write the formula for the mean as

$$\bar{X} = \bar{X}' + \frac{\sum\limits_{i=1}^{k} f_i d_i}{N} \tag{5.4}$$

where
$$d_i = X_i - \bar{X}'$$

and we can set up our computations in a table such as Table 5.2. Again, the correction factor involves taking the total deviation from the guessed mean (here $-63,000$) and then dividing by the number of cases to obtain the average amount the guessed mean deviates from the true mean.

Table 5.2. Computation of Mean from Grouped Data, Using Short Method

True limits	Mid-points	f_i	d_i	$f_i d_i$
$1,950–2,950	$2,450	17	$-3,000	$-51,000
2,950–3,950	3,450	26	-2,000	-52,000
3,950–4,950	4,450	38	-1,000	-38,000
4,950–5,950	5,450	51	0	0
5,950–6,950	6,450	36	1,000	36,000
6,950–7,950	7,450	21	2,000	42,000
Totals		189		$-63,000

Short Method

$$\bar{X} = \bar{X}' + \frac{\sum\limits_{i=1}^{k} f_i d_i}{N}$$

$$= 5,450 + \frac{-63,000}{189} = 5,450 - 333$$

$$= \$5,117$$

In this example the correction factor turned out to be negative, indicating that the guessed mean was too high. It should be noted that had we guessed any other value for the mean we would have obtained the same result. Selecting the mid-point of the third interval ($4,450) as the guessed mean yields a correction factor of $667 which, when *added* to $4,450, gives the correct result. Incidentally, this serves as a useful check on our work. Notice that had we selected the mid-point of any other interval, we would have made more work for ourselves since the numbers to be added in the $f_i d_i$ column would have been numerically larger. Had we failed to use a mid-point, deviations from the guessed mean would have involved much less simple numbers, and we would not have saved ourselves any work. Once the process becomes clearly understood, it will be possible to omit the mid-points column from the computing table.

You have undoubtedly already noticed that each of the deviations from the guessed mean in the above example is an exact multiple of 1,000, the size of the interval used. This will always be the case provided all intervals are exactly the same width. We can therefore factor out the width of the interval in each of the products $f_i d_i$, and then multiply by the interval width when we have finished summing. In other words, we could have obtained the sum $-63,000$ as follows:

$$-63,000 = 1,000(-51 - 52 - 38 + 0 + 36 + 42)$$

In what amounts to the same thing, we could have expressed the original deviations in terms of the number of *intervals* (or "step deviations") from the guessed mean. We then determine how many intervals the guessed mean is from the true mean and, finally, we translate the amount of error back into the original units by multiplying this correction factor by the size of the interval. Referring to the deviation in interval widths as d', we can revise our table as in Table 5.3.

Table 5.3. Computation of Mean from Grouped Data, Using Short Method and Step Deviations

True limits	Mid-points	f_i	d'_i	$f_i d'_i$
$1,950–2,950	$2,450	17	−3	−51
2,950–3,950	3,450	26	−2	−52
3,950–4,950	4,450	38	−1	−38
4,950–5,950	5,450	51	0	0
5,950–6,950	6,450	36	1	36
6,950–7,950	7,450	21	2	42
Totals		189		−63

The modified formula for the mean now becomes

$$\bar{X} = \bar{X}' + \frac{\sum_{i=1}^{k} f_i d'_i}{N} i \tag{5.5}$$

where i is the interval width. Therefore

$$\bar{X} = 5,450 + \frac{-63}{189} 1,000 = 5,117$$

If unequal intervals have been used it will be necessary to modify this second form of the short method. Some persons may find it easier to go back to the earlier method, using d_i instead of d'_i, and writing in the actual differences in the original units. Alternatively, if only one or two intervals differ from the rest in width we may take as the interval width i the width of the majority of class intervals. The deviations of the mid-points of the remaining intervals from the guessed mean can then be expressed in terms of fractions of whole intervals. For example, had the last interval been $6,950 to $8,950 instead of $6,950 to $7,950, the mid-point would have been $7,950 instead of $7,450. The deviation from the guessed mean would therefore be $2,500 or 2.5 interval widths. Had the interval run to $9,950 the d'_i value would have been 3.0 as can easily be verified.

Computation of Median. In computing the median from grouped data we shall treat all cases within a given interval as though they were distributed at equal distances throughout the interval. We first locate the interval containing the middle case, and we then interpolate to find the exact position of the median. In determining the interval containing the median it is usually desirable to obtain the cumulative-frequency distribution. Although not absolutely necessary, it is preferable to develop the habit of writing down the entire cumulative distribution as well as indicating in a separate column the meaning of each of the figures in the cumulative column (F). The cumulative distribution for the above data is given in Table 5.4. As a check on our adding, we note that all 189 cases must be less than $7,950.

Table 5.4. Computation of Median from Grouped Data

True limits	f	CF	No. of cases less than
$1,950–2,950	17	17	$2,950
2,950–3,950	26	43	3,050
3,950–4,950	38	81	4,950
4,950–5,950	51	132	5,950
5,950–6,950	36	168	6,950
6,950–7,950	21	189	7,950
Total	189		

Next, we locate the interval containing the middle or N/2nd case. Here $189/2 = 94.5$, so that we are looking for the interval containing the ninety-fourth and ninety-fifth cases. Note that had data been ungrouped we would have located the $(N + 1)$/2nd or ninety-fifth case. The reason for this apparent inconsistency will be discussed below. Since there are 81 cases less than $4,950 and 132 less than $5,950, the median must lie somewhere in the interval $4,950 to $5,950.   It is a good idea to indicate this interval with brackets since there is sometimes a tendency to look across from the figure 81, obtaining the incorrect interval $3,950 to $4,950.

Let us now look more closely at the interval containing the median. There are 51 cases within this interval, and therefore we shall divide the entire interval into 51 subintervals, each of width $1,000/51 or $19.61. We locate each of the 51 cases at the mid-point of its proper subinterval. The eighty-first case will be located in the last subinterval of the interval $3,950 to $4,950, and the 132nd case will be just slightly less than the upper limit of the interval containing the median.   We now simply count subintervals until we have come to the median.   Had the data been ungrouped, we should have located the score of the $(N + 1)/2$nd or ninety-fifth case.   According to our convention, the ninety-fifth case would be located at the *mid-point* of the fourteenth subinterval or

exactly 13.5 subintervals from the lower limit of the interval.   Notice that this same value of 13.5 could have been obtained by subtracting 81 from 94.5 or $N/2$.   It is because we are dealing with mid-points of small intervals that we count exactly $N/2$ intervals in order to locate the position of the $(N + 1)/2$nd case.

The value of the median can now be obtained by simply multiplying the number of subintervals covered by the size of each subinterval, adding the result to the lower limit of the interval.   The whole process can be summarized by the formula

$$\text{Md} = l + \frac{N/2 - F}{f} i \qquad\qquad (5.6)$$

where F = cumulative frequency corresponding to lower limit
f = number of cases in interval containing median
l = lower limit of interval containing median
i = width of interval containing median

The quantity i/f represents the size of each subinterval, and $N/2 - F$ gives the distance (in subintervals) between the lower limit of the interval and the median.   In our problem we get

$$\text{Md} = 4,950 + \frac{94.5 - 81}{51} 1,000 = 4,950 + 13.5 \frac{1,000}{51}$$
$$= 4,950 + 265 = \$5,215$$

There is an alternative but equivalent way of visualizing the process of obtaining the median. Instead of finding the width of each subinterval and then multiplying by the number of these subintervals, we can reason that since there are 51 cases in the entire interval and since we need to go 13.5 of these smaller intervals in order to get to the median, we must travel 13.5/51 of the entire interval. Therefore, if we multiply the width of the interval (1,000) by the fraction of the total distance we must go, we obtain the desired result. When using the formula, it is, of course, irrelevant which explanation we find most satisfactory. Lest one become too dependent on formulas, it is best to reason out the process each time, using the formula as a check, until it is thoroughly understood. As another check it should be noted that the median could have been computed by *subtracting* a certain quantity from the *upper* limit u. As can easily be shown, the formula then becomes

$$\text{Md} = u - \frac{F - N/2}{f} i \qquad (5.7)$$

where F now represents the cumulative frequency corresponding to the upper limit of the interval. Numerically

$$\text{Md} = 5,950 - \frac{132 - 94.5}{51} 1,000 = \$5,215$$

5.4. Comparison of Mean and Median

Having discussed the computational procedures used in obtaining the mean and median from both grouped and ungrouped data, we now need to compare their properties. Several differences between the two measures are immediately apparent. First, the mean uses more information than the median in the sense that all of the exact scores are used in computing the mean whereas the median really only involves the score of the middle case. Returning to the scores 72, 81, 86, 69, and 57 we see that had the highest score been 126 instead of 86 the median would have been unaffected but the mean would have been increased substantially. Likewise, had the lowest score been zero the mean would have been lowered but the median would again be unchanged. We therefore may state a very important difference between the two measures: *the mean is affected by changes in extreme values whereas the median will be unaffected unless the value of the middle case is also changed.* In our example, as long as 72 remains the third case when data have been reranked, the median will be unchanged.

This important difference between the two measures enables us to decide in most instances which will be the more appropriate. Ordinarily, we desire our measure to make use of all information available. We somehow have more intuitive faith in such a measure. Although at this point it is impossible to bolster such a faith with a sound statistical argument, some justification for the preference for the mean under ordinary circumstances can be given. It turns out that the mean is generally a more stable measure than the median in the sense that it varies less from sample to sample. When we turn our attention to inductive statistics we shall see that the researcher is ordinarily much more interested in generalizing about a population than he is in his particular sample. He is well aware of the fact that had another sample been taken the results would not have been quite the same. Had a very large number of samples of the same size been drawn he would be able to see just how much the sample means differed among themselves. What we are saying, here, is that the sample medians will differ from one sample to the next more than will the means. Since, in actuality, we usually draw only one sample it is important to know that the measure we use will give reliable results in that there will be minimal variability from one sample to the next. We can therefore state the following rule of thumb: *when in doubt, use the mean in preference to the median.*

Because of the fact that it uses all the data, whereas the median does not depend upon extreme values, the mean may give very misleading results under some circumstances. We must keep in mind that in making use of a measure of central tendency we are attempting to obtain a simple description of what is "typical" of our scores. Suppose, to take an extreme case, that the highest score in the series of five numbers had been 962. The median would remain at 72, but the mean would become 1,241/5 or 248.2. Is this value in any sense "typical" of the scores? Certainly not. It is nowhere near the score of any of the five cases. It is true, of course, that in such an extreme example no single measure could be used to describe adequately the typical case, but since four out of the five scores are around 72, the use of the median would obviously be less misleading. We may say, then, that *whenever a distribution is highly skewed,* i.e., whenever there are considerably more extreme cases in one direction than the other, *the median will generally be more appropriate than the mean*.

The relationship between skewness and the relative positions of the mean and median is indicated in Fig. 5.1. Since the mean can be very much affected by a few extreme values, the mean will be "pulled" in the direction of skewness, i.e., toward the tail. If the distribution is perfectly symmetrical, the mean and median will coincide. We know that income distributions are usually skewed toward the higher incomes, with a very few extremely high incomes. It might therefore be misleading to report mean incomes within a corporation or small community. For this reason income data are usually reported using the median rather than the mean. If a distribution is highly skewed, of course, this fact should be mentioned in reporting the data. In such instances it might be of some value to report both the mean and the median, although this is seldom done in practice.

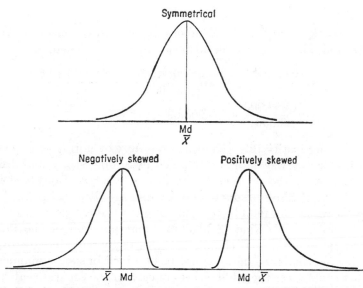

Fig. 5.1. Relationship between skewness and the relative positions of the mean and median.

The mean has a second property not possessed by the median: it is more easily manipulated algebraically. For example, it is sometimes necessary to obtain a weighted average from several sets of data. Suppose that we have the following mean incomes for three communities, A, B, and C:

Community	Size	Mean
A	10,000	$3,518
B	5,000	4,760
C	8,000	4,122

If the sizes of all three communities were exactly the same we could take the mean of these three scores as the over-all mean. But community A is twice as large as community B. In other words, the figure $3,518 represents twice as many cases as does $4,760. Had all 23,000 persons been thrown together and the over-all mean computed, the resulting figure would have reflected this fact. To obtain the correct mean we must weight each separate mean by the proper number of cases and then sum, dividing finally by the total number of cases (23,000). We thus get

$$\bar{X} = \frac{\sum_{i=1}^{k} N_i \bar{X}_i}{N} \tag{5.8}$$

where N_i and $\bar{X}_i$ represent the number of cases and the mean for the ith category, and k indicates the number of categories. Therefore

$$\bar{X} = \frac{10,000(3,518) + 5,000(4,760) + 8,000(4,122)}{23,000}$$

$$= \frac{91,956,000}{23,000} = \$3,998.09$$

We can easily justify this weighting procedure by noting that the mean of the ith category was actually obtained by adding scores and dividing by N_i. Therefore the product $N_i \bar{X}_i$ represents the *sum* of all scores in this category. Adding products and dividing by the total N thus gives us the same result as would have been obtained had categories been completely ignored. This kind of algebraic manipulation of the mean is sometimes quite useful. It should be readily apparent that the over-all median for the combined data cannot be obtained in such a manner. If we knew the values of the middle cases of each of the separate categories, we would still not know the value of the middle case for the combined data.

A final important difference between the mean and the median should be noted. The computation of the mean requires an interval scale. Without an interval scale it would be meaningless, of course, to talk about summing scores. It is obviously necessary to assume, for example, that the sum of the numbers 30 and 45 is equivalent to the sum of 20 and 55 since both pairs possess the same mean. The median, on the other hand, can be used for ordinal as well as interval scales. The actual numerical score of the median will be meaningless unless we have an interval scale, but it will certainly be possible to *locate* the middle score. This means that, among other things, we can separate the cases into one of two categories according to whether they are above or below the median. Positional measures can therefore be used with ordinal scales, a fact which is very useful in developing tests which do not require interval scales.

5.5. Other Measures of Central Tendency

There are several additional measures of central tendency, none of which are very commonly used in sociological research. One such measure is the *mode* which is simply the *most frequent* score or scores. If we take the following series of numbers

(1)   71, 75, 83, 75, 61, 68
(2)   71, 75, 83, 74, 61, 68
(3)   71, 75, 83, 75, 83, 68

we may say that the first has a mode of 75 since there are two individuals with this score and no other score appears twice. There is no mode in the second series of numbers, but there are two modes in the third (75 and

Fig. 5.2. A bimodal distribution.

83). The mode is perhaps more useful when there are a larger number of cases and when data have been grouped. We then sometimes speak of a modal category, taking the mid-point of this category as the mode. In the grouped data we have been using, the modal category would be $5,000 to $5,900. In a frequency distribution the mode will be indicated by the highest point on the curve. In a symmetrical distribution with a single mode at the center, the mean, median, and mode will of course all be identical. We also can distinguish between "unimodal" and "bimodal" distributions, the latter taking a form as in Fig. 5.2. In referring to bimodal distributions we usually do not assume that both peaks are of exactly the same height, as would be implied by the definition. It should be noted that since the mode refers to the category with the largest number of cases, we can make use of this concept in describing nominal as well as ordinal and interval scales.

Two other measures of central tendency which are practically never seen in the sociological literature are the *harmonic mean* and the *geometric mean*. They are defined by the formulas

$$\text{Harmonic mean} = \frac{N}{\displaystyle\sum_{i=1}^{N} \frac{1}{X_i}}$$

$$\text{Geometric mean} = \sqrt[N]{(X_1)(X_2) \cdots (X_N)}$$

In the latter formula, the N over the radical indicates that we are taking the Nth root of the product of the N scores.

5.6. Deciles, Quartiles, and Percentiles

In discussing the median, we pointed out that there are certain other positional measures such as percentiles which can be used to locate the position of scores which are larger than a given proportion of cases. These measures, although not necessarily measures of typicality or central tendency, are directly analogous to the median. Thus instead of finding a number which has half of the scores above or below it, we may wish to determine the value of the first quartile, which has the property that one-fourth of the scores are of lesser magnitude. Similarly, the third quartile represents the score having three-quarters of the cases below it in magnitude. If one prefers, he may divide the distribution into 10 deciles by locating scores that have one-tenth, two-tenths, or nine-tenths of the cases with lower values. You are perhaps more familiar with percentiles which divide the distribution into 100 portions of equal size. Thus a student falling at the ninety-first percentile on an examination knows that 91 per cent of the other students had lower scores than himself.

The computation of deciles, quartiles, and percentiles is directly analogous to the computation of the median. In the case of grouped data, we would first determine the interval within which the desired positional measure falls. Using the data of Table 5.4, we would obtain the first quartile by locating the position of the $N/4$th or the 47.25th case. From our cumulative-frequency column we see that the first quartile must lie somewhere within the interval \$3,950 to \$4,950. Since there are 38 cases within this interval, we must go $(47.25 - 43)/38$ of this distance. Thus, the value of the first quartile Q_1 would be

$$Q_1 = 3,950 + \frac{47.25 - 43}{38} \, 1,000 = 3,950 + 112 = \$4,062$$

Other positional measures can be computed in a similar manner. Notice, incidentally, that the median is by definition equivalent to the second quartile, the fifth decile, and the fiftieth percentile. Although deciles, quartiles, and percentiles are seldom used in sociological research, their meanings should at least be familiar.

GLOSSARY

Decile
Mean
Median
Mode
Percentile
Quartile
Skewed distribution

EXERCISES

1. Give the mean, median, and mode of the following numbers: 26, 37, 43, 21, 58, 26, 33, and 45.

2. Compute a mean and median for the data you grouped in Exercise 1, Chap. 4. Do the same for Exercise 2, Chap. 4.

3. Compute the third quartile, the fourth decile, and the seventy-first percentile for the data of Exercise 1, Chap. 4.

4. The following (hypothetical) data show the distribution of the percentage of farm families in 60 counties. Compute the mean and median.

Interval, %	Frequency
10–19	7
20–29	16
30–39	21
40–49	12
50–59	4
	60

5. Using the data for the previous example, indicate how the mean and median would be affected (raised, lowered, or remain the same) if

   a. The last interval were widened to read 50 to 69, with frequencies remaining the same;
   b. Ten per cent were added to each interval (making intervals 20 to 29, 30 to 39, etc.), with frequencies remaining the same;
   c. Intervals remained unchanged, but two cases in the 20 to 29 category were put in the 30 to 39 category (making frequencies 7, 14, 23, 12, and 4);
   d. Intervals remained unchanged, but each frequency were doubled.

6. A group of 10 boys and 7 girls take an algebra quiz. Suppose the mean score for the boys is 84, their median being 74. Both the mean and the median for the girls turn out to be 79. The teacher concludes that on this test the boys did better than the girls. Is her conclusion justified? Why or why not? How might you account for the large difference between the mean and median scores for the boys?

7. Suppose one finds the mean age of the 50 governors to be 51.6, the mean age of 100 senators to be 62.3, and the mean age of 435 representatives to be 44.7. What is the mean age of all of these politicians? Suppose the above figures represented median ages. Could you obtain the over-all median in the same manner? Why or why not?

REFERENCES

1. Dornbusch, S. M., and C. F. Schmid: *A Primer of Social Statistics*, McGraw-Hill Book Company, Inc., New York, 1955, chaps. 5 and 8.
2. Hagood, M. J., and D. O. Price: *Statistics for Sociologists*, Henry Holt and Company, Inc., New York, 1952, chap. 8.
3. Wallis, W. A., and H. V. Roberts: *Statistics: A New Approach*, Free Press, Glencoe, Ill., 1956, chap. 7.

Chapter 6

INTERVAL SCALES: MEASURES OF DISPERSION

In many instances in sociological research the focus of attention is on measures of central tendency. For example, we may wish to compare several religious denominations with respect to average attendance or income level. We may also wish to obtain measures of homogeneity, however. Perhaps we have hypothesized that one of the denominations will be more likely than the others to attract its membership from a single social stratum. But even if we are primarily interested in comparing measures of central tendency we still may need to know something about the dispersion in each group. We realize intuitively that if each denomination were extremely heterogeneous with respect to income background or church attendance, then a given difference between their means (say $2,000) would not be as important or indicative as would be the case if each group were quite homogeneous. When we come to inductive statistics we shall be in a position to justify this intuition and to see why measures of dispersion are so important. In the present chapter we must concentrate on mechanics. In the following chapter will be given an interpretation for the most important measure of dispersion, the standard deviation.

6.1. The Range

Of the several measures of dispersion to be discussed in this chapter, the range is by far the simplest. The range is defined as the difference between the highest and lowest scores. Thus, for the data given in the previous chapter (72, 81, 86, 69, and 57) the range would be the difference between 86 and 57, or 29. We usually indicate the range either by the actual difference (29) or by giving the two extreme scores, e.g., 57 and 86. If data have been grouped we take as the range the difference between the *mid-points* of the extreme categories. Thus, if the mid-point of the lowest interval is 2,450 and that of the highest is 7,450, the range will be 5,000.

The extreme simplicity of the range as a measure of dispersion is both an advantage and a disadvantage. The range may prove useful if it is desirable to obtain some very quick calculations which can give a rough indication of dispersion or if computations must be made by persons unacquainted with statistics. If data are to be presented to a relatively unsophisticated audience, the range may be the only measure of dispersion which will be readily interpreted. The level of sophistication of social scientists is rapidly reaching the point, however, where we can assume that more satisfactory measures will be understood. The disadvantage of the range is obvious: it is based on only two cases, the two extreme cases at that. Since extremes are likely to be the rare or unusual cases in most empirical problems, we recognize that it is usually a matter of chance if we happen to get one or two in our sample. Suppose, for example, that there is one millionnaire in the community sampled. If we choose 10 persons at random he will probably not be included. But suppose he is. The range in incomes will then be extremely large and very misleading as a measure of dispersion. If we use the range as our measure, we know nothing about the variability of scores between the two extreme values except that the scores lie somewhere within this range. And, as implied in the above example, the range will vary considerably from one sample to the next. Furthermore, the range will ordinarily be greater for large samples than small ones simply because in large samples we have a better chance of including the most extreme individuals. For these reasons, the range is not ordinarily used in sociology except at the most exploratory levels.

6.2. The Quartile Deviation

Another measure which is sometimes used in the fields of psychology and education but which seldom appears in the sociological literature is the quartile deviation or semi-interquartile range. The quartile deviation Q is a type of range, but instead of representing the difference between extreme values it is arbitrarily defined as half the distance between the first and third quartiles. Symbolically,

$$Q = \frac{Q_3 - Q_1}{2} \tag{6.1}$$

where Q_1 and Q_3 represent the first and third quartiles respectively. Notice that the quartile deviation measures the range covered by the middle half of the cases. Since Q_1 and Q_3 will vary less from sample to sample than the most extreme cases, the quartile deviation is a far more stable measure than the range. On the other hand, it does not take advantage of all the information. We are not measuring the variability among the middle cases nor are we taking into consideration what is happening at the extremes of the distribution. We shall therefore turn our attention to two measures which do have this desirable property.

6.3. The Mean Deviation

If we wish to make use of all scores, common sense would suggest that we take the deviations of each score from some measure of central tendency and then compute some kind of average of these deviations in order to control for the number of cases involved. It would be possible to use the median or mode as our measure of central tendency, but we ordinarily take the mean since this is the most satisfactory single measure under most circumstances. Suppose we were simply to sum the actual deviations from the mean. Unfortunately, as we know, the result would always be zero since the positive and negative differences would cancel each other. This suggests that in order to obtain a measure of dispersion about the mean we must somehow or other get rid of the negative signs. Two methods immediately occur to us: (1) ignore signs, taking the absolute value of the differences, or (2) square the differences. These two methods lead to the two remaining measures of dispersion to be discussed in this chapter, the mean deviation and the standard deviation.

The mean deviation is defined as the arithmetic mean of the absolute differences of each score from the mean. In symbols

$$\text{Mean deviation} = \frac{\sum_{i=1}^{N} |X_i - \bar{X}|}{N} \tag{6.2}$$

The mean of the numbers 72, 81, 86, 69, and 57 is 73.0. Subtracting 73.0 from each of these numbers, ignoring the sign, and then adding the results and dividing by 5 we get

$$\frac{\sum_{i=1}^{N} |X_i - \bar{X}|}{N} = \frac{1 + 8 + 13 + 4 + 16}{5} = \frac{42}{5} = 8.4$$

We may therefore say that on the average the scores differ from the mean by 8.4.

Although the mean deviation has a more direct intuitive interpretation than the standard deviation it has several serious disadvantages. First, absolute values are not easily manipulated algebraically. Second, and more important, the mean deviation is not as easily interpreted theoretically nor does it lead to as simple mathematical results. For purely descriptive purposes, the mean deviation may be adequate although, as we shall see, the standard deviation can be interpreted more readily in terms of the normal curve.   When we come to inductive statistics we shall see that the standard deviation is used almost exclusively because of its theoretical superiority.   For this reason, we seldom see references to the mean deviation in sociological literature.

6.4. The Standard Deviation

Having more or less eliminated several other measures of dispersion, we can turn our attention to the most useful and frequently used measure, the standard deviation.   The standard deviation is defined as the square root of the arithmetic mean of the squared deviations from the mean. In symbols

$$s = \sqrt{\frac{\sum_{i=1}^{N} (X_i - \bar{X})^2}{N}} \tag{6.3}$$

where s is used to represent the standard deviation.[1]   In words, we take the deviation of each score from the mean, square each difference, sum the results, divide by the number of cases, and then take the square root. If we are to get the correct answer, it is essential that the operations be carried out in exactly this order.   In our numerical example the standard deviation could be obtained as follows:

X_i	$(X_i - \bar{X})$	$(X_i - \bar{X})^2$
72	−1	1
81	8	64
86	13	169
69	−4	16
57	−16	256
$\bar{X} = 73.0$	0	506

$$s = \sqrt{506/5} = \sqrt{101.2} = 10.06$$

The intuitive meaning of a standard deviation of 10.06 will not be apparent until later when we make use of s to give us areas under the normal curve.   For the present, we simply accept it as an abstract number.   Several properties of the standard deviation are readily apparent, however.   We notice that the greater the spread about the

---

[1] Some texts define s with $N - 1$ in the denominator rather than N.   The reason for this will not be apparent until Chap. 11.

mean, the larger the standard deviation. Had all five values been the same, the deviations about the mean would all have been zero and s would also be zero. Furthermore, we see that extreme deviations from the mean have by far the greatest weight in determining the value of the standard deviation. The values 169 and 256 dominate the other three squared deviations. In squaring the deviations, even though we later take a square root, we are in effect giving even more relative weight to extreme values than was the case in computing the mean. This suggests that we must qualify our initial enthusiasm about the standard deviation as the single "best" measure of dispersion. Certainly if there are several extreme cases we want our measure to indicate this fact. But if the distribution has a few very extreme cases, the standard deviation can give misleading results in that it may be unusually large. In such instances we would probably use the median as our measure of central tendency and, perhaps, the quartile deviation as a measure of dispersion. For most data the standard deviation will be appropriate, however.

It is reasonable to ask, "Why bother to take the square root in computing a measure of dispersion?" One easy but unsatisfactory answer would be that this is the way the standard deviation is defined. It would be possible to justify taking the square root by pointing out that since we have squared each deviation we are essentially compensating for this earlier step. It makes more sense, however, to justify taking a square root in terms of its practicality. Since we shall make considerable use of the normal curve later on, the standard deviation, as defined, turns out to be a very useful measure. For other purposes we shall make use of the square of the standard deviation or *variance* which is defined as

$$\text{Variance} = s^2 = \frac{\sum_{i=1}^{N} (X_i - \bar{X})^2}{N}$$

Mathematicians have found the concept of variance of more theoretical value than the standard deviation. Beginning with Chap. 16 we shall make increasing use of the variance, but for the present we can confine our attention to the standard deviation. The two concepts are so easily interchangeable that we can pass readily from the one to the other. Whether one defines the variance as the square of the standard deviation or the standard deviation as the square root of the variance is unimportant.

Computation of Standard Deviation from Ungrouped Data. Although the standard deviation can always be computed from the basic formula given above, it is often simpler to make use of computing formulas which do not require the subtraction of the mean from each separate score. Not only will the mean not ordinarily be a whole number, but rounding errors will usually be made if the above formula is used. In order to see how we can simplify the computations, let us expand the expression under the radical. We get

$$\frac{\sum_{i=1}^{N} (X_i - \bar{X})^2}{N} = \frac{\sum_{i=1}^{N} (X_i^2 - 2X_i\bar{X} + \bar{X}^2)}{N} = \frac{\sum_{i=1}^{N} X_i^2 - 2\bar{X} \sum_{i=1}^{N} X_i + N\bar{X}^2}{N}$$

Notice that since $\bar{X}$ is a constant we were able to take it in front of the summation sign in the second term of the numerator. In the third term, we have made use of the fact that for any constant k

$$\sum_{i=1}^{N} k = Nk$$

But since $\bar{X} = \sum_{i=1}^{N} X_i/N$, the middle term reduces to $-2\bar{X}^2$ and we may write

$$\frac{\sum_{i=1}^{N} (X_i - \bar{X})^2}{N} = \frac{\sum_{i=1}^{N} X_i^2}{N} - 2\bar{X}^2 + \bar{X}^2 = \frac{\sum_{i=1}^{N} X_i^2}{N} - \bar{X}^2$$

Therefore
$$s = \sqrt{\frac{\sum_{i=1}^{N} X_i^2}{N} - \bar{X}^2} \tag{6.4}$$

Some alternative computing formulas are as follows:

$$s = \sqrt{\frac{\sum_{i=1}^{N} X_i^2}{N} - \left(\frac{\sum_{i=1}^{N} X_i}{N}\right)^2} \tag{6.5}$$

$$= \sqrt{\frac{\sum_{i=1}^{N} X_i^2 - \frac{\left(\sum_{i=1}^{N} X_i\right)^2}{N}}{N}} \tag{6.6}[2]$$

$$= \frac{1}{N} \sqrt{N \sum_{i=1}^{N} X_i^2 - \left(\sum_{i=1}^{N} X_i\right)^2} \tag{6.7}$$

[2] The derivation of equations (6.6) and (6.7) from equation (6.5) is left as an exercise.

Although any of the above forms may be used as computing formulas, equation (6.7) will involve the fewest rounding errors and is therefore recommended.

Let us make use of one of these computing formulas (Eq. 6.7) in the above problem where $N = 5$.

X_i	$X_i{}^2$
72	5,184
81	6,561
86	7,396
69	4,761
57	3,249
365	27,151

In addition to the total number of cases, the two quantities needed are $\sum_{i=1}^{N} X_i$ and $\sum_{i=1}^{N} X_i{}^2$. Both sums can be accumulated simultaneously on modern desk calculators. We now compute s from (6.7).

$$s = \tfrac{1}{5} \sqrt{5(27{,}151) - (365)^2} = \tfrac{1}{5} \sqrt{135{,}755 - 133{,}225} = 10.06$$

We have made use of this very simple problem in order to illustrate that the computing formula gives the same numerical result as the basic formula (Eq. 6.3). Since $\bar{X}$ turned out to be a whole number, the computing formula actually involved more work than did the original formula. Usually, of course, this will not be the case.

Computation of Standard Deviation from Grouped Data. When data have been grouped, we may simplify our work considerably by treating each case as though it were at the mid-point of an interval and by making use of a guessed mean. Of course, we thereby introduce certain inaccuracies, but the saving in time will be substantial. Following a common convention, suppose we let $x_i = X_i - \bar{X}$. The small x's therefore represent deviations from the mean, and the basic formula for the standard deviation becomes

$$s = \sqrt{\frac{\sum_{i=1}^{N} x_i{}^2}{N}}$$

We can now modify the formula to take into consideration the fact that there will be a large number of cases all treated as having the same value, i.e., one of the mid-points. If we multiply the number of cases in each class by the proper mid-point and then sum these products, we can save ourselves the work of adding up all N cases. The formula for the standard deviation then becomes

$$s = \sqrt{\frac{\sum\limits_{i=1}^{k} f_i x_i^2}{N}} \tag{6.8}$$

where f_i is the number of cases in the ith interval and k is the number of intervals.

Now suppose we were to guess a mean and to take deviations from the guessed mean instead of the true mean. We have shown in the previous chapter that the sum of the squared deviations from the mean will be less than the sum of the squared deviations from any other value. In particular, the sum of the squared deviations from the guessed mean will be larger than the figure obtained using the true mean unless, of course, the guessed mean actually equals the true mean. It can also be shown that the closer the guessed mean is to the true mean, the smaller the sum of the squared deviations from the guessed mean. In other words, if we use a guessed mean we expect to find a sum of squares which is too large. We can, as before, make use of a correction factor which we then subtract from the value obtained using the guessed mean. The formula for the standard deviation then becomes

$$s = \sqrt{\frac{\sum\limits_{i=1}^{k} f_i d_i^2}{N} - \left(\frac{\sum\limits_{i=1}^{k} f_i d_i}{N}\right)^2} \tag{6.9}$$

where the d_i represent the differences between each score and the guessed mean and are directly analogous to the x_i in equation (6.8).

Before taking up a numerical example, let us examine the above formula more carefully. The second term under the radical represents the correction factor to be subtracted from the mean of the squared deviations from the guessed mean. Recalling the formula for the mean expressed in terms of the guessed mean, i.e.,

$$\bar{X} = \bar{X}' + \frac{\sum\limits_{i=1}^{k} f_i d_i}{N}$$

we see that

$$\frac{\sum\limits_{i=1}^{k} f_i d_i}{N} = \bar{X} - \bar{X}'$$

and therefore

$$\left(\frac{\sum\limits_{i=1}^{k} f_i d_i}{N}\right)^2 = (\bar{X} - \bar{X}')^2$$

Thus the correction factor turns out to be the square of the difference between the true and guessed means. We see immediately that had we guessed the mean exactly, the correction factor would have been zero. Also, the greater the difference between the true and guessed means, the larger the correction factor. A poor guess will always lead to the correct result but will involve larger numerical scores for both terms in the formula.

The formula can be modified still further if we prefer to think in terms of step deviations d_i'. As in Chap. 5, we factor out the width of the interval from each d_i, multiplying the final result by i when we have finished the process. The formula then becomes

$$s = \sqrt{\frac{\sum_{i=1}^{k} f_i d_i^2}{N} - \left(\frac{\sum_{i=1}^{k} f_i d_i}{N}\right)^2} = \sqrt{\frac{i^2 \sum_{i=1}^{k} f_i d_i'^2}{N} - \left(\frac{i \sum_{i=1}^{k} f_i d_i'}{N}\right)^2}$$

Therefore

$$s = i \sqrt{\frac{\sum_{i=1}^{k} f_i d_i'^2}{N} - \left(\frac{\sum_{i=1}^{k} f_i d_i'}{N}\right)^2} \tag{6.10}$$

$$= i \sqrt{\frac{\sum_{i=1}^{k} f_i d_i'^2 - \frac{\left(\sum_{i=1}^{k} f_i d_i'\right)^2}{N}}{N}} \tag{6.11}$$

$$= \frac{i}{N} \sqrt{N \sum_{i=1}^{k} f_i d_i'^2 - \left(\sum_{i=1}^{k} f_i d_i'\right)^2} \tag{6.12}$$

Notice that in effect we have merely taken the interval width i outside the radical.

When computing the standard deviation from grouped data, we can now extend the procedure used for the mean by adding the column $f_i d_i'^2$. Although we could actually obtain the squared deviations $d_i'^2$ and then multiply by f_i, it will be much simpler to multiply the last two columns used in obtaining the mean (i.e., $d_i' \times f_i d_i'$). Having in effect multiplied d_i' by itself, we see that all negative numbers now become positive. Let us now compute the standard deviation for the grouped data used in the previous chapter. For illustrative purposes we shall use equation (6.10), although equation (6.12) will ordinarily involve fewer rounding errors.

We thus have obtained a mean of $5,117 and a standard deviation of $1,444. These two numbers can now be used to summarize the data or to compare them with data from another sample. As will be seen later,

Table 6.1. Computation of Standard Deviation, Using Grouped Data

True limits	Mid-points	f_i	d_i'	$f_i d_i'$	$f_i d_i'^2$
$1,950–2,950	$2,450	17	−3	−51	153
2,950–3,950	3,450	26	−2	−52	104
3,950–4,950	4,450	38	−1	−38	38
4,950–5,950	5,450	51	0	0	0
5,950–6,950	6,450	36	1	36	36
6,950–7,950	7,450	21	2	42	84
Totals		189		−63	415

$$s = i \sqrt{\frac{\sum\limits_{i=1}^{k} f_i d_i'^2}{N} - \left(\frac{\sum\limits_{i=1}^{k} f_i d_i'}{N}\right)^2}$$

$$= 1,000 \sqrt{\frac{415}{189} - \left(\frac{-63}{189}\right)^2} = 1,000 \sqrt{2.196 - .111}$$

$$= 1,444$$

they can also be used to test hypotheses or to estimate population measures.

6.5. The Coefficient of Variability

It is sometimes desirable to compare several groups with respect to their relative homogeneity in instances where the groups have very different means. It therefore might be somewhat misleading to compare the absolute magnitudes of the standard deviations. One might expect that with a very large mean he would find at least a fairly large standard deviation. He might therefore be primarily interested in the size of the standard deviation *relative to that of the mean*. This suggests that we can obtain a measure of the relative variability by dividing the standard deviation by the mean. The result has been termed the *coefficient of variability*, denoted by V. Thus

$$V = \frac{s}{\bar{X}}$$

To illustrate the advantages of the coefficient of variability over the standard deviation, suppose a social psychologist is attempting to show that for all practical purposes two groups are equally homogeneous with respect to age. In the one group the mean age is 26 with a standard deviation of 3. In the other, the mean age is 38 with a standard deviation of 5. The coefficients of variability for the two groups are therefore $3/26 = .115$ and $5/38 = .132$, a much smaller difference than that between the two standard deviations. In view of the fact that exact age usually becomes less important in determining interests, abilities, and social status as the average age of group members is increased, a comparison of the two coefficients of variability in this instance might very well be much less misleading than if the standard deviations were used.

It is also possible to make use of a relative variance if one so desires. Unfortunately, these relative measures of dispersion are rather infrequently reported in the sociological literature. More commonly, one finds the means and standard deviations listed in adjacent columns.

6.6. Other Summarizing Measures

We have discussed only two types of summarizing measures, measures of central tendency and measures of dispersion. Other kinds of measures are possible, although they are seldom used in sociological research. Of course we often find the entire frequency distribution given, but this is not a single summarizing measure. It is sometimes desirable to indicate the degree of skewness in a distribution. One measure of skewness takes advantage of the fact that the greater the skewness the larger the difference between the mean and the median. This measure is given by the formula

$$\text{Skewness} = \frac{3(\bar{X} - \text{Md})}{s}$$

If the distribution is skewed to the right (large positive scores), the mean will be greater than the median and the result will be a positive number. A distribution skewed to the left will produce a negative result.

Very infrequently in sociology we also find references to the general peakedness of a distribution. The term *kurtosis* is used to refer to this type of measure which will be discussed very briefly after we have taken up the normal curve. Statistics texts written primarily for students of economics usually go more deeply into both skewness and kurtosis. Perhaps as we begin to attain greater precision in describing the exact forms of distributions of sociological variables we may find more use for these other descriptive measures.

GLOSSARY

Coefficient of variability
Mean deviation
Quartile deviation
Range
Standard deviation
Variance

EXERCISES

1. Compute the mean deviation and standard deviation for the data given in Exercise 1, Chap. 5.

2. Compute the standard deviation and the quartile deviation for the data grouped in Exercise 1, Chap. 4. Do the same for Exercise 2, Chap. 4.

3. Compute the standard deviation for the data given in Exercise 4, Chap. 5. Check your computations by selecting a different guessed mean and a different computing formula.

4. Indicate how the standard deviation would be affected by each of the changes indicated in Exercise 5, Chap. 5.

REFERENCES

1. Dornbusch, S. M., and C. F. Schmid: *A Primer of Social Statistics*, McGraw-Hill Book Company, Inc., New York, 1955, chaps. 6 and 8.

2. Hagood, M. J., and D. O. Price: *Statistics for Sociologists*, Henry Holt and Company, Inc., New York, 1952, chap. 9.

3. Wallis, W. A., and H. V. Roberts: *Statistics: A New Approach*, Free Press, Glencoe, Ill., 1956, chap. 8.

(2)   mean = 4.3

S.D. = 3.24

Chapter 7

THE NORMAL DISTRIBUTION

The notion of a frequency distribution is already a familiar one. The present chapter is concerned with a very important kind of frequency distribution, the normal curve. This distribution is useful not only because a large number of empirical distributions are found to be approximately normal but also because of its theoretical significance in inductive statistics. At this point you should not be concerned about applications in which the normal curve is used. The purpose of this chapter is to indicate the properties of the normal curve and to enable you to gain facility in using tables based on the normal curve. This distribution is discussed under descriptive rather than inductive statistics for two principal reasons. First, the normal curve can be used to provide an interpretation for the standard deviation. Second, you will find it helpful to become familiar with the normal distribution several chapters before you are exposed to statistical tests which require facility with it. Therefore, the better your understanding of the materials in the present chapter the less difficulty you will experience later on.

7.1. Finite Versus Infinite Frequency Distributions

Frequency distributions discussed up to this point have involved a finite number of cases. Actually, of course, all empirical distributions necessarily involve a finite although perhaps very large number of cases. Mathematicians frequently find it useful to think in terms of distributions based on an indefinitely large number of cases, however. Rather than dealing with empirical distributions having a jagged appearance, as exemplified by a histogram or frequency polygon, it is possible to conceive of smooth curves which are based on an indefinitely large number of cases and which can be expressed in terms of relatively simple mathematical equations. The normal distribution is one such curve. Before studying this specific distribution it will be necessary to examine the nature of the process by which such a smooth curve is developed.

Let us start with a histogram involving five intervals (Fig. 7.1a). For simplicity we shall assume the frequency distribution to be symmetrical. We have already seen that if the number of intervals is increased without changing N, the form of the histogram is likely to become irregular. Suppose, however, that the number of cases is also increased. Then, as

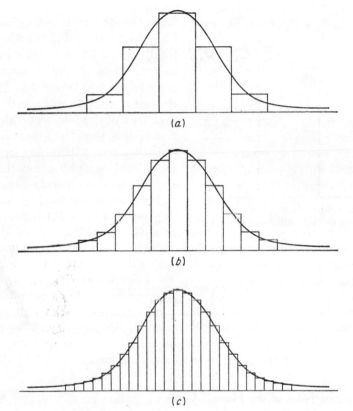

(a)

(b)

(c)

Fig. 7.1. Comparisons of smooth curves with histograms having different interval widths.

in Fig. 7.1b, it will be possible to make use of a larger number of narrower intervals, each of which has a sufficiently large number of cases to maintain regularity. If the number of cases is further increased, still more rectangles can be used while retaining the regular pattern (Fig. 7.1c). Smooth curves have been drawn through the mid-points of the top of each rectangle. It is clear that the rectangles form better and better approximations to the smooth curve as the number of rectangles increases, i.e., as the width of each interval decreases. We now imagine an ever-increasing number of cases and correspondingly narrower intervals until the rectangles approximate the smooth curve so closely that we can no longer see any difference. We refer to the smooth curve approximated by the ever-narrowing rectangles as the *limiting* frequency distribution.[1] Although we cannot possibly imagine an infinite number of cases, we can conceive of such a large number that the rectangles approximate the smooth curve to within any desired degree of accuracy.

It will be remembered that the *area* of each rectangle can be used to represent the proportion of cases within the interval. As indicated in

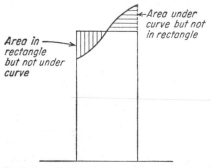

Chap. 4, it is customary to set the total area of all rectangles equal to unity. Thus if the proportion of cases in the first interval is .10, then this same number represents the actual area of the first rectangle. We now notice that the area under the smooth curve within any given interval can be approximated by the area of the corresponding rectangle. This is indicated in Fig. 7.2. As the number of rectangles is increased, the total area of the rec-

Fig. 7.2. Comparison of areas under smooth curve and under rectangle.

tangles becomes a better and better approximation to the area under the smooth curve. This can be seen by noting that the shaded areas become relatively smaller and smaller. In the limit, then, the area under the smooth curve can be obtained by summing the areas of an indefinitely large number of rectangles. Since the area under the rectangles is unity, the area under the smooth curve will also be unity. The process we have just described is exactly the kind of process underlying that branch of mathematics referred to as the calculus.

7.2. General Form of the Normal Curve

The normal curve is a special type of symmetrical smooth curve. Since the normal curve is smooth, perfectly symmetrical, and based on an indefinitely large number of cases, it can only be approximated by frequency distributions involving actual data. It is bell-shaped in form and has a number of remarkable mathematical properties, some of which will be indicated shortly. Since it is symmetrical and unimodal, its mean, median, and mode all coincide. The general form of the normal distribution is indicated in Fig. 7.3.

*The mathematical equation for the normal curve is relatively simple by mathematicians' standards. Although you will never have to use this formula for computations since tables have been constructed for this

[1] The notion of a limit is also discussed in Sec. 9.1.

purpose, it will be instructive to use it to point out and verify some of the properties of this theoretical distribution. The formula is as follows:

$$Y = \frac{1}{s\sqrt{2\pi}}\, e^{-(X-\bar{X})^2/2s^2}$$

where Y is the height of the curve for any given value of X. Since both π and e are constants (equal to 3.14 and 2.72, respectively), the formula involves only two summarizing measures, the mean $\bar{X}$ and the standard

Fig. 7.3. General form of the normal curve.

deviation s.[2] Therefore, the exact form of the normal curve will be known if we are given the values of both the mean and standard deviation. In other words, there are many different normal curves, one for every combination of mean and standard deviation.

*Recalling that a quantity with a negative exponent can be written as the reciprocal of that quantity raised to a positive power, we may rewrite the formula as follows:

$$Y = \frac{1}{s\sqrt{2\pi}}\left(\frac{1}{2.72^{(X-\bar{X})^2/2s^2}}\right)$$

where the constant e has been replaced by its numerical value. Let us assume that s has a fixed value and find the value of X for which Y will be a maximum. Clearly, Y will be at its maximum when the denominator within the parentheses is a minimum. But this denominator consists of a positive number greater than unity raised to a power which cannot be negative since a squared real number can never be less than zero. The denominator will therefore take on its minimum value when the exponent is zero. This will occur when X takes on the value $\bar{X}$ since we will then have $X - \bar{X} = 0$. This shows that the mode (and therefore the mean and median) is actually $\bar{X}$, a fact that has already been pointed out but not demonstrated. Also, we can see that the equation yields a curve which is symmetrical about $\bar{X}$. Since the quantity $X - \bar{X}$ is squared and therefore cannot be negative, deviations from $\bar{X}$ in either direction will produce identical values of Y.

[2] Other notation for the mean and standard deviation will be introduced when we come to inductive statistics. The formula for the normal curve is usually written in terms of a mean of μ (mu) and a standard deviation of σ.

The specific equation for any particular normal curve can be obtained by using the proper values of $\bar{X}$ and s. Normal curves having the same standard deviations but different means are drawn in Fig. 7.4. On the other hand, curves having different standard deviations will vary in

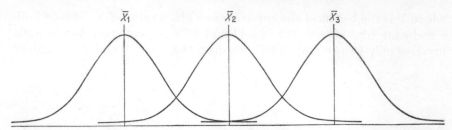

Fig. 7.4. Comparison of normal curves with the same standard deviations but different means.

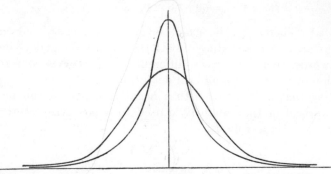

Fig. 7.5. Comparison of two normal curves with the same means but different standard deviations.

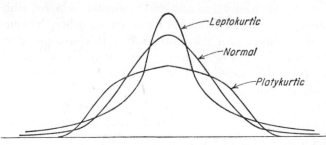

Fig. 7.6. Comparison of normal curve with curves having the same standard deviation but which differ with respect to peakedness.

peakedness as indicated in Fig. 7.5. The smaller the standard deviation the more peaked the curve.

It should be pointed out that all symmetrical bell-shaped curves are not normal. Although the curves in Fig. 7.5 differ with respect to peakedness, this is due only to differences in their standard deviations.

They are all normal in form. In general, unimodal symmetrical curves may be either more peaked or more flat than the normal curve even though their standard deviations are all the same. Several such curves are drawn in Fig. 7.6. Curves which are more peaked than the normal curve are referred to as *leptokurtic* and those which are flatter than normal as *platykurtic*. Unlike the normal curve, the equations of leptokurtic and platykurtic curves are likely to involve summarizing measures in addition to the mean and standard deviation.

7.3. Areas under the Normal Curve

It is frequently necessary to determine the proportion of cases falling within a given interval. Fortunately, the normal curve has an important

Fig. 7.7. Areas under the normal curve.

property which makes this task a relatively simple one. It turns out that regardless of the particular mean or standard deviation a normal curve may have, there will be a *constant area* (or proportion of cases) *between the mean and an ordinate which is a given distance from the mean in terms of standard deviation units.* Fig. 7.7 helps to illustrate the meaning of the above statement.

Thus if we go one standard deviation to the right of the mean we shall always find .3413 of the area included between the mean and an ordinate drawn at this point. Therefore twice this area, or .6826, will be included between the two ordinates which are located one standard deviation on either side of the mean. In other words, slightly over two-thirds of the cases will always be within one standard deviation of the mean. Similarly, the area between the mean and an ordinate two standard deviations away will always be .4773, and therefore slightly over 95 per cent of the area will be included between the pair of ordinates which are two standard deviations on either side of the mean. Practically all the cases will be within three standard deviations of the mean even though the normal curve theoretically extends infinitely far in either direction. Distances from the mean need not always be exact multiples of the standard deviation, of course. By means of a procedure to be described shortly it is possible to determine the areas between any two ordinates. For example, if we go out 1.96 standard deviations on either side of the mean we shall include almost exactly 95 per cent of the area; 99 per cent of the area will be included between ordinates which are 2.58 standard deviations from the mean.

This property of the normal curve affords an interpretation for the standard deviation and a method of visualizing the meaning of this measure of dispersion. A number of empirical frequency distributions are sufficiently similar to the normal distribution that these relationships between areas and the standard deviation will hold up reasonably well. Even in the case of income distributions which are likely to be skewed in the direction of high incomes, we usually find approximately two-thirds of the cases within one standard deviation of the mean. It should be kept in mind that although the normal curve provides an *interpretation* for the standard deviation, this property cannot be used to *define* what is meant by a standard deviation. The definition is in terms of its formula. The above property holds only in the case of normal or approximately normal distributions.

It is possible to take any particular normal curve and to transform numerical values for this curve into such a form that a single table can be used to evaluate the proportion of cases within any desired interval. We can illustrate the process with a numerical example. Suppose we have a normal curve with mean 50 and standard deviation 10. Let us find the proportion of cases within the interval 50 to 65. We first determine how many standard deviations 65 is from the mean 50. In order to do this, we take the difference between these two values, i.e., 15, and divide by the size of the standard deviation. In this case the result is 1.5. Generally, we can make use of the formula

$$Z = \frac{X - \bar{X}}{s}$$

$$= \frac{65 - 50}{10} = 1.5$$

where X is the value of the ordinate and where Z represents the deviation from the mean in standard-deviation units.

*Before discussing how the numerical value of Z can be used to determine the proportion of cases between the mean and the ordinate corresponding to Z, let us give an alternative interpretation of Z. We can think in terms of an actual transformation from the X variable to a new variable Z. Whereas the distribution of the X variable is normal with a mean $\bar{X}$ and standard deviation s, the new variable is normal with a mean of zero and a standard deviation of one.[3]   A normal distribution with mean zero and standard deviation one is referred to as the *standard form* and the Z is often called a *standard score*.   The transformation of variables is illustrated in Fig. 7.8.   From every X we subtract the constant $\bar{X}$.   In subtracting this constant value (here, 50) from each X we have shifted every original score 50 units to the left and have therefore in effect moved the original normal curve to a position directly over the origin.   This takes care of the numerator in the expression for Z.   We

Fig. 7.8. Comparison of standard and general forms of the normal curve.

now divide each difference $X - \bar{X}$ by the size of the standard deviation. In so doing we either squeeze the original curve or spread it out depending on whether or not its standard deviation is greater or less than unity. We can thus think of having first shifted the position of the original normal curve and then having changed the size of the standard deviation so as to superimpose it on the standard form.   In dividing by the standard deviation of 10 we have essentially changed units along the horizontal axis so that a distance of 10 along the X axis corresponds to a distance of 1 along the Z axis.

Regardless of which interpretation is given, a value of $Z = 1.5$ indicates that the ordinate is 1.5 standard deviations from the mean.   In the case of the standard form this of course means that the ordinate itself falls at the value 1.5 on the Z scale.   Tables showing exact areas have been constructed for the standard form of the normal curve.   Table C in Appendix 2 is one such table.   The values of Z are given down the left-hand margin and across the top.   The first two digits of Z are obtained by reading down and the third by reading across.   Figures within the body of the table indicate the proportion of the area between the mean (i.e., 0) and the ordinate corresponding to Z.   In the above example, we see that .4332 of the area is within these limits.   Had Z turned out to be 1.52 the corresponding area would have been .4357.

[3] The verification of this fact is left as an exercise.   (See Exercise 3.)

7.4. Further Illustrations of the Use of the Normal Table

Suppose we wish to find the shaded area in the normal curve indicated by Fig. 7.9.   The value of Z in this case is

$$Z = \frac{143 - 168}{12} = \frac{-25}{12} = -2.08$$

The fact that Z is negative simply indicates that the shaded area is to the left of the mean.   The sign of Z can be ignored when using the

Fig. 7.9. Normal curve, with shaded portion representing the area in a single tail.

normal table since the curve is perfectly symmetrical.   From the table we see that the area between the mean and a Z of 2.08 is .4812.   Since the total area is unity, the area to the left of the mean must be .5 (by symmetry).   The shaded area therefore can be obtained by subtracting the area between the mean and the ordinate from the total area to the left of the mean.   Thus,

$$(\text{Proportion of cases} \leq 143) = .5000 - .4812 = .0188$$

Therefore, fewer than 2 per cent of the cases have scores less than or equal to 143.[4]   The type of problem illustrated in this example is a very common one because of the fact that tests of hypotheses practically always involve the tails of a frequency distribution.   We therefore are often interested in the areas of one or both of these tails.   Had we wanted to obtain the total area outside of the region defined by 168 ± 25 (as indicated by the shaded areas in Fig. 7.10), we would simply have

[4] In a continuous distribution the proportion of cases which are exactly 143.0 will be zero.   This can be seen if we imagine two ordinates extremely close together. The proportion of cases between these ordinates will also be very small.   Now if we allow these ordinates to move closer and closer together, the proportion of cases will become infinitely small.   A mathematical line, it will be remembered, has no width. In practice there may be some cases with scores of 143.0 owing to measurement inaccuracies.   Since we are dealing with a theoretical distribution, however, it makes no difference whether or not the ordinate itself is included within the interval.   Henceforth, we shall simply refer to the area between (but not including) two ordinates or the area less than a given value.

doubled the above result since the two shaded areas are exactly equal in size.

To take another example, suppose we need to obtain the shaded area indicated in Fig. 7.11. This area is calculated by first finding the proportion of cases between the mean and ordinate B and subtracting

Fig. 7.10. Normal curve, with shaded portions representing areas in both tails.

Fig. 7.11. Normal curve, with shaded portion representing the area between two ordinates.

from this number the proportion of cases between the mean and ordinate A. The Z's corresponding to B and A are 2.0 and 1.2 respectively. Thus we have

Proportion between B and mean	.4773
Proportion between A and mean	.3849
Proportion between A and B	.0924

Therefore slightly over 9 per cent of the cases fall between .42 and .46. Notice that had we desired the area between two ordinates on opposite sides of the mean, the result could have been obtained by addition rather than subtraction.

GLOSSARY

Leptokurtic
Limiting-frequency distribution
Normal curve
Platykurtic
Standard score

EXERCISES

1. You have already computed the mean and standard deviation for the data given in Exercise 1, Chap. 4. What proportion of the 65 cases were within one standard deviation of the mean? Two standard deviations? Three standard deviations? How well do these figures approximate those we would expect if the distribution were exactly normal? Answer these same questions for Exercise 2, Chap. 4. Contrast and account for any differences between the results for the two sets of data.

2. If the mean of a normal distribution is 80 and its standard deviation 12:

   a. What proportion of the cases is between 80 and 93?

   b. What proportion of the cases is between 90 and 105?   70 and 105?

   c. What proportion of the cases is less than 68?

   d. How many standard deviations on either side of the mean would you need to go in order to obtain two tails each containing 2 per cent of the total area? Ten per cent of the total area?

   e. What score has 4 per cent of the cases above it?   (In other words, locate the ninety-sixth percentile.)

*3. Verify that the standard form of the normal curve has a mean of zero and a standard deviation of unity. [*Hint:* Rewrite the formula for the normal curve in terms of Z, using the fact that $Z = (X - \bar{X})/s$.]

4. Raw scores on various aptitude and attitudinal tests are often treated as interval scales by psychologists. These raw scores are then often converted to standard scores with convenient means and standard deviations. Suppose the mean raw score on a college entrance examination is 117 with a standard deviation of 28.5. Assume that these raw scores are distributed normally.

   a. What is the proportion of raw scores above 131?   Below 79?

   b. What are the raw scores corresponding to the first, second, and third quartiles?

   *c. On College Board exams, raw scores are standardized so that the mean of the normal distribution is exactly 500 and the standard deviation 100. Specifically, how would one go about standardizing the above set of scores to obtain a mean of 500 and a standard deviation of 100?   (*Hint:* How would you standardize to get a mean of zero and a standard deviation of unity?)

REFERENCES

1. Dornbusch, S. M., and C. F. Schmid: *A Primer of Social Statistics*, McGraw-Hill Book Company, Inc., New York, 1955, chap. 13.

2. Hagood, M. J., and D. O. Price: *Statistics for Sociologists*, Henry Holt and Company, Inc., New York, 1952, chap. 14.

Part III

INDUCTIVE STATISTICS

Chapter 8

INTRODUCTION TO INDUCTIVE STATISTICS

The purpose of this brief chapter is to give a general overview of inductive statistics and in particular the logic underlying the testing of statistical hypotheses. It is very easy to become so overwhelmed with the details of each particular test encountered that one is unable to see the similarities underlying all tests. The learning of statistics can then become a mere "cookbook" exercise in memorizing formulas and procedures. Therefore this chapter is a very important one and should be reread carefully after you have been exposed to two or three specific tests.[1]

8.1. Statistics and Parameters

The purpose of statistical generalizations is to say something about various characteristics of the population studied on the basis of known facts about a sample drawn from that population or universe.[2] We shall refer to the characteristics of the population as *parameters* as contrasted with characteristics of a sample which are called *statistics*. You are already familiar with a number of parameters and statistics: means, medians, proportions, standard deviations, etc. At this point you should learn to make a careful distinction between those characteristics which refer to the population and those which refer to a sample. Greek letters are usually used to refer to population characteristics; Roman letters indicate sample characteristics.[3] Thus, the population mean will henceforth be designated by μ and the sample mean by $\bar{X}$, the population standard deviation by σ and the sample standard deviation by s.

An important distinction between parameters and statistics can be

---

[1] A good point for review would be after Chap. 11.
[2] The terms *population* and *universe* are generally used interchangeably in the statistical literature.
[3] Unfortunately, there are a number of exceptions to this rule.

made. Parameters are *fixed* values referring to the population and are generally *unknown*.[4] For example, at any given time the mean age or grade-point average of all students at Harvard University may be unknown but presumably would be found to be the same value by all observers. Statistics, on the other hand, vary from one sample to the next. If 10 different samples of college students were selected at random, we would not expect them all to have exactly the same mean ages. In fact, we would be very suspicious if they did. In contrast to parameters, the values of statistics for a particular sample are known or can be computed. We do *not* know, however, how representative the sample actually is of the population or how closely the statistic obtained approximates the comparable unknown parameter.

It is the population, rather than any particular sample, in which we are really interested. We have selected a sample as a matter of convenience, and our goal is practically always to make inferences about various population parameters on the basis of known, but intrinsically unimportant, sample statistics. In tests of hypotheses, we make assumptions about the unknown parameters and then ask how likely our sample statistics would be if these assumptions were actually true. In so doing, we attempt to make a rational decision as to whether or not the assumed values of these parameters are reasonable in view of the evidence at hand. Hypothesis testing can thus be viewed as a special type of decision-making process. Since the basic logic underlying the testing of hypotheses is rather complex, it will be helpful at this point to discuss this logic briefly. In later chapters you will see how it is applied to specific tests.

8.2. Steps in Testing an Hypothesis

In the social sciences the term *hypothesis* is used in a number of different senses. Sometimes it is used to refer to a theoretical proposition which has some remote possibility of being tested indirectly. At other times it is used to refer to the kind of statement which can actually be tested statistically. In order to minimize confusion it will therefore be necessary to specify how the term will be used in this text. The criteria used in defining what we shall mean by a test of an hypothesis are rather strict and would rule out many of the so-called tests made in the current social science literature. They are, however, consistent with the rather

---

[4] Parameters will always be treated as fixed even though they may actually vary over time. Thus the median age of a population will change from one moment to the next. For this reason, you should conceptualize the notion of repeated sampling in terms of a large number of samples drawn simultaneously rather than in temporal sequence.

rigid requirements laid down by the statistician.   As such, they represent an ideal against which the adequacy of any actual test can be compared.

An hypothesis is a statement about a future event, or an event the outcome of which is unknown at the time of the prediction, set forth in such a way that it can be rejected.   In more precise language, let us say that we have tested an hypothesis if the following steps have been taken:

1. All possible outcomes of the experiment or observation were anticipated *in advance of the test.*[5]

2. Agreement was reached prior to the test on the operations or procedures used in determining which of the outcomes actually occurred.

3. It was decided in advance which of the outcomes, should they occur, would result in the rejection of the hypothesis and which in its nonrejection.   As implied above, rejection must have been a possible result.

4. The experiment was performed, or the event observed, the outcomes noted, and a decision made whether or not to reject the hypothesis.

The steps outlined above are very general ones.   Statistical inference is primarily concerned with steps 3 and 4 since the statistician must assume that the first two steps have already been accomplished.   We shall have occasion to see how the last two steps become more specific in a statistical test.   Perhaps the most important general implication in the above list is that all decisions must be made prior to the test.   All possible outcomes are divided into two classes: those which will result in rejection and those which will not.   If this is not done prior to the test it becomes possible to retain an hypothesis by simply changing the rules as one goes along.   This is directly analogous to the child flipping a coin to decide whether or not to go to the movies.   He decides, "Heads I go, tails I don't."   If the coin turns up heads he goes.   If it comes up tails he decides on the best two out of three and continues to flip.   In this way he always ends up going to the movies unless he loses the coin (an unanticipated outcome).

*It was mentioned in Chap. 2 that a test can only be made on a proposition which has been stated in terms of concepts which have been operationally defined.   Step 2 indicates that operational definitions must be agreed upon in advance of the test.   Unless this has been done, it is always possible to retain an "hypothesis" regardless of the outcome of the experiment by rejecting the methods used.   Suppose one states as his "hypothesis" that "the higher one's social class position, the less likely that he will be highly ethnocentric."   If the results do not seem to

---

[5] The term *experiment* is used in a very broad sense by the statistician.   For example, an experiment might consist of interviewing a housewife and recording a "yes" or "no" to a specific question.

confirm this proposition, he may claim that the measure of "social class" or "ethnocentrism" was not really measuring what he intended it to measure and that some other index (which happens to confirm his theory) is a better one. It thus seems desirable to reserve the term *hypothesis* to refer to statements which are on the operational level and are clearly rejectable. If agreement cannot be reached beforehand on the procedures to be used, then agreement on the outcomes can hardly be expected. As indicated in Chap. 2, this point of view does not deny the importance of theory nor does it imply that operational definitions are the only definitions necessary for the development of a science.

The third step is a crucial one since the decision made will usually involve certain risks of error. In some instances the problem is relatively simple. Not all tests of hypotheses involve induction. An hypothesis may be formulated concerning the outcome of a specific event such as a football game. We may predict, for example, that team A will beat team B. As long as there are criteria for determining whether or not the procedures agreed upon have been adequately carried out, there is little chance of error in deciding whether or not to reject this kind of hypothesis. When information is based on a sample of events taken from a larger population there is a greater risk of error, however. We reject or fail to reject the hypothesis realizing that since our judgment is based only on a sample we always have to admit the possibility of error due to the lack of representativeness of the sample. It is probability theory which enables us to evaluate the risks of error and to take these risks into consideration in deciding upon the criteria to be used in rejecting the hypothesis. In the next sections, two kinds of possible errors will be discussed. We can then return to the question of the role played by statistics in tests of inductive hypotheses.

8.3. The Fallacy of Affirming the Consequent

There is often no direct way of checking up on our most important propositions or theories. Instead, we derive from these a number of consequences which should occur if the original proposition or theory were true, and it is the validity of these consequences which can be determined by empirical methods.[6] Thus, evidence for the original theory is indirect. The theory A implies certain consequences B or, written symbolically, $A \rightarrow B$. It should be emphasized that purely logical or deductive reasoning rather than empirical evidence is used in going from A to B. Therefore, if A is true, B must also be true provided our reasoning in deducing B from A is valid. We then look to see whether or not B

---

[6] Strictly speaking, this statement is not quite accurate since a purely deductive theory does not lead *directly* to testable hypotheses. See [3].

has occurred; if B has not occurred (B false), then we know that theory A must also be false. $A \rightarrow B$ & B false then A false. B true then A true? No

But what if B turns out to be true? Can we conclude that A *must* be true? We cannot. If we do, we shall be committing the fallacy of affirming the consequent, as logicians refer to it. If B is true, we can say that A *may* be true, but there could be any number of alternative theories which also predict B. We cannot be assured that A is *necessarily* true unless we can also show that there is no valid alternative theory C for which $C \rightarrow B$. Unfortunately, it is practically never possible to do this, and therefore we have to proceed by *eliminating* of theories rather than by definitely establishing them. A good theory is one which successfully resists elimination—provided, of course, that it is stated in such a way that it can be eliminated.[7] In other words, it must lead to hypotheses which themselves can be eliminated. If we fail to reject A when B is true, we run the risk of making an error since A may actually be false. In statistics this type of error, *the error of failing to reject an hypothesis when it is actually false,* is referred to as a *type II or β error.*

Perhaps a simple example will make the above argument seem less abstract. Suppose we have a theory A consisting of the following three propositions: (1) All persons will conform to all norms of their society; (2) it is a norm of society X not to steal; and (3) Jones is a member of society X. If all portions of the theory are correct, we may conclude B, that Jones will not steal. Suppose that for some reason we are unable to verify the truth or falsity of A directly, but we are able to ascertain Jones's behavior. Clearly, if Jones does steal, the theory must be at least in part incorrect. Therefore, if B is false we reject A. But, certainly, if we learn that Jones does not steal, we would not want to conclude that theory A is correct. Perhaps Jones is simply more honest than others. Or he may not even be a member of society X. In this case if we were to accept the theory as true we would be running a considerable risk of error. We would probably conclude that, although this particular individual may be honest, it would be best to withhold judgment.

The absurdity of the above example should not be allowed to obscure the main point that whenever we are in the position of having a theory which implies certain consequences, and these consequences but not the theory are subject to verification, we are in the logical position of being able to reject the theory, whereas we cannot accept it without running the risk of making an error.

[7] The role of the crucial experiment is to enable the scientist to choose among several alternative theories, each of which has previously resisted elimination. For example, theories A and A' may both predict events $B_1, B_2, \ldots, B_k$, all of which occur. But A may predict that B_{k+1} will be true whereas A' predicts it will be false. If B_{k+1} actually is false, then A may be eliminated and A' retained for the time being.

8.4 The Form of Statistical Hypotheses

In the social sciences we do not find propositions of the sort used in the above example for the simple reason that theories about the real world do not imply certainty. Instead of holding that if A is true, B *must* follow, we claim only that if A is true, B will *probably* also be true. We thus have to admit the possibility that B may be false even when A is true. If we follow the rule of rejecting A whenever B is false we also run the risk of making another kind of error, that of *rejecting a true hypothesis*. We refer to this kind of error as a *type I* or α *error*. Using the above example our propositions would be modified to read, "*Most* members will conform to societal norms," and "Jones will *probably* not steal." If Jones does steal we reject the revised theory with some risk of error since it may actually be true, Jones being one of the few dishonest members.

There are thus two kinds of error which must be taken into consideration. The first type discussed (type II) stems from the purely logical fallacy of affirming the consequent. When we introduce probability statements into our theory we admit of an additional type of error (type I). Although we have as yet said nothing about inductive as contrasted with deductive reasoning, it is because of the necessity of generalizing beyond the limits of one's data that we are required to make use of such probability statements.

What specific forms do statistical hypotheses take? What do the A and B look like? Actually the theory A consists of a number of assumptions about the nature of the population and the sampling procedures used, together with the mathematical reasoning necessary to make probability statements concerning the likelihood of particular sample results if the assumptions made are in fact true. By means of these probability statements we decide ahead of time which results are so likely that we would reject the assumptions A should these outcomes B *not* occur. We are reasoning, in effect, that if the assumptions are correct, then most of the time our sample results will fall within a specified range of outcomes. Of course we draw only one sample, but if our particular result happens to fall outside of this range into what is called the *critical region*, we shall reject the assumptions, running the risk of making a type I error. The B, then, is represented by a certain range of sample results. If the results are outside this range, then B is false and the hypothesis rejected. In deciding on how big a range to include under B we must (ideally) take into consideration the risks of errors of types I and II.

To illustrate the process, suppose we wish to compare samples of white-collar and blue-collar workers with respect to the percentage desiring a college education for their children. If we actually wish to show that there is a difference between these two groups, we proceed by trying to eliminate the alternative hypothesis that there is no difference. This seems like an extremely devious way of proceeding, but we must remember that we shall not be in a position to establish directly that there is a difference. To avoid the fallacy of affirming the consequent, we must proceed by the elimination of false hypotheses. In this case there are logically only two possibilities, there either is or is not a difference. If the latter possibility can be eliminated, we can then conclude that some difference in fact exists.

We therefore hypothesize that the percentage desiring college education is the same for both populations. We might then show mathematically that for 99 per cent of all possible pairs of such samples, the differences between the two sample percentages would be less than 10 per cent *if the assumptions were in fact true*. In other words, *B* consists of sample differences which are less than 10 per cent. If there are actually no differences between the two populations, it is highly likely that the percentages for the two samples will be within 10 per cent of each other. It can therefore be decided that if the difference between sample percentages turns out to be 10 per cent or more the assumptions *A* will be rejected. This is done with the knowledge that 1 per cent of the time a difference of this magnitude could occur even though *A* were true. In other words, the risk of making a type I error (rejecting a true hypothesis) would be one chance in a hundred.

Let us return to the original list of steps necessary in the testing of hypotheses. It has been pointed out that statistical inference is basically concerned with steps 3 and 4 in the process. The researcher is anticipating all possible sample results and is dividing these into two classes: those for which he can reject and those for which he cannot reject his hypothesis. Actually, all that statistics does is to provide the criteria to be used in dividing the outcomes into the two classes. Outcomes are put in one or the other of the two classes according to the risks one is willing to take of making types I and II errors. The major advantage of statistical procedures over intuitive methods is in the knowledge they provide about these risks of error.

Explained this way statistics hardly seems to be worth the trouble. But step 3 is by no means an easy one to accomplish by any other method. Imagine, for example, an experiment consisting of 25 tosses of a coin, the honesty of which is called into question. Suppose we try to decide upon the outcomes which, if they should occur, would result in our challenging the person doing the flipping. Would we reject the hypothesis that the coin is honest if 15 or more heads turned up? More than 18? Only if all tosses resulted in heads? If there were 10 heads in a row regardless of the results on other tosses? Probability theory enables us to evaluate the probabilities of getting any particular set of results if the coin were actually an honest one. We could then select those outcomes which would be quite unlikely under this assumption.

It is not expected that a student exposed for the first time to statistical inference will understand on first reading everything that has been said about the logic of testing hypotheses. The process is admittedly an involved one, and one which seems to give students more difficulty than any other part of statistics. The student should therefore make a special effort to understand this logic by looking for the basic similarities among all statistical tests. Once the underlying logic is thoroughly understood the learning of statistics is greatly simplified.

GLOSSARY

Hypothesis
Parameter
Population
Statistic
Types I and II errors

REFERENCES

1. Ackoff, R. L.: *The Design of Social Research*, University of Chicago Press, Chicago, 1953, chap. 5.

2. Festinger, L.: "Assumptions Underlying the Use of Statistical Techniques," in M. Jahoda, M. Deutsch, and S. W. Cook (eds.), *Research Methods in Social Relations*, The Dryden Press, Inc., New York, 1951, part 2, pp. 713–726.

3. Northrop, F. S. C.: *The Logic of the Sciences and the Humanities*, The Macmillan Company, New York, 1947, chaps. 7 and 8.

Chapter 9

PROBABILITY

We all undoubtedly have some intuitive notion of what is meant by the concept *probability* even though we may not be able to give the term a precise definition.   There are a number of words and phrases used almost interchangeably with the concept probability in ordinary language: words such as *likelihood, chance, odds,* etc.   These concepts are frequently used in a number of very different senses.   A few illustrations are sufficient to indicate some of these diverse usages.   We ask, "What is the probability that it will rain today?" referring to a single event (raining today) which may or may nor occur in the future.   The statement "Jones probably did not murder his mother-in-law" is similar to the above example but refers to an event that has already occurred but about which we lack sufficient information to make a statement of certainty. Or we can refer to what may happen in the long run: "If you gamble you will probably lose your shirt."   Here, the reference is presumably not to losing one's shirt in a single throw of the dice but to what will happen if the experiment is repeated a large number of times.   "A male baby born in the United States of native-white parentage will probably live at least 65 years."   Such a statement seems to refer to the kind of generalized baby which exists in actuarial tables rather than to a concrete Jimmy Brown.

Obviously, if we are to talk intelligently about probability and especially if the mathematician is to be brought into the picture, the concept must be defined with sufficient precision that we can all use it in the same sense.   Unfortunately, however, it is no simple matter to obtain a definition which at the same time satisfies the mathematician and also our intuitive notion of what we ordinarily mean by the term.   As we shall see, the mathematician finds it necessary to think in terms of a priori probabilities which cannot actually be obtained empirically.   In the next sections the concept probability will be defined in mathematical language and some of its important mathematical properties discussed.   At the same time, there will be an attempt to make this definition and these mathematical properties seem reasonable in the light of everyday usage and experience.

9.1. A Priori Probabilities

In statistics we are concerned with generalizing to a population ordinarily made up of a large number of individuals. Such a population may be a finite existing one which is clearly delimitable—such as the population of the United States or native-white males over 65. In such a case we would ordinarily take some sort of a sample from the population, and interest would be primarily in the population itself (or some subpopulation) rather than in those individuals who happen to appear in one particular sample. The population may also be a hypothetical one involving, say, an unlimited number of experiments performed "under similar conditions." The statistician is therefore not interested in the single event or individual except in so far as this event or individual may help him obtain information about the population. Since this is a text in statistics, we shall use the term *probability* to refer not to single events (raining today, Jones a murderer, etc.) but to a large number of events or to what happens in the long run.[1]

How can we approach probability from the point of view of repeated events? First, it is necessary to think in terms of an idealized experiment which can be carried out a large number of times "under similar conditions." Of course in reality conditions change, but it should at least be possible to imagine that they don't. All outcomes must be anticipated in each of these perfect experiments. Thus we must learn to think in terms of an ideal coin being flipped a very large number of times under identical circumstances and with only two outcomes (H or T) possible on each flip. We ignore the fact that a real coin might become worn unevenly in the process of being flipped or that occasionally it might stand on end. We learn to conceive of a perfectly shuffled deck of cards, none of which tend to stick together, even though such a deck could never be found in real life.

Let us call any outcome or set of outcomes of an experiment an "event." An event can be simple (nondecomposable) or compound (a combination of simple events). Thus, event A may be a 6 on a single toss of a die; event B (compound) may consist of the outcomes 2, 4, or 6 on a single toss of a die; event C (also compound) may be the obtaining of a 7 in two

---

[1] It is possible to approach probabilities from the standpoint of the single event and still make use of the same mathematical properties as discussed in the next section (see [3]). This latter approach presents at least as many conceptual difficulties as the one used in this text, however.

tosses. It is conventional to use the term *success* whenever the event under consideration occurs and *failure* when it does not occur.[2] The experiment can then be performed a very large number of times and the proportion of times any particular event occurs can be obtained.

We are not yet quite ready to give a formal definition of probability. First it is necessary to appeal to your knowledge of what happens empirically when an experiment such as the flipping of a coin is repeated a large number of times. Let us suppose that we begin to flip, and with every

Fig. 9.1. Oscillation of the proportion of successes, approaching a limit of .50.

tenth flip we record the ratio of successes (say, heads) to total number of trials. The results obtained are likely to be similar to those indicated in Fig. 9.1.

On the first 10 flips we would usually not expect to get exactly 5 heads, even with an honest coin. Perhaps there will be 7 heads. The next set of trials may contain a long sequence of tails so that at the end of 20 trials the proportion of heads may be .45. The next sequence may also result in more tails than heads, the next slightly more heads than tails, and so forth. After we have made 100 trials with an honest coin we would expect the proportion of successes to be in the neighborhood of .5; after 1,000 trials it should be even closer to this figure. Thus we would expect

[2] This technical use of the terms *success* and *failure* need not conform to general usage. Thus *success* may indicate the contraction of polio or the election of a demagogue.

the ratio of successes to *total* number of trials to settle down in the sense that it ceases to fluctuate very much from one sequence of 10 flips to another. After 10,000 trials, even if we were to get 20 successive tails (an extremely unlikely event), the effect on this ratio would be negligible.[3] Had this happened on the third and fourth sequences the effect would have been pronounced. Therefore, the larger the number of trials the closer and closer the ratio approaches a given value which mathematicians call a "limit." If we can imagine the experiment being carried on indefinitely, we can probably also imagine the ratio becoming exactly this limiting value, say .5. Since we are becoming involved with the notion of infinity, and since mathematicians have found this to be a notoriously ambiguous concept, it may be preferable to think in terms of an extremely large number of trials.

*The notion of a limit can be defined somewhat more precisely. We say that the ratio approaches a limit if, having previously decided how close an approximation we want, we can flip the coin a finite number of times until we can be virtually sure that the obtained ratio approximates the limit within the desired degree of accuracy. In other words, we first choose a very small number ϵ representing the degree of approximation desired. Suppose we set $\epsilon = .0001$. If a limit exists, there is a finite large number of flips N such that we can be almost positive that the obtained proportion of successes will be within $\pm.0001$ of the true probability.[4] Furthermore, no matter how small an ϵ we select we can always find a finite number of flips for which this is true. If a limit does not exist, then this will not in general be possible.

It is by no means a *logical* necessity that the ratios obtained in this manner settle down to a limiting value. Indeed, it is at least conceivable that such ratios continue to fluctuate indefinitely. If this were actually the case we could not speak of a single probability of heads associated with the coin. When such a limit does exist, however, we can define a *probability as a limit of the ratio of successes to total number of trials.* Put more crudely, a probability is the proportion of successes "in the long run."

It will be convenient in later discussions to speak as though we were

---

[3] Notice that it is not being claimed that the absolute numbers of heads and tails will be nearly equal or that if there is initially an excess of heads that the tails will eventually catch up. There may continue to be an excess of heads indefinitely, but the *ratio* will approach .5 even when this is the case. Thus, if we had 35 heads and 15 tails on the first 50 trials the proportion of heads would be .7. An excess of 20 heads in 100 trials (i.e., 60 heads) gives a proportion of .6; the same excess in 200 flips (i.e., 110 heads) gives a value of .55.

[4] The discussion of confidence intervals (Chap. 12) should help to indicate why we can never be absolutely certain that the true probability is within the interval obtained.

thinking in terms of the probabilities of single events. Thus we may ask, "What is the probability of getting a 6 on a single toss of a die or of getting a red ace in a single drawing from a deck of cards?" Actually, in using the phrase "a single toss of a die," we are merely attempting to avoid the use of clumsy phrasing. What we really mean is, "What proportion of times in the long run would we expect to get a 6 if a single die were tossed repeatedly?" As a convenience, then, we shall refer to a single toss when we actually mean an indefinitely large number of single tosses of the same die.

Several points need to be made before we proceed with a discussion of the mathematical properties of probabilities. Real-life experiments, when repeated, actually seem to follow the general pattern discussed above and diagramed in Fig. 9.1. That is, a limit is actually approached and can be estimated. This leads us to speak of "the law of averages" and to expect that most coins will come up heads about half the time or that good bridge hands will be mixed with poor ones. A word of caution is necessary regarding this law of averages, however. Some persons have interpreted such a law to mean that if a coin comes up heads 10 times in a row, then the next time it is more likely to come up tails "because of the law of averages." Such an interpretation involves a prediction about a single event (i.e., the result of the eleventh flip). As will be discussed below, we usually assume that what has happened on previous flips is absolutely irrelevant to what follows.[5] A coin is possessed of neither a memory nor a conscience. As a matter of intelligent strategy, if a player were to witness 10 successive heads in 10 trials he would do well to predict heads on the eleventh under the assumption that the coin is dishonest.

It should be perfectly clear that a priori probabilities, as defined in this section, cannot be obtained *exactly* by empirical methods although they may be *estimated*. This is not only because we have had to imagine idealized experiments but also because no experiment can be repeated indefinitely. With a sufficient number of trials, however, a probability can be estimated to any degree of accuracy. The mathematical rules given in the next section and all the mathematical reasoning underlying statistical inference are concerned with a priori probabilities rather than the kinds of probabilities that can actually be obtained by the researcher.[6]

In applying statistical reasoning to any science dealing with the real world we are thus going to find ourselves in the logical position described in Chap. 8. We have to assume some a priori probability in order to

[5] This cannot be assumed in the case of human beings, a fact which must be kept in mind whenever repeated measurements are taken on humans or other animals. See Sec. 9.4.

[6] Strictly speaking, the researcher can only obtain *proportions* since the number of trials or cases will always be finite.

apply mathematical reasoning. We can then say that *if* this is the correct a priori probability *then* certain empirical results are likely (or unlikely). Thus A is the mathematical theory, B the predicted empirical results, and there is no way of testing the theory directly. If B turns out to be false we can reject A, but if B is true some other theory C, involving different a priori probabilities, may also account for the results. If we wish to avoid the fallacy of affirming the consequent, it will be necessary to assume probabilities which we really suspect are false and to proceed by elimination. In the next chapter we shall take up specific examples where this will be done.

9.2. Mathematical Properties of Probabilities

Although you may never again have to calculate probabilities, it is important to realize that underlying every table you will use to make tests of hypotheses there are a number of fairly simple properties of probabilities. It is not possible in a text such as this to go very deeply into probability theory. The purpose of the discussion which follows is merely to give some insight into the way mathematicians operate with probabilities in laying the foundations for statistical inference. We can begin by identifying three mathematical properties of a priori probabilities.

The first property hardly requires much comment. Since we can obtain no fewer than zero successes and no more than N successes in N trials, it follows that for any event A the probability of A occurring [written $P(A)$] must be greater than or equal to 0 and less than or equal to 1. Thus

$$0 \leq P(A) \leq 1$$

where the symbol $\leq$ should be read as "less than or equal to." If $P(A) = 1$, the event A is certain to occur; if $P(A) = 0$, then A cannot possibly occur.

The Addition Rule. The second property of probabilities is a somewhat more interesting one. Because of its simplicity, we shall first take up a special case of the addition rule which can be stated as follows: *If events A and B are mutually exclusive, the probability of getting either A or B [written $P(A \text{ or } B)$] is equal to the probability of A plus the probability of B, i.e.,*

$$P(A \text{ or } B) = P(A) + P(B) \qquad \text{(if } A \text{ and } B \text{ are mutually exclusive)} \qquad (9.1)$$

By mutually exclusive, we mean that A and B cannot possibly occur simultaneously in the same experiment. Thus it is impossible to get both an ace and a king in a single draw from an ordinary deck of cards. Therefore, applying the addition rule to a hypothetical perfect deck we have

$$P(A \text{ or } K) = P(A) + P(K) = \tfrac{4}{13} + \tfrac{1}{13} = \tfrac{2}{13}$$

Of course, we could have obtained this same result by noting that there are eight aces and kings in a deck, and with equal probability of selection the probability of getting one of these cards would be $\tfrac{8}{52}$ or $\tfrac{2}{13}$. Similarly, the probability of getting either a 5 or 6 in a single throw of a die would be $\tfrac{1}{6} + \tfrac{1}{6}$ or $\tfrac{1}{3}$.

The addition rule can be extended to cover more than two events. Thus, *if A, B, C, . . . , K are all mutually exclusive, then*

$$P(A \text{ or } B \text{ or } C \cdots \text{ or } K) = P(A) + P(B) + P(C) + \cdots + P(K) \quad (9.2)$$

If we have a population composed of 100 upper-, 200 upper-middle-, 400 lower-middle-, and 300 lower-class persons, for example, the probability of getting an upper-class, *or* an upper-middle-class, *or* a lower-middle-class person in a single draw would be

$$\frac{100}{1,000} + \frac{200}{1,000} + \frac{400}{1,000} = \frac{700}{1,000} = .7$$

if every person had an equal chance of being selected.

Since probabilities are essentially proportions it follows that if we have all possible simple events, each being mutually exclusive of the others, the sum of these events must be unity. Thus, if we add the probabilities of getting a spade or a heart or a club or a diamond, we must obtain a sum of 1. The probability of event A *not* occurring is equal to the sum of the probabilities of all the remaining (mutually exclusive) events. If we subtract $P(A)$ from unity, we thus have the probability of not getting A since

if $$1 = P(A) + P(B) + P(C) + \cdots + P(K)$$
then $$1 - P(A) = P(B) + P(C) + \cdots + P(K)$$

The probability of not getting a queen, for example, is $1 - \tfrac{1}{13}$, or $\tfrac{12}{13}$.

So far we have been concerned only with mutually exclusive events. A more *general form* of the addition rule can be stated as follows: *If A and B are any events* (not necessarily mutually exclusive)

$$P(A \text{ or } B) = P(A) + P(B) - P(A \& B) \quad (9.3)$$

where $P(A \& B)$ represents the probability of getting *both* A and B.[7] In the general case, the probability of getting either A or B can be obtained by first adding the probability of A to the probability of getting B and then subtracting out the probability of getting both A and B simul-

---

[7] The word *or* as used by the mathematician includes the possibility that both A and B hold. Therefore, the expression "A or B" means "A and/or B."

taneously.   The reason for subtracting out $P(A \& B)$ is that the probability of this joint occurrence has been figured in twice, once in $P(A)$ and
again in $P(B)$.   Figure 9.2 may help to indicate why this is the case.

In Fig. 9.2 the probabilities of A and B have been represented by
certain areas which are proportional to their numerical values, the area
of the rectangle being taken as unity.   In the general case there will

Fig. 9.2. Geometric representation of probabilities, with areas proportional to $P(A)$,
$P(B)$, and $P(A \& B)$.

ordinarily be some overlap, i.e., A and B will not be mutually exclusive.
The probability of obtaining either A or B (or both) is represented by
the total cross-hatched area.   Since the smaller shaded area will have
been added in twice, once in A and again in B, we see why it is necessary
to subtract out $P(A \& B)$ in order to obtain the total cross hatched area.[8]

Let us take a numerical example.   Suppose A is the event that one
obtains a queen in a single draw, and let B be the event that the card is a
spade.   Then A and B are not mutually exclusive since it is possible to
draw both simultaneously (i.e., the queen of spades).   Therefore,

$$P(A \text{ or } B) = P(A) + P(B) - P(A \& B)$$
$$= \tfrac{4}{52} + \tfrac{13}{52} - \tfrac{1}{52} = \tfrac{16}{52} = \tfrac{4}{13}$$

This result can be verified intuitively by noting that either A or B could
be obtained by drawing any spade or one of the three remaining queens,
i.e., any one of 16 cards.   Had we simply added $P(A)$ and $P(B)$, the
queen of spades would have been considered twice.   In the next section
we shall take up a general rule for computing $P(A \& B)$ since it will not
always be so simple to obtain this quantity.   Notice that if the two
events are mutually exclusive there will be no overlap and $P(A \& B) = 0$.

[8] You should convince yourself that in order to obtain the probability of A or B
but not both we would subtract $2P(A \& B)$ from $P(A) + P(B)$.   You should also
attempt to extend the general form of the addition rule by drawing a similar diagram
for events A, B, and C.   (See Exercise 4b.)

Therefore, the general rule reduces to the special case of the addition rule discussed above.

The Multiplication Rule. A third property of probabilities enables us to obtain the probability of two (or more) events occurring jointly. We can state this property as follows: If *A and B are any two events, the probability of getting both A and B is the product of the probability of getting one of these events times the conditional probability of getting the other given that the first event has occurred.* In symbols,

$$P(A \& B) = P(A)P(B|A) = P(B)P(A|B) \qquad (9.4)$$

The symbols $P(A|B)$ and $P(B|A)$ represent what are called conditional probabilities. $P(A|B)$ should be read "the probability of A given that B has occurred." The term *conditional probability* means that we recognize that the probability of A may be dependent on whether or not B occurs. In other words, the probability of A given B may differ from the probability of A given that B has *not* occurred. Thus, if B is the event that a man drives recklessly and A the event that he is in a traffic accident, then we would expect $P(A|B)$ to be greater than $P(A)$ since reckless driving is a cause of accidents.

Before illustrating the use of the multiplication rule, let us introduce a new and important concept. Two events A and B are said to be *independent* if and only if $P(A|B) = P(A)$ and $P(B|A) = P(B)$. Thus, if the probability of A occurring remains the same regardless of whether or not B has occurred, and if the same holds true for B, the two events are independent of each other. Practically speaking, this means that knowledge that one of the events has occurred does not help one predict the other. For example, the probability of getting an ace, given that the card is red, is $\frac{2}{26}$ since there are two red aces and a total of 26 red cards. This is numerically the same as the unconditional probability of getting an ace $(\frac{4}{52})$. Therefore color and face value are independent. Knowledge that a card is red does not help one predict whether or not it is an ace. Likewise, knowing the card to be an ace does not help one predict its color. Notice, incidentally, that mutually exclusive events are not independent. If A and B are mutually exclusive, we must always have $P(A|B) = P(B|A) = 0$. Why?

In the case where A and B are actually independent, we have $P(B|A) = P(B)$ and the multiplication rule takes on the simple form

$$P(A \& B) = P(A)P(B) \qquad \text{(if } A \text{ and } B \text{ are independent)}$$

We shall in general find this special case of the multiplication rule much easier to use than the more general rule.

We shall first illustrate the multiplication rule in the special case where A and B are independent. Ordinarily we think of replications of an experiment as being independent of each other. Thus, if we flip a coin once we expect that the result will have no effect on what happens on the next flip; the probability of heads remains constant from one flip to the next. Knowing that we get a head does not help us predict the outcome of the second toss.[9] Using the multiplication rule we can therefore calculate the probability of getting successive heads on two flips by multiplying the probabilities of getting a head on any given trial. For an honest coin the probability of two successive heads would be $(\frac{1}{2})(\frac{1}{2})$ or $\frac{1}{4}$. Similarly, if A is the event that we get a red card and B the event that we get an ace, the probability of getting a red ace $[P(A \& B)]$ would be

$$P(A \& B) = P(A)P(B) = \frac{1}{2}\,\frac{1}{13} = \frac{1}{26}$$

Let us take up two examples in which independence does not hold. The first of these involves a situation in which two variables are related so that knowledge of one helps us predict the other. Suppose we have the following purely hypothetical data:

Trait	Brunettes	Blondes	Redheads	Total
Aggressive	300	600	300	1,200
Nonaggressive	600	100	100	800
Total	900	700	400	2,000

If a girl is drawn at random[10] from this population as a blind date, what is the probability that she will be an aggressive redhead? Since there are 300 aggressive redheads out of 2,000 girls, the probability of getting one of this select group is clearly 300/2,000 or .15. This same probability will now be obtained using the multiplication rule.

Let A be the event that we get a redhead and B be the event that the date is aggressive. Since there are 400 redheads in all, $P(A) = 400/2,000$ or .2. Among the 1,200 aggressive girls, however, there are 300 redheads.

[9] We are assuming that the true probability is known and that our task is to predict the outcome of any specific trial. It is of course true that without this knowledge, the probability might be *estimated* by using results of previous trials and this estimate then used to predict future results. This is *not* what we mean when we say that in the case of independence, knowledge of one event does not help us predict another. Thus, knowledge of 20 successive heads would lead us to predict a biased coin, i.e., that the true probability of getting a head is some value greater than .5. This in turn would lead to a prediction of a head on the twenty-first trial. The assumption is, however, that such a bias if it exists is already known. Therefore, if it is known that p actually is .8, knowledge of 20 successive heads will not improve our ability to predict the next outcome.

[10] A random sample will be defined later in this chapter. In a random sample all individuals, and all combinations of individuals, have an equal chance of being selected.

Therefore, if we are given knowledge that the date is aggressive, the probability of her being a redhead is 300/1,200 or .25. Similarly the probability of getting an aggressive girl is 1,200/2,000 or .6, but if it is known that the date is a redhead the probability of her being aggressive is 300/400 or .75. We thus have

$$P(A) = .2 \qquad P(A|B) = .25$$
$$P(B) = .6 \qquad P(B|A) = .75$$

Using the multiplication rule we obtain the following probability of getting an aggressive redhead:

$$P(A \& B) = P(A)P(B|A) = (.2)(.75) = .15$$
$$= P(B)P(A|B) = (.6)(.25) = .15$$

For the second example, let us suppose we want to calculate the probability of getting two aces in two draws from an ordinary deck of cards. Let A be the event that we get an ace on the first draw and B the event that an ace turns up on the second draw. Are A and B independent? This depends on whether or not we replace the first card and reshuffle before drawing the second. If we sample *with replacement* our two draws will be independent since the probability of getting an ace remains constant from one draw to the next and the result of the first cannot possibly affect the second. In this case $P(A \& B) = P(A)P(B) = (1/13)(1/13) = 1/169$.

Now suppose we sample *without* replacement, i.e., we do not put the first card back in the deck. If we should happen to get an ace on the first draw, the probability of getting a second ace would then be $3/51$ since there would be only three aces in the remaining 51 cards. On the other hand, if we did not get an ace on the first draw the probability of getting one on the second draw would be $4/51$. Therefore, we do not have independence in this case and would have to use conditional probabilities to compute $P(A \& B)$. Thus,

$$P(A \& B) = P(A)P(B|A) = 4/52 \cdot 3/51 = 1/221$$

It should be mentioned that the multiplication rule we have been discussing can also be extended to cover more than two events. For example, *if A, B, and C are all independent of each other*

$$P(A \& B \& C) = P(A)P(B)P(C)$$

Although the rule for conditional probabilities becomes rather complicated in form, the principles can readily be applied to certain simple examples. If, for instance, we were to draw four cards without replacement, we could calculate the probability of obtaining four aces as follows:

$$P(4 \text{ aces}) = \frac{4}{52} \frac{3}{51} \frac{2}{50} \frac{1}{49} = \frac{1}{270,725}$$

The Order of Events. Before completing this brief discussion of the mathematical properties of probabilities, it is necessary to introduce a further complication. So far we have taken up very simple problems, ones that could easily have been solved almost intuitively. Needless to say, most problems in probability are far more complex than those discussed up to this point. In order to handle problems of somewhat greater complexity we shall find it necessary to take into consideration the order in which the events may occur. For example, suppose we wish to find the probability of getting an ace, king, and queen in three draws with replacement. We can obtain the probability of getting an ace on the first draw, a king on the second, and a queen on the third. This probability would be $(\frac{1}{13})^3$. But this represents the probability of getting an ace *followed by* a king *followed by* a queen. There are other ways of getting an ace, king, and queen in three draws *if we are not concerned about the order in which they are drawn.* As a matter of fact there are six ways they could be obtained: AKQ, AQK, KAQ, KQA, QAK, and QKA. Each of these possibilities can be seen to have the same probability. Therefore, if we are interested in the probability of getting these cards *in any order* we can add their separate probabilities (since they are mutually exclusive) obtaining $6(\frac{1}{13})^3$. replacement

Thus, in using the multiplication rule we have let event A refer to the outcome of the first draw, B to that of the second, and so forth. In other words, we have taken order into consideration, whereas usually we are more interested in the probabilities of obtaining a certain set of outcomes. We may want to know the probability of four aces in a bridge hand or the probability of getting a certain percentage of Negroes in a sample, regardless of the order in which they were drawn. In computing such probabilities *it will usually be simplest first to determine the probability of any given ordering of outcomes,* and if all other orderings are equally likely we can simply multiply the number of orderings by the probability of any one of them occurring. In so doing, it will be noticed, we are employing both the multiplication and the addition rules. There are definite formulas which can be used to enable one to count exactly how many orderings there will be in a given problem. One of these formulas will be presented in the next chapter when we take up the binomial.

9.3. Independence and Random Sampling

All the statistical tests to be discussed in this text make use of the assumption that there is independence between events and that therefore conditional probabilities do not have to be used when multiplying probabilities.[11]   In other words, it is assumed that there is independence of selection within a sample—the choice of one individual having no bearing on the choice of another individual to be included in the sample. There are many instances in which this important assumption is likely to be violated, however.   One should therefore develop the habit of always asking himself whether or not the independence assumption is actually justified in any given problem.   It will be helpful at this point to indicate a few examples of situations in which this assumption is likely to be overlooked.

Statisticians often obtain what is called a *random sample* (or *simple random sample*) in order to meet the required assumption of independence as well as to give every individual in the population an equal chance of appearing in the sample.   By using a table of random numbers or some equivalent device, one can obtain a sample in essentially the same way that one would draw cards from a well-shuffled deck or numbers in a bingo game.   A random sample has the property *not only of giving each individual an equal chance of being selected but also of giving each combination of individuals an equal chance of selection.*[12]

Strictly speaking, since we practically always sample without replacement, the assumption of independence is not quite met.   Whenever the population is large relative to the size of the sample, however, one can safely neglect the resulting minor distortion because no individual is given a chance to be drawn a second time.   For example, if 500 persons are selected out of a population of 100,000, the chances are very slight of any one person being selected again if his name were replaced.   Likewise, it makes relatively little practical difference if we replace when drawing only three cards from a deck, but if we were to draw 35 cards it would make considerable difference.   If the sample is relatively large as compared with the population, a correction factor can sometimes be applied to compensate for lack of replacement.[13]

*Although the problems introduced by failure to replace are not serious ones, the failure to give every *combination* of individuals an equal chance of appearing in the sample may result in a serious violation of the independence assumption.   Suppose, for example, that one were to sort ordinary playing cards into four piles, one for clubs, one for spades, etc. Then suppose he were to select one of these piles randomly.   Clearly, every card in the deck would have an equal chance (1 in 4) of being

[11] This will be seen in the case of the binomial discussed in the next chapter.   In the case of other tests, however, you will simply have to accept the truth of this statement.

[12] In Chap. 22, random sampling will be distinguished from other commonly used types of sampling such as systematic, stratified, and cluster sampling.

[13] See Sec. 22.1.

selected, but certainly all combinations would not be possible, let alone equally probable.   Knowing that the top card is a spade tells us immediately that all others in the sample are also spades.

*Area or cluster samples commonly used in social surveys do not meet the assumption of independence for this same reason.   If 100 blocks in a city are selected at random and then every third household in these 100 blocks is included in the sample, it is quite clear that all combinations of households do not have an equal chance of appearing in the sample.   For example, two houses in the same block have a much better chance of appearing in the same sample than do two houses in different blocks. Since city blocks are usually relatively homogeneous with respect to characteristics such as the income and education of the head of the household, the result of this type of sampling is to yield less accuracy than a random sample of the same size.   This can be seen intuitively if we imagine a situation in which all blocks are completely homogeneous (as was true for the piles of cards).   In this case we would need to obtain information about only one household in each block, and the number of "cases" would in effect be the number of *blocks* selected, i.e., a much smaller N.   As will be seen later, it is possible to get some extremely misleading results if, having obtained such a cluster sample, a researcher then makes use of statistical tests which assume a random sample.

*An analogous problem is likely to be encountered whenever one is interested in behavioral acts of individuals.   For example, suppose a social psychologist runs an experiment in which he uses 30 subjects, each of whom makes 50 separate judgments.   There would then be 1,500 judgments, and one might be tempted to make use of such an artificially inflated N in a statistical test, assuming in effect that the 1,500 judgments constituted a random sample of judgments from some sort of a population. But, obviously, it would be absurd in most instances to assume that the judgments of a single individual are independent of each other. His first 30 judgments are very likely to affect the remaining ones since, unlike a coin, a person does have a memory.

*Suppose a social scientist is primarily interested in pairs of persons rather than in the single individual as a unit.   He may have a group of 20 persons, each of whom is in interaction with all of the others.   He would therefore have $(20)(19)/2$ or 190 pairs of persons but would not be in a position to consider each pair as being independent of the others. Obviously, knowledge about the Smith-Brown pair is likely to yield some information about the Smith-Jones or Brown-Jones pairs since the same persons appear in several pairs.

*Ecologists, anthropologists, and other social scientists interested in generalizing about communities, societies, or other spatially defined units also need to be concerned about lack of independence in much of their work. Here the problem seems to stem from the fact that units selected are often not clearly distinct. The boundaries of a society or community may be difficult to define, and one such unit may shade into another with the division points being more or less arbitrary.[14] For example, if census tracts within a city or counties within a state are used as units, it is often possible to predict from one unit to a contiguous one. If the delinquency rate is high in one tract it is also likely to be high in an adjacent one since it is even possible that the same gangs of delinquents will be drawn from both tracts. That "something is wrong" in relation to the assumption of independence can be seen intuitively by realizing that whenever units are not clearly distinct it would be possible to inflate the number of "units" to any desired size by simply slicing the cake into many small pieces. Thus, if there are not enough societies in the world to obtain statistical significance, one might subdivide each society into 10 subregions and obtain 10 times as many "cases."

In a text such as this it is not possible to discuss solutions to problems involving violations of the independence assumption. To the writer's knowledge, many of these problems have not been satisfactorily resolved. It is often rather difficult to assess the seriousness of errors introduced when required assumptions, such as that of independence, are *not* met. We are on safe ground whenever we can be assured that assumptions required for any test *are* met; if they are not met it is seldom possible to determine just how much we are departing from these assumptions. To be on the safe side, you should develop the habit of examining every assumption carefully. If you have reason to question the validity of a particular assumption, you should consider seriously the possibility of making use of another procedure which does not involve such an assumption. For example, you might decide to make use of a different unit of analysis—the person rather than behavioral acts or pairs of persons, or individual delinquents rather than delinquency rates for a census tract.

Although social scientists and others who use applied statistics have sometimes tended to ignore assumptions, thereby reaching unwarranted conclusions, it is also possible to be overly perfectionistic. Since we never deal with situations as simple as coin flipping or drawing cards from a perfect deck, it is always possible to question every procedure as falling short of the ideal. One can be so much afraid of violating assumptions that he refuses to use any statistical technique at all. Especially in a discipline characterized by exploratory studies and relatively imprecise scientific techniques, it is necessary to make compromises with reality.

[14] This situation would be somewhat analogous to a deck of cards each of which gradually shades into the others so that it is difficult to determine where one card ends and another begins. Also, each card would be capable of influencing the face values of its nearest neighbors!

The most sensible procedure would seem to be to make as few compromises as possible within the limits of practicality.

GLOSSARY

Event
Independent events
Limit
Mutually exclusive events
Probability
Random sample

EXERCISES

1. In a single toss of an honest die what is the probability of:

 a. Getting a 6? $\frac{1}{6}$
 b. Not getting a 6?
 c. Getting a 1 or a 6? $\frac{1}{3}$
 d. Getting a 1 and a 6? 0
 e. Getting either an odd number or a 6? $\frac{2}{3}$

2. What is the probability of getting each of the following in *three* draws from a well-shuffled deck of cards:

 a. Three jacks, with replacement? $\frac{4}{52} \times \frac{4}{52} \times \frac{4}{52}$
 b. Three jacks, without replacement? $\frac{4}{52} \times \frac{3}{51} \times \frac{2}{50}$
 c. A spade, heart, and diamond (in any order), with replacement? $6\left(\frac{13}{52} \times \frac{13}{52} \times \frac{13}{52}\right)$
 d. Exactly two aces, with replacement?
 e. At least one ace, with replacement? (*Hint:* What is the alternative to at least one ace?) see notes $\frac{12}{13} \times \frac{12}{13} \times \frac{12}{13}$
 *f. At least one ace *and* at least one king, with replacement? (*Hint:* In (f) and in certain of the exercises that follow, it will be helpful to divide the problem into three steps: (1) determine the various combinations of cards which will yield at least one ace and at least one king (e.g., one ace, one king, and one other card; two aces and one king, etc.); (2) determine the probability of getting these cards in any particular order; and (3) for each of these combinations determine the number of possible orderings.

3. Suppose 1,000 freshmen are asked about their musical tastes. It is found that 400 of these students are lovers of classical music; the remainder are not. Of these lovers of classical music, only 100 like "rock and roll." There are 400 persons who do not like either type of music and the remainder like "rock and roll" only. 300 likerock

 a. If a student is selected at random from this population, and if A is the event that he likes classical music and B the event that he likes "rock and roll," what are $P(A)$, $P(B)$, $P(A|B)$ and, $P(B|A)$?
 b. Verify numerically that

$$P(A \& B) = P(A)P(B|A) = P(B)P(A|B)$$

 c. What is the probability of getting a person who likes one of the two types of music but not both?
 *d. Noting that a person can have one of four kinds of tastes (likes both, likes neither, etc.), what is the probability that three persons selected at random as roommates will *all* have the same set of tastes? (Assume replacement.)

  *e. What is the probability that there will be *at least* two "rock and roll" fans in
      a corridor of eight persons?   (Assume random sampling, with replacement.)

*4. In the data given below, let A be the event of getting a male, B be the event
of getting a college-educated person, and C be the event of getting a person with
high prejudice.

Degree of prejudice	College-educated		Less than college-educated	
	Male	Female	Male	Female
High	100	50	200	250
Low	150	100	150	200

  a. Find $P(A \ \& \ B \ \& \ C)$ on a single draw without using a formula.   Now extend
     the formula used to determine $P(A \ \& \ B)$ by writing a general formula for
     obtaining $P(A \ \& \ B \ \& \ C)$.   Verify that your formula holds for the numerical
     data of this exercise.
  b. Do the same for $P(A \text{ or } B \text{ or } C)$.
  c. What is the probability of getting exactly one college-educated male, exactly
     one female with a college education, and exactly one person with high preju-
     dice in a random sample of three persons?   (Assume replacement.)

*5. Students enrolled in introductory sociology at the University of Michigan
were classified as to occupational aspirations for self or spouse, depending on the sex
of the respondent.   The following data were obtained:

Sex	High aspirations	Low aspirations	Total
Male	43	10	53
Female	71	93	164
Total	114	103	217

Suppose you were to draw individuals randomly from this population of 217 students.

  a. What is the probability of getting a student with high aspirations?   What is
     the probability of getting a student with high aspirations, given that the
     student is a male?   A female?
  b. Suppose you were to select individuals at random (without replacement) from
     this population, each time guessing whether the individual had high or low
     aspirations.   How often would you guess he had high aspirations?   Low
     aspirations?   Why?   In 217 trials, how many errors would you expect to
     make?
  c. Suppose the sex of the student were known.   Given that the individual is a
     male, how many errors would you expect to make in assigning the 53 males
     to either the high- or low-aspirations category?   How many expected errors
     for females?

d. How might you construct an index showing the proportional reduction of errors if the respondent's sex is known as compared with errors expected if sex is unknown? As will be seen in Chap. 15, such an index can be used to measure the strength or degree of relationship between the respondent's sex and his occupational aspirations.

REFERENCES

1. Freund, J. E.: *Modern Elementary Statistics*, Prentice-Hall, Inc., Englewood Cliffs, N.J., 1952, chap. 7.

2. McCarthy, P. J.: *Introduction to Statistical Reasoning*, McGraw-Hill Book Company, Inc., New York, 1957, chap. 7.

3. Savage, L. J.: *The Foundations of Statistics*, John Wiley & Sons, Inc., New York, 1954, chaps. 1–3.

Chapter 10

TESTING HYPOTHESES:
THE BINOMIAL DISTRIBUTION

In the social sciences we frequently encounter simple dichotomies such as whether or not an individual possesses a certain attribute or whether an experiment has been a success or failure. Whenever it is possible to hypothesize a certain probability of success in such instances, whenever trials are independent of each other, and whenever the number of trials is relatively small, it is possible to make use of statistical tests involving what is known as the binomial distribution. Although there are numerous statistical tests which are more practical than those which make use of the binomial, it is advisable to devote considerable time to this distribution primarily because of its simplicity. In using the binomial distribution, you can follow relatively easily all of the steps involved and can thereby gain insight into the general procedures used in all statistical tests.

You will probably find this chapter an unusually difficult one because of the fact that a number of new ideas are presented in fairly compact fashion. Many of these same ideas are again taken up in Chap. 11, and you may prefer to treat these two chapters as a single unit, reading Chap. 11 before really mastering materials in the present chapter. In particular, you may wish to postpone reading Sec. 10.3 dealing with various applications of the binomial.

10.1. The Binomial Sampling Distribution

Before discussing each of the steps involved in statistical tests, it will be necessary to examine how binomial distributions are obtained. For the time being, it will simplify matters if we confine our attention to the flipping of coins. In this type of problem the number of flips constitutes the sample size, and our interest centers on the number of heads (successes) obtained in N trials.

Assuming that the N trials (coin flips) are independent of one another, we can immediately evaluate the probability of getting r heads and $N - r$ tails in some particular order. For example, we can obtain the probability of getting r successive heads followed by $N - r$ tails. Let p be the probability of obtaining a head; the probability of getting a tail, denoted by q, will then be $1 - p$. Since the trials are independent, we can simply multiply the unconditional probabilities. The probability of getting exactly r heads *in the order described above* will then be

$$\underbrace{p\,p\,p\;\cdots\;p}_{r \text{ terms}}\,\underbrace{q\,q\,q\;\cdots\;q}_{N - r \text{ terms}} = p^r q^{N-r}$$

Clearly, under the assumptions of independence and a constant probability of success (e.g., the coin doesn't wear thin unevenly), the probability of getting any other particular ordering of r heads and $N - r$ tails will also be $p^r q^{N-r}$. Therefore, in order to obtain the probability of getting *exactly* r heads *in any order* it is only necessary to count the number of distinct ways we can get r heads and $N - r$ tails. If N is even moderately large this task becomes very tedious, however. Fortunately there is available a mathematical formula which makes such a counting operation unnecessary. The number of possible ways we can order r successes and $N - r$ failures, written symbolically as $\binom{N}{r}$ or sometimes as C_r^N, is

$$C_r^N = \binom{N}{r} = \frac{N!}{r!(N - r)!} \tag{10.1}$$

where $N!$ (read factorial N) $= N(N - 1)(N - 2) \cdots (3)(2)(1)$ and similarly for $r!$ and $(N - r)!$[1]

Formula (10.1) may be simplified for computational purposes by noting that some of the terms in the numerator and denominator cancel each other out. Since $r \leq N$, we can write $N!$ as a product of two terms as follows:

$$N! = [N(N - 1)(N - 2) \cdots (N - r + 1)][(N - r) \cdots (3)(2)(1)]$$
$$= [N(N - 1)(N - 2) \cdots (N - r + 1)][(N - r)!]$$

and we see immediately that $(N - r)!$ can be taken out of both numerator and denominator. We are then left with

$$\binom{N}{r} = \frac{N(N - 1)(N - 2) \cdots (N - r + 1)}{r!} \tag{10.2}$$

[1] The symbol $\binom{N}{r}$ is not to be confused with N/r or N divided by r.

TESTING HYPOTHESES: THE BINOMIAL DISTRIBUTION **117**

Thus if we want to find the number of ways of getting four heads in ten flips we have

$$N - r + 1 = 10 - 4 + 1 = 7$$

and therefore

$$\binom{10}{4} = \frac{(10)(9)(8)(7)}{(4)(3)(2)(1)} = 210$$

$$\frac{N(N-1)\dots(N-R(+1))}{R}$$

Notice that in using equation (10.2) there are the same number of factors in both numerator and denominator. This will always be the case. This second form is computationally simpler than the first. If $r > N/2$ we begin to get certain terms appearing in both numerator and denominator and therefore canceling each other. For example, if $r = 6$ we have

$$\binom{10}{6} = \frac{(10)(9)(8)(7)}{(1)(2)(3)(4)}\left[\frac{(6)(5)}{(5)(6)}\right] = 210$$

which gives us the same result as obtained in computing $\binom{10}{4}$. In general it can be shown that

$$\binom{N}{r} = \binom{N}{N-r} \qquad \text{or} \quad C_r^N = C_{N-r}^N$$

so that either r or $N - r$ may be used, depending on whichever is the smaller.

If we now wish to obtain the probability of getting *exactly* r successes in N trials and are not interested in the order in which they occur, we can multiply the probability of getting any particular sequence by the number of possible orders $\binom{N}{r}$. Denoting the desired probability by $P(r)$, we have

$$P(r) \quad = \quad \binom{N}{r} \qquad\qquad p^r q^{N-r}$$

| Probability of exactly r successes | = | no. of ways of getting r successes | × | probability of any given sequence | (10.3) |

If the coin were an honest one, i.e., if $p = q = \frac{1}{2}$, the probability of getting exactly four heads in ten trials would be

$$P(4) = \binom{10}{4}\left(\frac{1}{2}\right)^4\left(\frac{1}{2}\right)^6 = 210\left(\frac{1}{2}\right)^{10} = \frac{210}{1,024} = .205$$

Similarly, we can obtain the probabilities of getting exactly 0, 1, 2, . . . , 10 heads in 10 trials.

No. of heads	Probabilities (with $p = \frac{1}{2}$)
0	$1/1{,}024 = .001$
1	$10/1{,}024 = .010$
2	$45/1{,}024 = .044$
3	$120/1{,}024 = .117$
4	$210/1{,}024 = .205$
5	$252/1{,}024 = .246$
6	$210/1{,}024 = .205$
7	$120/1{,}024 = .117$
8	$45/1{,}024 = .044$
9	$10/1{,}024 = .010$
10	$1/1{,}024 = .001$
	1.000

Notice that whenever r is zero the quantity $\binom{N}{r}$ is undefined and the formula breaks down. We see, however, that there can be only one possible order when $r = 0$ (all tails). In this example, the distribution of probabilities is perfectly symmetrical. Using the fact that $\binom{N}{r} = \binom{N}{N-r}$, you should satisfy yourself that $\binom{N}{r}$ will always be symmetrical but that the factor $p^r q^{N-r}$ will be exactly symmetrical only when $p = q = \frac{1}{2}$.

In the above example, probabilities have been associated with each of the 11 possible outcomes of the experiment. In this simple example there were only a small number of conceivable outcomes, given the assumption that only two outcomes were possible on each flip. In other experiments the number of possible outcomes may be very large or even infinite, and it may be necessary to group certain outcomes together and to associate a probability with the entire set of outcomes. Thus, if the coin had been flipped 1,000 times we might have obtained the probabilities of getting 400 to 449, 450 to 499, or 500 to 549 heads.

Whenever we associate probabilities with each possible outcome of an experiment, or with sets of outcomes, we refer to the resulting probability distribution as a sampling distribution. Remembering that we are using the concept *probability* to refer to the limit of the ratio of successes to total number of trials, we see that *a sampling distribution refers to the relative number of times we would expect to get certain outcomes in a very large number of experiments.*

In the numerical example under consideration, each experiment consists of flipping a coin ten times and noting the number of heads. Our computations tell us that if we were to perform the experiment 1,024,000 times, we could expect to get approximately (but not exactly) 1,000 occurrences of no heads, 10,000 occurrences of exactly one head, 45,000 of two heads, etc. Furthermore, we would expect that the larger the number of times the experiment is performed the closer the empirical proportions will be to these theoretical probabilities.

The researcher never actually obtains a sampling distribution by empirical means since he usually only performs an experiment or draws a sample once or at most a very few times. It is important to realize that sampling distributions are hypothetical, theoretical distributions which would be obtained only if one were to repeat an experiment an extremely large number of times. A sampling distribution is obtained by applying *mathematical* or deductive reasoning as was done in the previous example.

Since sampling distributions are not the kind of distributions a researcher actually sees from his data, persons who are not mathematically inclined are likely to have difficulty understanding the role of these hypothetical distributions in statistical inference. Yet, unless the notion of sampling distribution is clearly grasped you will find it almost impossible to obtain anything more than a "cookbook" understanding of statistics. For this reason, it will be helpful at this point to discuss more systematically the steps made in testing a statistical hypothesis and to see exactly how these sampling distributions are used.

10.2. Steps in Statistical Tests

There are a number of specific steps involved in all statistical tests. It should again be emphasized that each of these steps should be carried out prior to the inspection of one's data. They can be listed as follows:

1. Making assumptions
2. Obtaining the sampling distribution
3. Selecting a significance level and critical region
4. Computing the test statistic
5. Making a decision

Each of these steps will be discussed in some detail in this chapter and again in Chap. 11 so that you may become familiar with the general processes involved in all statistical tests.

1. *Making Assumptions.* In order to make use of probability theory in obtaining a sampling distribution the researcher must make certain assumptions about both the *population* to which he is generalizing and the *sampling* procedures used. The assumptions made about the population and sampling procedure usually fall into one of two categories: (1) those of which the researcher is relatively certain or which he is willing to accept, and (2) assumptions which seem most dubious and in which he is

therefore most interested. Assumptions in the first category can be lumped together into what we shall call the *model*. The assumptions in the second category are the ones which the researcher wants to test and are called *hypotheses*.

Usually, at least in the simpler tests taken up in the next several chapters, there will be only one hypothesis. It is important to realize that *from the standpoint of the statistical test itself all assumptions have the same logical status.* If the results of the test warrant rejection of the assumptions, all that one can say *on the basis of the test itself* is that at least one (and possibly all) of the assumptions is probably false. Since the test itself can supply no information as to which of the assumptions is erroneous, it is essential if results are to be meaningful that only one of the assumptions be really in doubt. It will then be possible to reject this assumption (the hypothesis) as the faulty one.

Students often ask the following type of question: "On what basis does one choose a particular statistical test in preference to another?" One criterion that can be given at this point is an appropriate model. In other words, the researcher should select a test which involves only a single dubious assumption (his hypothesis). If a certain test requires two or more assumptions which are in doubt it will be difficult, if not impossible, to decide which should be rejected. In such an instance one should attempt to find an alternative test which does not require as many doubtful assumptions.

To illustrate with our coin example, the binomial test requires the assumption that the 10 flips constitute a random sample of all possible flips with the same coin and that the flips are independent of each other. We are also assuming that the coin is an honest one. The latter assumption would ordinarily be our hypothesis and the former our model since interest would probably center on whether or not the coin were honest. Conceivably, however, we might be suspicious of the person doing the flipping. If we were relatively sure of the coin, having previously determined that it usually produced about half heads, we could turn the problem around and test an hypothesis concerning the method of flipping (the method of sampling). Suppose we were unwilling to accept as our model the honesty of the coin or the honesty of the flipper. If 50 heads came up in succession we would decide that at least one of our assumptions was undoubtedly wrong, but we would be unable to choose between them. Usually, of course, we pay careful attention to our sampling methods in order to be reasonably assured that assumptions regarding sampling are actually justified.

Taking a sociological example to illustrate the same point, let us suppose that we are required to make only two assumptions in a particular statistical test: (1) that in the population sampled the proportions of middle- and lower-class persons with high mobility aspirations are the same, and (2) that a random sample of all persons has been obtained. Suppose also that these assumptions lead to certain conclusions which cannot be supported by the data.   Perhaps the sample data show a much higher percentage of middle-class persons with high aspirations.   We conclude that one or the other of the assumptions is probably erroneous. But which of the two should be rejected?   We might like to conclude that the first is wrong, but perhaps we have used biased sampling methods. We must have additional knowledge beyond what can be learned from the test itself.

In this particular example, if we have gone to great lengths to assure the selection of a random sample, we can take assumption (2) as our model and conclude that (1) is probably false.   Here, our willingness to accept (2) is based on knowledge about the sampling methods used, i.e., our research methodology.   In other instances we may accept certain assumptions on the basis of previous research findings.   The important point is that *the test itself cannot be used to enable one to locate the faulty assumption or assumptions*.   It is in this sense that the assumptions all have the same logical status.   To emphasize this fact and to call your attention to the assumptions in the model, we treat the hypothesis actually being tested as merely one among a number of assumptions required by the test.

As previously mentioned, a researcher is usually interested in setting up an hypothesis which he really would like to reject.   The hypothesis which is actually tested is often referred to as a *null hypothesis* (symbolized as H_0) as contrasted with the *research hypothesis* (H_1) which is set up as an alternative to H_0.   Usually, although not always, the null hypothesis states that there is no difference between several groups or no relationship between variables, whereas the research hypothesis may predict either a positive or negative relationship.   The researcher may actually expect that the null hypothesis is faulty and should be rejected in favor of the alternative H_1.   Nevertheless, in order to compute a sampling distribution he must for the time being proceed as though H_0 is actually correct. He would assume that the coin is an honest one, for example.

Notice that the assumption of an honest coin provides a way of computing exact probabilities using the binomial formula.   If one were to hypothesize that the coin is "dishonest," he would find that he could not obtain a sampling distribution until he made his hypothesis more specific. He would have to commit himself on a specific value for p, say .75. Seldom will he be in a position to do this.   Likewise, the research hypothesis that there is a larger proportion of persons with high mobility aspirations among the middle class is not as specific as the null hypothesis that there is absolutely no difference between the two classes.

2. *Obtaining the Sampling Distribution*. Having made the necessary assumptions, we are in a position to make use of mathematical reasoning to obtain the sampling distribution in which we associate probabilities with outcomes. Such a distribution of probabilities will tell us just how likely each of the possible outcomes is *if the assumptions made are actually correct*. If the above assumptions about the coin and the flips were actually true, we have seen that in the long run only one time in 1,024 would we expect to get all heads, only ten times in 1,024 would we get nine heads, etc.

Knowledge of the likelihood of any particular outcome occurring by chance if the assumptions were really true can now be used to make a rational decision about the conditions under which we could risk rejecting these assumptions. Suppose, for example, that we were to get all 10 heads. There are two possibilities: (1) either the assumptions are correct and this is one of those occasions on which a very rare event occurred, or (2) at least one of the assumptions (presumably the null hypothesis) is false. Unfortunately, we can never be positive which alternative is the correct one. If we could, we would have known ahead of time about the assumptions and there would have been no point in performing the experiment. But we can say that the first alternative is very unlikely.

Let us establish the rule that every time we get 10 heads in 10 trials we automatically conclude that at least one of the assumptions is false and should be rejected. In the long run, we shall occasionally make erroneous decisions in adhering to this rigid rule since we know that even with an honest coin we can expect to get all 10 heads one time in 1,024 simply by chance. Such a rule will not help us determine the correctness of our decision for any particular experiment, but the laws of probability tell us exactly what proportion of the time we can expect to make correct decisions *in the long run*. In a sense, our faith is in the procedure we are following rather than in the decision we make on any particular occasion. This *procedure* will yield correct decisions most of the time even though we cannot be absolutely certain of being correct on any specific decision.

3. *Selecting a Significance Level and Critical Region*. Ideally, the researcher's decisions should be made prior to the actual experiment or analysis of data. From his knowledge of the sampling distribution he selects a set of alternatives which, should they occur, would require him to reject his assumptions. These unlikely outcomes are referred to as the *critical region*. Thus, he divides the possible outcomes into two categories: (1) those for which he will reject (the critical region), and (2) those whose occurrence would not permit him to reject. In order to make a choice of critical region he must make two decisions in addition to his choice of model and hypothesis. First, he must determine the risks he is willing to take of making types I and II errors. Second, he must decide

whether or not he wants his critical region to include both tails of the sampling distribution.

As indicated in Chap. 8, one must take into consideration two types of possible errors. The first type of error consists of rejecting a set of assumptions when they are in fact true. A type II error, on the other hand, involves a failure to reject assumptions when they are actually false. From the sampling distribution one can determine the exact probabilities that certain outcomes will occur *if the assumptions are actually true*. If the researcher decides that he will reject whenever a specified set of unlikely outcomes (say either zero or ten heads) occurs, then if the assumptions are true he will make a type I error whenever he obtains any of these outcomes.

The probability of making a type I error is the sum of the probabilities of each of the outcomes within the critical region. For example, if the critical region consists of zero or ten heads, the probability of a type I error would be 2/1,024 or .002. If a larger critical region were selected the risk of this type of error would be greater. Suppose it were decided to reject the assumptions if zero, one, nine, or ten heads were obtained. Then the probability of a type I error would be $(1 + 1 + 10 + 10)/1,024$ or .022. The probability of making a type I error is referred to as the *significance level* of the test and can be set at any desired level.

Before discussing possible criteria for deciding upon the significance level to be used, something should be said about type II errors. In view of our earlier discussion of the fallacy of affirming the consequent, it is clearly incorrect to conclude that if certain assumptions cannot be rejected they therefore must be true. Another set of assumptions might also have led to a sampling distribution for which similar conclusions would have been reached. For example, if the true probability of heads were .51 rather than .50, the correct sampling distribution would be almost identical to the one we calculated. Therefore, exactly the same critical region would probably have been selected, and the decision as to whether or not to reject might have been identical. Yet, strictly speaking, the hypothesis that $p = .5$ would be false and should be rejected. If we were unable to reject it, we would not want to accept it outright as the single correct hypothesis since there are a large number of additional hypotheses which also could not be rejected. We simply decide that we should "not reject" our hypothesis.

Even if we conservatively refuse to accept an hypothesis, we would still like to be able to eliminate as many false hypotheses as possible. In this sense we are making an error whenever we fail to reject a false hypothesis. What can be said about the probability of making a type II error? Unfortunately, it is no simple matter to compute type II errors as was the case with type I errors. We shall have to defer our discussion of type II errors until Chap. 14.   One important fact should be noted, however.   For any given test the probabilities of types I and II errors are inversely related.   In other words, *the smaller the risk of a type I error, the greater the probability of a type II error*.   This can be seen in our coin flipping example.   You should convince yourself that if one selects a small critical region (say, zero and ten heads) he will be less likely to reject *any* assumptions than if he were to use a more inclusive region (say, zero, one, nine, and ten heads).   In the former case, while he is less likely to reject true assumptions he is also less likely to reject false assumptions.   Therefore he is more likely to make a type II error.

It is thus impossible to minimize the risks of both types of errors simultaneously unless one redesigns his study and selects additional cases or a different statistical test.   In practice, we set the probability of a type I error at a fixed level (say .05) and then try to select the statistical test which minimizes the risk of a type II error.   In choosing among alternative tests, we select that test which has an appropriate model and which is most powerful in the sense of minimizing the risk of a type II error.[2]

The decision as to the significance level selected depends on the relative costs of making the one or the other type of error and should be evaluated accordingly.   Sometimes a practical decision must be made according to the outcome of the experiment.   A manufacturer may decide to install expensive equipment, a researcher may decide to draw another sample and replicate his study, or public health authorities may have to decide whether or not to attempt mass innoculations of polio serum.   In other instances there is no practical decision required.   A sociologist may simply report the results of his study in a journal article and may not have to take the consequences of one or the other type of error.

It is in situations in which a practical decision has to be made that the choice of a significance level is especially difficult.   In the coin flipping example suppose that the decision involved refusing to continue gambling with a coin the honesty of which were in doubt.   If our hypothetical gambler were faced with the prospects of a nagging wife should he return home with empty pockets, he would do well to quit the game if there were even a reasonable doubt about the coin.   In such a case he would select a large critical region since the penalty for making a type II error (i.e., staying in the game when the coin is actually dishonest) would be quite large.   On the other hand, if he were to run the risk of insulting his boss if he claimed that the coin was dishonest, he would want to be very sure of this fact before he made his decision.   In the latter case he should select a very small critical region, thereby minimizing the risk of a type I error. Similarly, if the cost of mass polio innoculations were considerable or if the serum were potentially harmful, one would want to be quite sure of its

[2] For further discussion of this point, see Sec. 14.1.

effectiveness before putting it to use.   He would want to make it quite difficult to reject the null hypothesis that the serum has no beneficial effect.

If there is no practical decision to be made other than whether or not to publish the results of a study, another rule of thumb should be followed. *The researcher should lean over backwards to prove himself wrong or to obtain results that he actually does not want to obtain*.   Usually, but not always, one sets up a null hypothesis that he really wants to reject.   Since he would like to be able to reject, he should make it very difficult to achieve the desired result by using a very small critical region.

There are occasions—and you should be alerted to their existence—in which one actually does not wish to reject the null hypothesis.   For example, the null hypothesis may take the form of a prediction that there will be no class or religious differences with respect to fertility rates.   If one really wishes to establish such differences he should select a very small critical region, making it difficult for him to reject the null hypothesis. But suppose he actually wishes to show that there are no such differences. Perhaps he is attempting to demonstrate that certain commonly held theories about fertility differentials are incorrect or inadequate.   Or he may be hoping that these differences do not exist so that he will not have to control for class or religion in relating fertility rates to other variables.

In the above instances the researcher is in one sense on the wrong end of the hypothesis and should be primarily interested in minimizing the risk of a type II error.   In other words, he should be especially concerned that he not retain the null hypothesis of no differences when it is actually false.   One is therefore not always being conservative by selecting a small critical region, thus making it difficult to reject a null hypothesis which he may really want to retain.   Significance levels commonly used in statistical research are the .05, .01, and .001 levels.   It should be realized in view of the above discussion that there is nothing sacred or absolute about these levels.   Although a person would usually be conservative in using such levels, if he actually did not want to reject the null hypothesis he would be on safer ground using perhaps the .10, .20, or even .30 level, thereby reducing his risk of a type II error.

*A word of caution is necessary in interpreting the results of significance tests since it is possible to obtain rather misleading results even when the .001 level is used and when rejection is desired.   Significance tests tell us how likely a given set of results would be if certain assumptions were true.   There are several factors which determine the likelihood that we shall be able to reject these assumptions.   The first is how inadequate these assumptions really are.   If, for example, the true probability of heads is .9 it is quite likely that we shall be able to reject the hypothesis that p is .5 because we are actually apt to get a sufficiently high proportion of heads to end up in the critical region.   On the other hand, if the

true probability is .53 we are less likely to get the extreme results necessary for rejection.

*The *number of cases* is another important factor in determining how
extreme the results must be before rejection is possible.   With only 10
flips or cases it has been seen that very extreme results are required in
order to reject.   But if N is large the *proportion* of successes need differ
from the hypothesized p by only a small amount in order to reject.   If
the coin were flipped 10,000 times instead of 10, we would be able to reject
the hypothesis if, say, we were to get over 5,200 heads.   In other words,
under the assumption that p is *exactly* one-half, 5,200 or more heads in
10,000 trials would be just as unlikely as 10 heads in 10 trials even
though the results would not be nearly as extreme.   This is, of course,
consistent with our greater intuitive faith in large samples and with the
realization that in the case of very small samples extreme results could
occur quite frequently by chance.   Similarly, with a sample of 10,000
persons we could obtain very small differences in the fertility rates
between middle- and lower-class women and still be able to reject the null
hypothesis that there are *no* differences whatsoever in the population.

*With a very large number of cases it is practically always possible to
reject any false hypothesis we might set up, regardless of how far our
hypothesized value may differ from the true one.   This means that if
we have 10,000 cases we should not be very surprised if we are able to
reject at the .001 level, and we should be on guard against reporting our
finding as though it were a highly important one.   Statistical significance
should not be confused with practical significance.   Statistical significance can tell us only that certain sample differences would not occur very
frequently by chance if there were no differences whatsoever in the
population.   It tells us nothing directly about the magnitude or importance of these differences.   A factor which is large enough to produce
differences which are statistically significant in a small sample is therefore
much more worthy of one's attention than a factor which produces small
differences which can only be shown to be statistically significant with a
very large sample.   If the study involves a large number of cases, we are
usually more interested in other kinds of problems than tests of significance.   This question will be discussed more thoroughly in Chap. 15
when we take up measures of degree of relationship.   For the present it is
sufficient to point out that statistical significance does not necessarily
imply striking differences or ones which are important to the social
scientist.

Another kind of decision must be made before the critical region can be
determined.   There are a number of outcomes or sets of outcomes the
probability of which may be less than the significance level selected.
For example, the probability of getting *exactly* eight heads is 45/1,024 or

.044. Therefore it would be possible, although not very sensible, to decide to reject the null hypothesis if exactly eight heads were to occur but otherwise not to reject. The probability of a type I error would then be .044. The choice of such a critical region would seldom make sense theoretically, however, since one would ordinarily be even more hesitant about accepting the null hypothesis if nine or ten heads were to turn up, and yet these alternatives would not belong to the critical region. We are practically always interested in using at least an entire tail of the distribution. We are not interested in the probability of getting *exactly* eight heads but in the probability of getting eight *or more* heads, i.e., the probability of getting eight heads or something *even more unusual*.

But why not also include zero, one, and two heads in the critical region since these alternatives are just as unlikely as eight, nine, and ten heads? Often we are not in a position to predict ahead of time the direction in which the unusual results may occur. In this example we may merely suspect that the coin is dishonest but may have no hint as to whether it is biased in favor of heads or tails. Furthermore, we may not care. In such a case we would want to play safe and make use of both tails of the sampling distribution. For if we were to make use of a critical region consisting only of eight, nine, and ten heads, then were we to obtain exactly one head we would be in the unfortunate position of not being able to reject the null hypothesis even though it might be incorrect.

There are a number of occasions, however, either when we are able to predict the direction of deviance or when we are primarily interested in deviations in one direction only. For example, previous information may have led us to predict that the coin is biased in favor of heads. Or we may be betting on tails each time so that if the coin happens to be biased in favor of tails we need have no fear of continuing in the game. In more realistic examples it is often possible to predict direction on the basis of theory or previous studies. It may have been predicted that Catholics will have larger families than Protestants, for instance. If one is interested in showing his theory to be correct, he will make significance tests only when results occur in the predicted direction. If they occur in the opposite direction he need make no test since the data obviously do not support the theory anyway.

Whenever direction has been predicted, one-tailed tests will be preferable to two-tailed tests at the same significance level since it will be possible to obtain a larger tail by concentrating the entire critical region at the proper end of the sampling distribution. This advantage of a one-tailed test is illustrated in Fig. 10.1 in the case of a smooth sampling distribution having the form of a normal curve. In this figure the probabilities of making a type I error are the same in both instances since the two critical regions are of the same size (as measured in terms of areas).   But if the results actually occur in the predicted direction, the researcher will be more likely to reject the hypothesis using a one-tailed test since there is a greater probability of falling into the larger critical region in this direction.   The risk of making a type II error if the true probability is in the predicted direction is less than the risk when using a two-tailed test.

At this point you should not really expect to understand intuitively the relationship between type II errors and one- and two-tailed tests.

Fig. 10.1. Comparison of critical regions for one- and two-tailed tests, using .05 significance level.

Many of these rather difficult notions will become clear only after several practical examples have been discussed.   A more detailed treatment of type II errors must be postponed until Chap. 14.

To be specific in this example, let us select the .05 level and make use of a two-tailed test.   The critical region will consist of the alternatives zero, one, nine, and ten since including additional alternatives would increase the probability of a type I error beyond the .05 level.   In this example the significance level actually used will be $(1 + 1 + 10 + 10)/1,024$ or .022.   In other instances in which the sampling distribution is continuous rather than discrete, it will be possible to use the exact level desired (e.g., .05, .01, or .001).

4. *Computing the Test Statistic.*   It is always necessary to compute what is referred to as a test statistic, the sampling distribution of which is to be used in the test.   Up to now we have dealt only with statistics such as sample proportions, means, and standard deviations which are directly comparable to the same quantities in the population and which may be used as measures for summarizing the data.   A test statistic is a statistic which usually is of no inherent interest descriptively but which is used in testing hypotheses.   It is this statistic which has the sampling distribution which is directly used in the test.   In other words, we compute a quantity from sample data which varies in a known way according to probability theory.   We then compare its value with the sampling distribution and make a decision by evaluating the probability of its occurrence.   Of course there are numerous quantities which can be

computed from sample data, but only a relatively small number have known sampling distributions which can be used for purposes of testing hypotheses.

In this example of the binomial test the test statistic is so simple that it seems hardly worthwhile calling it to your attention.   It is merely the number of successes in N trials and does not require any further computations.   In other problems, however, the test statistic will have to be computed.   In the case of the binomial test, we have let the number of successes r take on all possible values from zero to N, and we have associated probabilities with each value.   Let us suppose in this particular problem involving 10 flips that the number of successes (heads) actually turns out to be eight.   We now have all the information necessary in order to make our decision.

5.) *Making a Decision.*   After having selected his critical region and computed the test statistic, the researcher will either reject or fail to reject the assumptions depending upon the outcome of the experiment.   If the outcome falls within the critical region he will reject with a known probability of a type I error.   If it does not fall within the critical region, he will not reject the assumptions and will take the risk of making a type II error.   In this example, since the outcome of eight heads does not fall within the critical region, he should not reject the null hypothesis that the coin is an honest one.

Ideally, all decisions prior to steps 4 and 5 should be made before the tabulation of results.   Often in exploratory work a person will first examine his data and then make tests of significance.   Although this is sometimes necessary, it should be noted that whenever this occurs one is not completely living up to the rules of the game.   In such instances it would be better not to put forth the claim that hypotheses were actually being tested.   Results could be presented as suggestive, however, and anyone doing a follow-up study would then be in a position to make legitimate statistical tests.

The above comments may sound overrigid and perfectionistic in view of the exploratory nature of much social science research.   The writer takes the position, however, that it is preferable to establish a strict "statistical conscience" rather than to leave the impression that anything goes.   Unless one makes his decisions prior to the analysis of data he cannot legitimately make use of probability theory since his analysis is essentially ex post facto.   The trouble with ex post facto analyses is that the experiment can be set up so that the researcher can't possibly lose.   Suppose, for example, that he has tentatively decided to use the .05 level of significance.   If he finds his results to be significant at the .07 level he may then decide to reject his hypothesis anyway.   But suppose they had been significant at the .09 or .13 or .18 level?   Where does one stop?

Another way of cheating is to wait until after the experiment to decide whether or not to use a one-tailed test. Then if the results show more heads than tails one simply decides that he should have used a one-tailed test since he was subconsciously predicting a bias in favor of heads. This way, no matter what the direction of deviance, he can obtain a larger critical region than with a two-tailed test.

*10.3. Applications of the Binomial

The Sign Test. Suppose a social scientist is making use of a simple "before-after" or "after-only" experimental design in which there are a small number of cases and in which he is only able to determine for each case whether or not his experiment has been successful.[3] For example, he may want to find out whether or not an experience in an interracial camp is successful in reducing stereotypes toward Negroes. He gives a stereotype test to his subjects both before and after the experiment and is able to determine whether or not this type of prejudice has been reduced. Let us indicate by a + ("success") each instance in which prejudice is reduced and by a − ("failure") the cases for which prejudice is increased. If there are any persons showing absolutely no change these persons will be excluded from the analysis. Unless measurement has been extremely crude there should be relatively few of these persons.

The binomial requires the assumption of independence of trials. The social scientist will therefore want to assume that his experimental group constitutes a random sample drawn from some population about which he wishes to generalize and that there has been little or no mutual influence among participants with respect to prejudice scores. Let us suppose that he wishes to establish that the camping experience is actually effective in reducing prejudice. Since this cannot be done directly, he can set up the null hypothesis that the experiment has no effect. If it actually has no effect, then if the entire population from which the sample has been drawn were to undergo similar experiences, we would expect to find the same number of persons whose prejudice was reduced as persons having increased prejudice. In other words, there would be equal proportions of pluses and minuses.

Since each member of the population has an equal chance of appearing in a random sample, the *probability* of getting a + in any given draw will be .5 under the null hypothesis. An assumption about the *proportion* of pluses in the population, when combined with the assumption of randomness, thus permits us to say something about the *probability* of success in any given trial. Randomness also assures independence of trials. Let us emphasize again that *it is necessary to make assumptions about both the*

[3] For a discussion of these and other types of experimental designs, see [3].

population and the method of sampling. In this example, interest is centered on the effectiveness of the experiment, i.e., the proportion of successes in the population.   Therefore, the social scientist will want to make sure that he uses correct procedures for obtaining a random sample.

If there are eight persons in the sample, the sampling distribution of successes would be as follows:

No. of successes	Probability	
0	$\frac{1}{256}$ =	.004
1	$\frac{8}{256}$ =	.031
2	$\frac{28}{256}$ =	.109
3	$\frac{56}{256}$ =	.219
4	$\frac{70}{256}$ =	.274
5	$\frac{56}{256}$ =	.219
6	$\frac{28}{256}$ =	.109
7	$\frac{8}{256}$ =	.031
8	$\frac{1}{256}$ =	.004
		1.000

Let us suppose that the social scientist wishes to use the .05 level of significance.   Since direction has been predicted, a one-tailed test can be used.   The critical region can be determined by cumulating probabilities starting with eight successes, then seven, etc., until the sum becomes greater than the significance level.   It will ordinarily not be necessary to obtain the entire sampling distribution since only the tails are actually used in determining the size of the critical region.   In this case, the probability of eight successes is .004; the probability of seven or eight successes is .035; and the probability of six, seven, or eight successes is .144.   Since the sum of the probabilities of outcomes within the critical region must be less than or equal to the significance level selected, we see that the critical region can consist only of seven or eight successes.

Suppose the social scientist carries out the experiment and finds that in six cases prejudice has been reduced while in the remaining two it has been increased.   He therefore will not reject the hypothesis that the experiment has no effect since the probability of getting such a result, or one even more unusual, is greater than .05.

Testing for Nonrandomness.   In the above example randomness was assumed and interest was centered on the proportion of successes in the population.   In other types of problems there may be information about the proportion of persons in a population having a certain characteristic, but there may be a question about selectivity.   For example, one may test to see whether or not professionals are overrepresented on boards or Negroes underrepresented on jury panels.   Suppose a mayor appoints nine persons to a commission, claiming that these persons are representative in the sense that all types of adults have an equal chance of being selected.   If it is known that 35 per cent of the labor force is white-collar and yet six out of nine members of the commission are white-collar, a binomial test can be used in order to determine how likely such an occupational distribution would be under the assumption of random sampling. In this particular problem the probability of success under the null hypothesis would be .35, and the sampling distribution would not be symmetrical.   We would look upon each of the nine positions on the commission as a "trial."   The probability of getting a white-collar worker as the first commissioner would be .35, and similarly for each of the eight remaining positions.

Other Uses of the Binomial.   The binomial can be used in a number of other types of problems in addition to those mentioned above.   Positional measures, such as the median or quartiles, can sometimes be used to enable one to test whether a small subsample of persons is significantly different from what we would expect by chance.   From a large survey it may be possible to obtain a very good estimate of the income distribution for a particular city.   If data have been obtained for only seven Armenians and if six of these persons are in the lowest quartile, we may test to see how likely this would be, provided, of course, that decisions have been made prior to the test.[4]   Since by definition one-fourth of a population will be in the lowest quartile, the binomial distribution gives the probability of getting a certain proportion of a subsample below the population quartile, under the assumption that such a subsample essentially constitutes a random sample from the larger population.

For example, since the probability of any given person being in the bottom quartile is .25, the probability of getting exactly six Armenians in the lowest quartile would be

$$P(6) = \binom{7}{6}\left(\frac{1}{4}\right)^6\left(\frac{3}{4}\right)^1 = \frac{21}{16{,}384}$$

Also

$$P(7) = \binom{7}{7}\left(\frac{1}{4}\right)^7\left(\frac{3}{4}\right)^0 = \frac{1}{16{,}384}$$

Since we need to obtain the probability of getting six *or more* successes, we add these probabilities getting

$$P(6) + P(7) = \frac{21 + 1}{16{,}384} = .0013$$

Another use of the binomial might involve testing the adequacy of a

---

[4] We must have a very large number of cases in order to obtain an accurate estimate of the positional measure (e.g., Q_1).   Otherwise there will be sufficient sampling error in this estimate to require the use of a two-sample test.   The reason for this should become clearer after two-sample tests have been presented in Chap. 13.

theory which correctly predicted the direction of certain differences in, say, 11 out of 15 independent trials. In order for such trials to be independent, they would have to involve different samples. For example, one sample might consist of young Protestant males, another of young Protestant females, a third of older Catholic males, etc. Each subsample might be too small to yield statistical significance separately, but if the subsamples were independently selected a binomial could legitimately be used to test whether or not a sufficient number of subsamples gave results in the predicted direction. Each subsample would constitute a trial, and the probability of the result being in the predicted direction on any given trial would be .5 under the null hypothesis that the theory has absolutely no predictive value, i.e., that it predicts direction wrongly as often as it does so correctly. Notice that such a test could not be used if 15 observations were taken on the *same* sample of persons.

GLOSSARY

Binomial distribution
Critical region
Model versus hypothesis
One- and two-tailed tests
Sampling distribution
Significance level

EXERCISES

1. In 11 flips of an honest coin, what is the probability of getting exactly four heads? Exactly seven heads? Less than three heads?

2. Suppose the coin in Exercise 1 is dishonest and that the probability of getting a head is actually .6. Without doing the computations, indicate how this would affect each of the probabilities obtained above (i.e., raise, lower, or leave them unchanged).

3. Suppose you wish to test the null hypothesis that the coin is honest by flipping it 11 times. Indicate the critical region you would use:

    a. For a two-tailed test at the .05 level
    b. For a two-tailed test at the .10 level
    c. For a two-tailed test at the .01 level
    d. For a one-tailed test at the .05 level, predicting that $P(\text{head}) > .5$
    e. For a one-tailed test at the .10 level, predicting that $P(\text{head}) < .5$

*4. In a particular community 10 per cent of the population is Jewish. A study of the boards of directors of various service agencies indicates that of a total of seven chairmen of the boards, four are Jewish. How likely is it that this could happen by chance? In this and other exercises involving tests of hypotheses, indicate your reasoning and list the assumptions being made.

*5. A social psychologist takes 12 groups which he matches, pair by pair, according to size. He thus has six pairs of groups, with one group in each pair constituting an experimental group and the other the control group. The experiment involves an attempt to increase the cohesiveness of the groups, and the experimenter is able to evaluate whether or not the experimental group is more cohesive than the control group with which it has been paired. How can he make use of the binomial to test the null hypothesis that the experiment has no effect? In this problem you should indicate all assumptions required, compute the sampling distribution, and make a choice of critical region.

*6. Suppose you are studying a small group of 12 persons and wish to test the hypothesis that the higher the degree of conformity to group norms, the higher one's status in the group. For both variables (conformity and status) you are simply able to evaluate whether the individual is above or below the median. How would you use the binomial to test the null hypothesis that there is no relationship between these two variables? Be sure to indicate your reasoning.

REFERENCES

1. Freund, J. E.: *Modern Elementary Statistics*, Prentice-Hall, Inc., Englewood Cliffs, N.J., 1952, chap. 7.

2. McCarthy, P. J.: *Introduction to Statistical Reasoning*, McGraw-Hill Book Company, Inc., New York, 1957, chap. 8.

3. Selltiz, C., M. Jahoda, M. Deutsch, and S. W. Cook: *Research Methods in Social Relations*, Henry Holt and Company, Inc., New York, 1959, chap. 4.

4. Siegel, S.: *Nonparametric Statistics for the Behavioral Sciences*, McGraw-Hill Book Company, Inc., New York, 1956, pp. 36–42.

5. *Tables of the Binomial Probability Distribution*, National Bureau of Standards, Applied Mathematics Series, no. 6, 1950.

Chapter 11

SINGLE-SAMPLE TESTS INVOLVING MEANS AND PROPORTIONS

In this chapter we shall be concerned with tests of hypotheses about population means and proportions. A sample mean or proportion, obtained from a single sample, will be compared with the hypothesized parameter and a decision made as to whether or not to reject the hypothesis. You will soon discover that tests of the form discussed in this chapter have much less practical utility than tests involving several samples. At this point, however, it is more important to obtain a good understanding of fundamental ideas than to be overly concerned with practical applications. Unfortunately, the simplest tests are not always the most useful ones.

You will recall that statistical tests involving the binomial made use of the multiplication rule in order to obtain a sampling distribution. We were thus able to see exactly how probability theory was used in obtaining the sampling distribution. From here on, mathematical considerations become far more complex, so much so that in spite of the fact that it would be desirable to understand what is behind every argument, you will have to begin taking more and more statements on faith. Mathematical proofs are available, of course, but most involve calculus or even considerably more mathematical background.

11.1. The Central-limit Theorem and the Law of Large Numbers

A rather remarkable theorem, which can be stated in a number of ways and which has been referred to as the *central-limit theorem*, is based on the same principles and rules of probabilities as is the binomial but cannot be proved in a text such as this. This theorem can be stated as follows: *If repeated random samples of size N are drawn from a normal population, with mean μ and variance σ^2, the sampling distribution of sample means will*

135

be normal, with mean μ and variance σ²/N. Let us now take a careful look at what the central-limit theorem says.

We first start with a normal population, recognizing, of course, that in real life there is no such thing as a perfectly normal population. We then imagine ourselves drawing a very large number of random samples of size N from this population.[1] For each of these samples we obtain a mean $\bar{X}$. These sample means will naturally vary somewhat from sample to sample, but we would expect them to cluster around the true population mean μ. This is what the central-limit theorem tells us. It says that

Fig. 11.1. Comparison of normal sampling distributions for different-sized samples.

if we plot the distribution of these sample means the result will be a normal curve. Furthermore, the standard deviation of this normal distribution of sample means will be $\sigma/\sqrt{N}$. Therefore, the larger the sample size selected, the smaller the standard deviation in the sampling distribution, i.e., the more the clustering of sample means (see Fig. 11.1). If we consider the sample means as estimates of the population mean, we can say that there is a certain amount of error in our estimation process owing to sampling fluctuations. Therefore, we refer to the standard deviation of a sampling distribution as the *standard error*. In this case the standard error of the *mean*, indicated symbolically as $\sigma_{\bar{X}}$, is $\sigma/\sqrt{N}$.

You should keep clearly in mind that there are three distinct distributions involved, two of which happen to be exactly normal. *First,* there is the population which is assumed to be normal with a mean of μ and a variance of σ^2 [hereafter written in abbreviated form as $Nor(\mu,\sigma^2)$]. *Second,* there is a distribution of scores *within each sample.* If N is large, this distribution will probably be reasonably representative of the population and may therefore be approximately normal. Notice that this is the only distribution that one actually obtains empirically.[2] *Third,* there

[1] Be careful not to confuse the *number of samples* (which is infinite) with the *size* (N) *of each sample.*

[2] Since this is the distribution which the researcher actually sees, there is likely to be a tendency to confuse this second kind of distribution with the sampling distribution.

is the sampling distribution of a statistic (here, the mean).   We have just seen that the sampling distribution for the mean will also be normal but will have a smaller standard deviation than the population (unless the sample size N is one).

The relationship between the population and the sampling distribution is diagramed in Fig. 11.2.   The larger the sample size N, the more peaked will be the sampling distribution, as was shown in Fig. 11.1.   It should

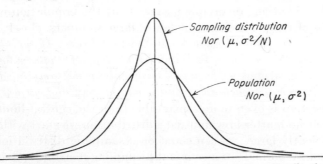

Sampling distribution
Nor $(\mu, \sigma^2/N)$

Population
Nor (μ, σ^2)

Fig. 11.2. Comparison between population and sampling distribution.

be kept clearly in mind that although their standard deviations are directly related to each other, they are completely distinct distributions. All of the "cases" in the sampling distribution are *means* of separate samples.   As was true in the case of the binomial and as will be true in all other statistical tests, it is the sampling distribution rather than the parent population which is used directly in significance tests.   Assumptions about the population may appear in the model.   It is through probability theory and the central-limit theorem that statements about the population and about the sampling methods become translated into statements about a sampling distribution.

In summary, the means and standard deviations of the three kinds of distributions are as follows:

	Mean	Standard deviation
Population	μ	σ
Sample	$\bar{X}$	s
Sampling distribution	μ	$\sigma/\sqrt{N}$

The central-limit theorem is consistent with the common-sense intuition that, assuming biases have been avoided, one can have more faith in estimating the mean from a large sample than a small one.[3]   In effect

---

[3] Notice that we have more faith in *estimates* which are based on large samples, but in rejecting a null hypothesis at the .05 level we take the same risk of a type I error regardless of the size of N.   As we shall presently see, the size of the critical region used in the test takes the sample size into consideration, thus accounting for the apparent inconsistency.

it says that sample means will vary less from sample to sample if N is large. But it is a considerable refinement of common sense in that it gives an indication of how much more faith we should have if N is increased by a given amount. For example, we can see that in order to cut the standard error in half we need to quadruple N. It also tells us that the more homogeneous the population is to begin with, i.e., the smaller the value of σ, the smaller the standard error $\sigma/\sqrt{N}$ and the greater the clustering of sample means about the population mean.

The Law of Large Numbers. A law of large numbers, closely related to the central-limit theorem, can be stated as follows: *If repeated random samples of size N are drawn from any population (of whatever form) having a mean μ and a variance σ^2, then as N becomes large the sampling distribution of sample means approaches normality, with mean μ and variance σ^2/N.*

This theorem is even more remarkable than the central-limit theorem. It says that no matter how unusual a distribution we start with, provided N is sufficiently large, we can count on a sampling distribution which is approximately normal. Since it is the sampling distribution, and not the population, which will be used in significance tests, this means that whenever N is large we can completely relax the assumption about the normality of the population and still make use of the normal curve in our tests.

You should require convincing that the law of large numbers makes sense empirically. The best way to obtain a good grasp of what the central-limit theorem means, and at the same time to convince yourself that the standard error is really $\sigma/\sqrt{N}$, is to draw a number of samples from a population with known mean and standard deviation, compute the sample means, find the standard deviation of these means, and compare the result obtained with $\sigma/\sqrt{N}$.[4] But the law of large numbers requires further intuitive justification. Why should the sampling distribution become normal if the parent distribution is not normal? Let us take a look at a population which is far from normal and see what happens as we take larger and larger samples.

*Imagine we are rolling some mathematically ideal dice for which the probabilities of getting each of the six faces are exactly $\frac{1}{6}$. The probability distribution for the toss of a single die is then rectangular, i.e., all numbers (from 1 to 6) have an equal chance of occurring. This type of distribution is in marked contrast to a normal distribution in which extreme values are less likely than those closer to the mean. Such a rectangular distribution can be represented as in Fig. 11.3. Strictly speaking, of course, the distribution would be discrete and not continuous as is implied in the diagram.

*Considering such a distribution as our population of all possible dice

---
[4] See Exercise 1 at the end of the chapter.

throws, let us calculate the sampling distribution of the means of samples of size 2.   This means that we shall toss two dice, sum of the face values, and divide by 2.   As experienced "craps" players are well aware, these sums range from 2 to 12, with 7 being the most likely value.   In obtaining

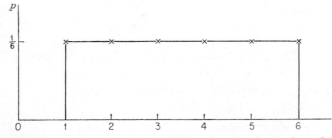

Fig. 11.3. Population distribution of probabilities of getting face values of 1, 2, 3, 4, 5, or 6 with a perfect die.

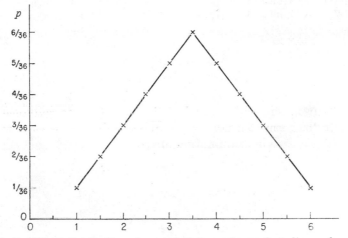

Fig. 11.4. Sampling distribution of means of faces, for perfect dice and samples of size 2.

the probabilities of occurrence of each of these sums, we first note that there are (6)(6) or 36 possible outcomes if the two dice are distinguished. Thus the first die can come up with any one of six faces showing, and so can the second.   To obtain the probability of getting a sum of scores of 7, and hence a mean of 3.5, we need only count the number of ways such a result can occur.   Clearly, there are six pairs which will yield a score of 7: (1,6), (2,5), (3,4), (4,3), (5,2), and (6,1).   A sum of 6 can be obtained in only five ways: (1,5), (2,4), (3,3), (4,2), and (5,1).   Likewise, there is only one way we can get a sum of 12 (6,6) or a sum of 2 (1,1).   The probability distribution of *means* can therefore be represented as follows:

Mean	Probability	Mean	Probability
1.0	$\frac{1}{36}$	4.0	$\frac{5}{36}$
1.5	$\frac{2}{36}$	4.5	$\frac{4}{36}$
2.0	$\frac{3}{36}$	5.0	$\frac{3}{36}$
2.5	$\frac{4}{36}$	5.5	$\frac{2}{36}$
3.0	$\frac{5}{36}$	6.0	$\frac{1}{36}$
3.5	$\frac{6}{36}$		$\frac{36}{36}$

When plotted, this sampling distribution takes the form of a triangle (Fig. 11.4).

*If three dice are tossed, the faces summed, and means obtained, the sampling distribution of means will be as follows:

Mean	Probability	Mean	Probability
1.00	$\frac{1}{216}$	3.67	$\frac{27}{216}$
1.33	$\frac{3}{216}$	4.00	$\frac{25}{216}$
1.67	$\frac{6}{216}$	4.33	$\frac{21}{216}$
2.00	$\frac{10}{216}$	4.67	$\frac{15}{216}$
2.33	$\frac{15}{216}$	5.00	$\frac{10}{216}$
2.67	$\frac{21}{216}$	5.33	$\frac{6}{216}$
3.00	$\frac{25}{216}$	5.67	$\frac{3}{216}$
3.33	$\frac{27}{216}$	6.00	$\frac{1}{216}$
			$\frac{216}{216}$

This distribution, as can readily be seen in Fig. 11.5, is beginning to approximate the form of a normal curve even though the sample size is only 3. After a careful examination of the above figures, you should be

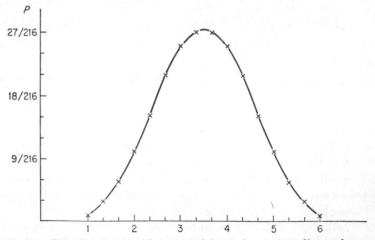

Fig. 11.5. Sampling distribution of means of faces, for perfect dice and samples of size 3.

able to grasp intuitively what is happening and why it is that a bell-shaped curve is being approximated as the sample size N becomes larger and larger.   Even though on a single toss a 6 is as likely as a 3 or 4, and as a matter of fact two 6's are as likely as two 3's, there is only one way of getting two 6's whereas there are a number of different ways of getting an *average* of 3.0 on 2 or more tosses.   In common language we say that large numbers are likely to be counterbalanced by small ones, especially if N is large.

11.2. Test for Population Mean, σ Known

Let us now see how the central-limit theorem and the law of large numbers can be used in statistical tests.   To begin with, we shall take up the simplest possible model for illustrative purposes.   Since some of the assumptions required in this model are impractical they will be relaxed later on.   Each of the five steps discussed in Chap. 10 will again be treated in some detail in order to help you gain greater familiarity with the process of developing statistical tests.

Problem. Suppose a researcher is interested in checking on the adequacy of the sampling procedures used in a local survey.   The survey has been taken by inexperienced interviewers, and the researcher suspects that middle- and upper-income families may have been oversampled, i.e., given a greater probability of appearing in the sample than lower-income families.   Census data, involving a complete enumeration, are available which show the mean family income of the community to be \$4,500 and standard deviation \$1,500.   The smaller survey involves 100 families, supposedly randomly selected, and the mean family income of this sample is found to be \$4,900.   Does the researcher have reason to suspect a biased sample?

1. *Making Assumptions*.   In order to make use of the law of large numbers certain assumptions must be made.   As previously indicated, there must always be an assumption about the method of sampling.   In this case we assume the sample to be random.   It is actually this assumption that we are interested in testing since we are skeptical of the interviewers' ability to give all families an equal chance of being selected.   Presumably, we are willing to accept certain assumptions about the population, i.e., that the census data are accurate.   If we cannot accept the census figures, there will be at least two assumptions in doubt, and interpretation of the results will be exceedingly difficult.   Random sampling, then, will be our hypothesis; the remaining assumptions about the population will constitute the model.

A normal population is required if N is not too large. Here the question arises, "How large does N have to be before we can relax the normality assumption and make use of the law of large numbers rather than the more restrictive central-limit theorem?" There is no simple answer to such a question since an answer depends, among other things, on (1) how precise an estimate of the probability of a type I error is desired, and (2) how good an approximation to a normal population we have. Although you should be wary of simple rules of thumb, it may be suggested that whenever $N \geq 100$ the normality assumption can practically always be relaxed. If $N \geq 50$ and if there is empirical evidence to the effect that departure from normality is not serious, then tests of the type discussed in the present section may also be used with a degree of assurance. If $N \leq 30$, however, one should definitely be on guard against the use of such tests unless the approximation to normality is known to be good. Whenever very small samples are used, one usually lacks such information since there are not enough cases in the sample to indicate the form of the population distribution. Therefore, other kinds of tests should ordinarily be used for small samples. Let us suppose in this problem that we can legitimately make use of the law of large numbers. As we know, income distributions are usually somewhat skewed. On the other hand, we have a reasonably large sample.

In addition to the above assumptions, if we are to use the law of large numbers, it is also necessary to accept the census figures for μ and σ and to assume an interval scale. Therefore we have the following assumptions:

Level of Measurement: Interval scale
Model: Normal population (can be relaxed)
 $\mu = \$4,500$
 $\sigma = \$1,500$
Hypothesis (null): Random sampling

2. *Obtaining the Sampling Distribution.* Fortunately, the task of getting the sampling distribution has already been done for us. Since we know that the sampling distribution of the sample means is normal or approximately normal, we can go directly to the normal table. From now on, sampling distributions will always be given in the form of tables in Appendix 2. It is important to realize, however, that these tables have been computed using probability theory. It is very easy to get so lost in computational details that one forgets that whenever he is making use of a table in his statistical tests he is actually making use of a sampling distribution.

3. *Choosing a Significance Level and Critical Region.* The choice of the proper significance level depends, of course, on the relative costs involved in making types I and II errors. If the researcher fails to

reject the hypothesis of random sampling when in fact the sample is biased, he runs the risk of reporting misleading findings.   On the other hand, if he rejects when the hypothesis is actually true, he may have to repeat the survey at considerable cost.   Ideally, he should make a rational decision based on the relative costs of these two kinds of error. Actually, he will probably have a difficult time doing this.   Let us assume that he decides on the .05 level.   Next, he should decide to use a one-tailed test since the direction of bias is predicted.   If the sample mean were to

Fig. 11.6. Normal sampling distribution, with shaded area representing a one-tailed critical region at the .05 significance level.

turn out to be less than $4,500, he would hardly suspect his interviewers of oversampling the middle- and upper-income groups.[5]   Given the choice of the .05 level and a one-tailed test, the critical region is determined from the normal table.   Since only 5 per cent of the area of the normal curve is to the right of an ordinate 1.65 standard deviations larger than the mean, we know that if the result is more than 1.65 standard deviations larger than μ the hypothesis should be rejected (see Fig. 11.6).

4. *Computing the Test Statistic.*   We know that if all assumptions are correct, the sampling distribution of $\bar{X}$'s will be $Nor(\mu,\sigma^2/N)$.   In terms of our example,

$$\mu = \$4,500$$

$$\sigma_{\bar{x}} = \frac{\sigma}{\sqrt{N}} = \frac{1,500}{\sqrt{100}} = \$150$$

In order to make use of the normal table it is necessary to convert to standard scores, or in other words to obtain a statistic Z which is $Nor(0,1)$. Previously we used the formula

$$Z = \frac{X - \bar{X}}{s}$$

---

[5] In this problem, the data for the sample have actually been given and we *know* the direction of the result.   You should imagine, however, that this decision is being made prior to one's knowledge of the outcome.

This formula holds for a sample which is $Nor(\bar{X},s^2)$ but *not* for the sampling distribution. Let us recall each of the steps in our procedure. We have made a series of assumptions in order to obtain a sampling distribution. This latter distribution tells us how likely a *given* $\bar{X}$ would be if the assumptions were actually true. The social scientist has obtained a single $\bar{X}$ from his sample and then will use the theoretical sampling distribution to help him evaluate the likelihood of getting a result as unusual or more unusual than his particular $\bar{X}$. It is the sampling distribution he is dealing with when he uses the normal table. Each "case" in this distribution is an $\bar{X}$, the mean is μ, and the standard deviation is $\sigma/\sqrt{N}$. Therefore, $\bar{X}$ replaces X, μ replaces $\bar{X}$, and $\sigma/\sqrt{N}$ replaces s in the above formula for Z. Hence

$$Z = \frac{\bar{X} - \mu}{\sigma/\sqrt{N}}$$

$$= \frac{4,900 - 4,500}{150} = 2.67$$

In other words, the sample mean is 2.67 standard errors larger than the population mean.

5. *Making a Decision*. Since $\bar{X}$ deviates from the assumed μ in the predicted direction by more than 1.65 standard deviations, the hypothesis should be rejected at the .05 level. In fact, having computed Z exactly, we can say more than this. The probability of getting a Z this large or larger is .0038, using a one-tailed test. In practice it is usually advisable to compute the exact significance level whenever possible. In so doing we indicate that the result has fallen within an even smaller critical region than the one originally established. Since the reader may prefer to use a different level of significance than does an author, it is ordinarily helpful to supply exact or more nearly exact probabilities so that the reader may draw his own conclusions about whether or not to accept the findings. In this example, the social scientist would reject the null hypothesis that the sampling was random. He would then want to decide whether or not to draw another sample.

11.3. Student's t Distribution

In most instances it is completely unrealistic to treat σ as known. Usually one goes to considerable trouble to assure randomness since he is primarily interested in testing assumptions about the population being studied. In tests of the sort being discussed in this chapter, he is likely to want to test an hypothesis concerning μ. But if this were the case, would he ever be in a position to know the value of σ? Practically never.

For if he possessed knowledge of σ he would undoubtedly also be in a position to know μ unless, of course, someone such as his statistics instructor were deliberately withholding information. Usually he would not know the values of either μ or σ. What can he do in such a situation? Since the law of large numbers involves σ, he cannot completely ignore its value. One solution would seem to be to replace σ with s, the *sample* standard deviation. As a matter of fact, this was commonly done prior to the development of modern statistics. In the formula for Z, $\sigma/\sqrt{N}$ was simply replaced by $s/\sqrt{N}$, and since s could be computed directly from the sample data there were no unknowns left in the formula. As it turns out, this procedure yields reasonably good results when N is large. As we shall see presently, however, probabilities obtained in this manner can be quite misleading whenever N is relatively small. Let us see why this is the case.

We can construct an alternative test statistic

$$t = \frac{\bar{X} - \mu}{s/\sqrt{N-1}}$$

This statistic was introduced by W. S. Gossett, writing under the name of "Student," and has a sampling distribution known as Student's t distribution. Comparing t with Z, we notice that whereas the numerators are identical, the denominators differ in two respects: (1) there is an $N - 1$ under the radical, and (2) σ has been replaced by s. In order to understand these modifications let us examine each in turn. In so doing we shall have to introduce several new ideas.

The sample standard deviation s can be used as an estimate of σ. Although the problem of estimation will be treated in the next chapter, it is sufficient at this point to mention that we often want an estimate to possess certain properties. One of the properties of a "good" estimate is that it be unbiased. Contrary to what one might expect, it turns out that s is not quite an unbiased estimate of σ. Another quantity, which we can designate as $\hat{\sigma}$ and which is obtained by the formula

$$\hat{\sigma} = \sqrt{\frac{\sum_{i=1}^{N} (X_i - \bar{X})^2}{N-1}}$$

can be shown mathematically to be an unbiased estimate of σ.[6] The only

---

[6] Strictly speaking, $\hat{\sigma}$ is not an unbiased estimate of σ, but $\hat{\sigma}^2$ is an unbiased estimate of σ^2. This subtle distinction need not bother us. In this text we shall commonly use a circumflex (∧) over a Greek letter to indicate an estimate of the parameter. Some texts define s with $N - 1$ in the denominator, but we shall keep the two formulas distinct.

difference between $\hat{\sigma}$ and s is in the $N - 1$ factor in the denominator. Thus, although you have learned to compute s, you are now faced with the fact that another formula should be used in estimating σ. In the present problem it is $\sigma/\sqrt{N}$ rather than σ which needs to be estimated since it is the former expression which appears in the denominator of Z. Although it is true that $\hat{\sigma}/\sqrt{N}$ is the best estimator of $\sigma/\sqrt{N}$, it is possible completely to avoid the computation of $\hat{\sigma}$ if s has already been obtained. Notice that

$$\frac{\hat{\sigma}}{\sqrt{N}} = \frac{\sqrt{\left[\sum_{i=1}^{N} (X_i - \bar{X})^2\right] / (N - 1)}}{\sqrt{N}}$$

Remembering that $\sqrt{a}/\sqrt{b}$ can be written as $\sqrt{a/b}$, we have

$$\frac{\hat{\sigma}}{\sqrt{N}} = \sqrt{\frac{\sum_{i=1}^{N} (X_i - \bar{X})^2}{N(N - 1)}}$$

$$= \frac{\sqrt{\left[\sum_{i=1}^{N} (X_i - \bar{X})^2\right] / N}}{\sqrt{N - 1}} = \frac{s}{\sqrt{N - 1}}$$

Thus we can take a somewhat biased estimate of σ, divide by a quantity which is slightly smaller than $\sqrt{N}$, and come out with $s/\sqrt{N - 1}$ as an unbiased estimate of $\sigma/\sqrt{N}$. It is for this reason that $N - 1$ appears in the denominator of t.[7]

In replacing Z with t, the modification introduced by using $N - 1$ is relatively slight, but the substitution of s in place of σ may be of considerable significance if N is small. Since s varies from sample to sample, the denominator of t varies as well as the numerator. For a given value of $\bar{X}$, if the s for a particular sample happens to be too small, t will be quite large; if s is large, t will be relatively small. There will thus be greater variability among t scores than among comparable Z values. This means that the sampling distribution of t will be flatter than normal. The t distribution will therefore have larger tails. Just how flat a t distribution is will depend on the size of the sample. If N is very small the t distribution will be very flat as compared with the normal curve. In other words, it will be necessary to go out a larger number of standard deviations from the mean in order to include 95 per cent of the cases.

[7] Some texts recommend the use of $N - 1$ for small samples and N for large ones. Such a procedure seems to add unnecessary confusion. In the case of large samples, of course, it makes little difference which figure is used.

As N becomes large, the t distribution comes closer and closer to approximating a normal distribution, always being slightly flatter than the normal curve, however. Thus there is a different t distribution for each size sample. The fact that t distributions approach normality makes sense intuitively when we realize that as N becomes large, s becomes a very accurate estimate of σ and it makes very little difference whether we use s or σ in the denominator. *In order to make use of the t distribution a normal population must be assumed, especially if N is relatively small.* The computation of the sampling distribution of t requires that the numerator $(\bar{X} - \mu)$ be normally distributed and that it also vary independently of the denominator $s/\sqrt{N - 1}$. Ordinarily, we would not expect independence between numerator and denominator since s is actually computed by taking deviations about $\bar{X}$, and therefore it would be surprising to find $\bar{X}$ and s independent of each other. Knowing the sample $\bar{X}$ we would expect to improve our ability to predict s for that same sample. It so happens that for normal populations and random sampling, the sample mean and standard deviation are independent, however. Since this property does not generally hold for all population distributions and since $\bar{X} - \mu$ will not generally be normally distributed unless N is large, we must assume a normal population when using the t test.

Problem. Suppose you are evaluating the programs of a random sample of 25 casework agencies selected from the population of all casework agencies in the state of New York. Each agency keeps a record of the percentage of successful cases judged according to some standard criterion. A standard has been set that the mean success percentage for all agencies ought to be 60 per cent. In your sample you find the mean percentage to be 52 per cent and the standard deviation to be 12 per cent. Do you have reason to suspect that for the population of agencies as a whole the level of performance is below the standard expected?

1. *Making Assumptions.* Necessary assumptions may be listed as follows:

> *Level of Measurement:* Interval scale
> *Model:* Random sampling
> Normal population
> *Hypothesis:* $\mu = 60$ per cent

Notice that no assumption about σ is necessary since s has actually been obtained empirically and can be directly used in the t test. A few comments about the level of measurement are needed. Since each client of an agency is either a success or a failure and since figures obtained for each agency are percentages of successes, it might be thought that we are dealing with a simple dichotomized nominal scale rather than an interval scale. Indeed, if the units of analysis were *clients* rather than agencies this would be the case. But remember that the units being studied are *agencies*. A score for each agency (e.g., percentage of successes) has been obtained, and this score represents a legitimate interval scale. For example, a difference between 30 and 40 per cent is the same as a difference between 70 and 80 per cent. Both differences can be translated into the same actual number of clients.

2. *Obtaining the Sampling Distribution.* Sampling distributions for t are given in Table D of Appendix 2. Since these distributions differ for each sample size, the table has been condensed so as to give only the tails of each distribution. In using the table it is first necessary to locate the proper sample size by looking down the left-hand column. These sample sizes are ordinarily given in terms of *degrees of freedom* (df), which in this type of problem is always $N - 1$.[8] Next, locate the proper significance level by reading across the top. Figures within the body of the table indicate the magnitude of t necessary to obtain significance at the designated level.

3. *Selecting a Significance Level and Critical Region.* Let us use the .05 level and a one-tailed test. From Table D we see that for 24 degrees of freedom a t of 2.064 or larger is needed in order to obtain significance at the .05 level for a two-tailed test. For a one-tailed test and the .05 level, we need a t of only 1.711 or larger. In the case of one-tailed tests we simply halve the significance levels required for two-tailed tests. This is because we go out the same number of standard deviations from the mean in order to obtain a one-tailed critical region of .05 as we would to get a two-tailed region of .10.

4. *Computing the Test Statistic.* Although it is true that the sampling distribution of $\bar{X}$ is $Nor(\mu, \sigma^2/N)$ and therefore that the distribution of Z is $Nor(0,1)$, this information is of no real use to us since σ is unknown. Instead, we compute the value of t, obtaining

$$t = \frac{\bar{X} - \mu}{s/\sqrt{N - 1}} = \frac{52 - 60}{12/\sqrt{24}} = -3.27$$

5. *Decision.* It has been determined that any t the numerical value of which is ≥ 1.711 will be within the critical region. Therefore we reject the hypothesis that $\mu = 60$ and conclude, with a certain risk of error, that the actual level of performance of the agencies is below the standard expected. Reading across the row corresponding to 24 degrees of freedom

[8] For a discussion of degrees of freedom, see Sec. 12.1.

in Table D, we see that for a one-tailed test the significance level corresponding to a t of 3.27 is somewhere between .005 and .0005.[9]

Several facts about the t distribution can be noted at this point. If you will examine the column corresponding to $p = .05$ for a two-tailed test, you will notice that as the sample size becomes larger t values become smaller and converge fairly rapidly to 1.96, the value necessary for significance if the normal table were used. These values should give a reasonably good idea of the degree of approximation to the normal curve for any given sample size. For values of $N - 1$ larger than 30, interpolation will ordinarily be necessary, and for values much larger than 120 the normal table will have to be used since t values are not given. Some texts arbitrarily state that it is only necessary to use the t table when $N \leq 30$. Although such a rule of thumb yields reasonable results, the position taken here is that it is always preferable to _use the t table whenever_ _σ is unknown_ and whenever a normal population can be assumed. Since the t table is no more difficult to use, it seems sensible to use exact values in preference to a normal approximation. It should also be emphasized that there is not a unique theory applying to small samples and an entirely different one applying to large samples as some texts imply.

As can be seen from the t table, only when the sample size is relatively small do the normal and t distributions differ considerably. Also, a normal population must be assumed whenever t is used unless N is quite large, in which case t can be approximated by Z. Therefore, the practical value of the t test is in situations where one has small samples and where a normal population can be assumed. Unfortunately, it is when samples are small that we are ordinarily most in doubt about the exact nature of the population. For example, if a researcher is doing an exploratory study with 17 cases, is he very likely to be in a position to accept the normality assumption? Probably not. This means that the t test is not a particularly useful test in spite of its popularity. As we shall see in Chap. 14, there are tests that can be used as alternatives to the t test and which do not involve the normality assumption. Probably in the next ten years or so these latter tests will come to replace the t test altogether. Since t is frequently used in the literature, however, you should be familiar with it and with the assumptions it requires.

11.4. Tests Involving Proportions

Up to this point in the chapter we have considered only examples involving an interval scale. Furthermore, normality of the population

---

[9] Although exact probabilities cannot be obtained from the table, interpolation is always possible. Usually, however, it is sufficient to indicate that p is between two values, e.g., $.0005 \leq p \leq .005$.

also had to be assumed for small samples. In this section we shall see how the law of large numbers can be used to cover tests involving proportions whenever N is fairly large. In fact, proportions will be treated as special cases of means so that our previous discussion will still apply.

Suppose we have a simple dichotomized nominal scale. We might want to test an hypothesis concerning, say, the proportion of males in a population. Let us arbitrarily assign the value one to males and zero to females and treat the scores as an interval scale. Although there is no clearly conceived unit, unless it be the attribute "maleness" which is either possessed or not possessed, we can treat these arbitrary scores as an interval scale because there are only two of them. If a third category were added this would no longer be possible, however, since it would become necessary to determine the exact position of this category relative to those of the other two. What we are in effect saying, here, is that it is unnecessary to make a distinction between nominal, ordinal, and interval scales in the case of a dichotomy since the problem of comparing distances between scores never arises.

We now have a population made up entirely of ones and zeros. This is a bimodal distribution, having all cases concentrated at one of two points, and is certainly not normal. But if N is sufficiently large we know that regardless of the form of the population, the sampling distribution of sample means will be approximately $Nor(\mu, \sigma^2/N)$. All that remains to be done is to determine the mean and standard deviation of this population of ones and zeros.

Let p_u represent the proportion of males in the population and q_u the proportion of females, the subscript u indicating that we are dealing with the entire universe. In order to obtain the mean of the ones and zeros in the population, we simply add the values and divide by the total number of cases. The *number* of ones will be the total number of cases multiplied by the proportion of males. Regardless of the number of zeros, their contribution to the sum will be zero. Therefore the population mean will be

$$\mu = \frac{M p_u}{M} = p_u$$

where M represents the size of the population (as distinguished from the sample size N). Therefore, the mean of a number of ones and zeros is exactly the proportion of ones. By similar reasoning $\bar{X} = p_s$, where p_s represents the proportion of males in the sample.

By using the general formula for the standard deviation, we can show that $\sigma = \sqrt{p_u q_u}$. Making use of the symbols for population parameters, the formula for σ becomes

$$\sigma = \sqrt{\frac{\sum_{i=1}^{M}(X_i - \mu)^2}{M}} = \sqrt{\frac{\sum_{i=1}^{M}(X_i - p_u)^2}{M}}$$

Looking at the numerator of the quantity under the radical, we see that there will be only two types of quantities representing the squared deviations from the mean p_u. For each score of one, the squared deviation from the mean will be $(1 - p_u)^2$, and for every zero it will be $(0 - p_u)^2$. Since there will be Mp_u ones and Mq_u zeros in the sum of squares, we get

$$\sigma = \sqrt{\frac{Mp_u(1 - p_u)^2 + Mq_u(0 - p_u)^2}{M}} = \sqrt{\frac{Mp_uq_u^2 + Mq_up_u^2}{M}}$$

Factoring Mp_uq_u from each term in the numerator, we get

$$\sigma = \sqrt{\frac{Mp_uq_u(q_u + p_u)}{M}} = \sqrt{\frac{Mp_uq_u}{M}}$$
$$= \sqrt{p_uq_u}$$

Notice, incidentally, that since M cancels out in both the formulas for μ and σ, the population mean and standard deviation are independent of the actual size of the population.

Therefore we can use the law of large numbers to give

$$\sigma_{\bar{X}} = \sigma_{p_s} = \frac{\sigma}{\sqrt{N}} = \sqrt{\frac{p_uq_u}{N}}$$

where the symbol σ_{p_s} indicates that we are dealing with the standard error of sample proportions.   In our new terminology, p_s replaces $\bar{X}$, p_u replaces μ, and σ_{p_s} replaces $\sigma_{\bar{X}}$ in the formula for Z.   Thus

$$Z = \frac{\bar{X} - \mu}{\sigma_{\bar{X}}} = \frac{p_s - p_u}{\sqrt{p_uq_u/N}}$$

Notice that although it appears as if we have a completely different formula from that previously used, there is really nothing new except a change of symbols.   This is true since we have been able to show that proportions can be treated as special cases of means.   It should be emphasized, however, that the law of large numbers requires that N must be large in order to make use of the normal approximation.   Whenever N is small the binomial would be a more appropriate test.

Problem.   You are interested in evaluating the program of a particular casework agency and have drawn a random sample of

125 cases from its files. The percentage of successful cases is found to be 55 per cent as compared with the standard of 60 per cent. Can you conclude that the agency is below standard performance?

1. *Making Assumptions.*

Level of Measurement: Dichotomized nominal scale
Model: Random sampling
Hypothesis: $p_u = .60$

This example is purposely similar to the previous one in order to emphasize the difference in units of analysis. Here, a single agency is being studied and the sample is of clients who are either successes or failures. In the earlier example agencies, rather than people, were the units being sampled, and the measure for each agency consisted of the *percentage* of successful cases. Notice that no assumption other than the hypothesis is required about the population, as it is implicitly assumed that it is bimodal.

2. *Obtaining the Sampling Distribution.* The sampling distribution will be approximately normal since N is large.

3. *Selecting a Significance Level and Critical Region.* Let us select, for sake of variety, the .02 level and a one-tailed test.

4. *Computing the Test Statistic.* We compute Z as follows:

$$Z = \frac{p_s - p_u}{\sqrt{p_u q_u / N}} = \frac{.55 - .60}{\sqrt{[(.60)(.40)]/125}} = \frac{-.05}{.0438} = -1.14$$

Note that p_u and q_u are used in the denominator rather than p_s and q_s. In case you might be tempted to use t rather than Z you should notice that given an hypothesized p_u, the value of σ is determined by the formula $\sigma = \sqrt{p_u q_u}$.

5. *Making a Decision.* From the normal table it can be seen that a Z of -1.14 or less would occur approximately 13 per cent of the time by chance if the assumptions were true. We therefore do not reject the hypothesis at the .02 significance level. On the basis of the evidence at hand it cannot be established that the agency is below standard.

GLOSSARY

Central-limit theorem
Law of large numbers
Rectangular distribution
t distribution

EXERCISES

1. Using the table of random numbers given in Table B of Appendix 2 (see Sec. 22.1 for an explanation of the use of this table), select 10 samples, each of size 4, from the

population of 65 cases given in Exercise 1 of Chap. 4. Compute the mean for each of these 10 samples and obtain the standard deviation of these 10 means. You now have a very rough and slightly biased estimate of the standard error of the mean. How does your figure compare with the standard error obtained by using the central-limit theorem, using the population standard deviation you computed in Exercise 2 of Chap. 6?

*2. Verify the sampling distribution of the mean of three dice throws which is diagramed in Fig. 11.5.

3. A sample of size 50 has a mean of 10.5 and a standard deviation s of 2.2. Test the hypothesis that the population mean is 10.0 using (a) a one-tailed test at the .05 level, and (b) a two-tailed test at the .01 level. Do the same for samples of size 25 and 100 and compare results.

4. Suppose it is known that the mean annual income of assembly-line workers in a certain plant is $4,000 with a standard deviation of $900. You suspect that workers with active union interests will have higher than average incomes and take a random sample of 85 of these active members, obtaining a mean of $4,200 and a standard deviation of $1,100. Can you say that active union members have significantly higher incomes? (Use the .01 level.)

5. You have taken a poll of 200 community residents of voting age and have found that of two candidates for an office, candidate A received 54 per cent of the votes sampled. Are you justified in concluding that A will win? Use the .05 level. List all of the assumptions you will have to make.

6. Suppose that a test measuring "conformity needs" has been standardized on college students across the country. Fifty per cent of these college students had raw scores of 26 or higher (high scores indicating high conformity needs). Suspecting that conformity needs would generally be higher in the case of adults without a college education, a social scientist selects a random sample of adults 25 or older residing within his community. He finds (1) that 67 per cent of the 257 adults without college education have scores of 26 or higher, and (2) that 59 per cent of the 80 adults with college education have scores in this range.

a. Can he conclude that the scores of either set of adults within his community are significantly higher than those of the college students on whom the test has been standardized? (Use .001 level.)

b. Suppose the social scientist knows the entire exact distribution of college students' scores on the test. On the basis of the materials in the present chapter, what are some alternative procedures for testing for the significance of the departures of the two sets of adults' scores from the standardized scores? Do these alternative procedures require any additional assumptions? Explain.

REFERENCES

1. Freund, J. E.: *Modern Elementary Statistics*, Prentice-Hall, Inc., Englewood Cliffs, N.J., 1952, chap. 10.

2. Hagood, M. J., and D. O. Price: *Statistics for Sociologists*, Henry Holt and Company, Inc., New York, 1952, chaps. 15 and 16.

3. Wallis, W. A., and H. V. Roberts: *Statistics: A New Approach*, Free Press, Glencoe, Ill., 1956, chaps. 11 and 13.

Chapter 12

POINT AND INTERVAL ESTIMATION

Up to this point the discussion of statistical inference has been concerned solely with the testing of hypotheses. There may also be an interest in *estimating* population parameters, and it is with this topic that the present chapter is concerned. After discussing the principles involved in estimation, we shall proceed to a discussion of the interrelationships between estimation and hypothesis testing. Modifications required for the t distribution and proportions will then be discussed. Finally, we shall take up the general question of the determination of sample size, illustrating the problem with estimation procedures.

In the previous two chapters you may have noted that in a number of practical problems the testing of specific hypotheses is not feasible because we are unable to specify a particular hypothetical value for the parameter, say μ. We shall presently see how estimation procedures can provide a very useful alternative to actual tests in such instances. Also, the social scientist may be directly interested in estimates rather than tests of hypotheses. For example, in survey research the practical aim of the study may be to estimate the proportion of persons using a certain product or voting in an election. Or it may be necessary to estimate the median income in an area or the mean number of children per married couple. Tests of specific hypotheses might be of some use in such instances, but estimation would be the more obvious procedure.

There are basically two kinds of estimation: point estimation and interval estimation. In point estimation we are interested in the best single value which can be used to estimate a parameter. For example, we may estimate that the median income in New York City is $4,500. Usually, however, we also want to obtain some idea of how accurate an estimate we have. We would like to predict that the parameter is somewhere within a given interval on either side of the point estimate. Thus we may want to make a statement such as, "The median income in New York City is somewhere between $4,000 and $5,000." These two types of estimation are discussed in the sections which immediately follow.

12.1. Point Estimation

The problem of what statistic to use as an estimate of a parameter seems, on the surface, to be completely straightforward and a matter of common sense. If one wants to estimate the *population* mean (or median or standard deviation), why not use the *sample* mean (or median or standard deviation)? Although common sense would not lead us too far astray in these instances, we shall see that the problem is not quite so simple. Obviously, we *could* estimate a population mean in a number of ways. In addition to the sample mean, we could use the sample median or mode, we could use a number half way between the two extreme values, or we could use as our estimate the value of the thirteenth observation. Certain of these procedures would be better than others. We therefore need criteria with which to evaluate each kind of estimate in order to determine just how good it is. The social scientist using statistics as an applied tool seldom has to worry about such criteria. He is usually simply told to use a particular estimate. Nevertheless, it seems to be worth while to know just what criteria are used by the mathematician in deciding which estimate to use. Two of the most important of the mathematician's criteria are bias and efficiency. We shall discuss each of these in turn. For other criteria, such as the principle of maximum likelihood, you should refer to more advanced texts.

Bias. An estimate is said to be *unbiased* if the *mean of its sampling distribution is exactly equal to the value of the parameter being estimated.* In other words, the expected value of the estimate in the long run is the parameter itself. Notice that nothing is said, here, about the value of any particular sample result. According to this definition $\bar{X}$ is an unbiased estimate of μ since the sampling distribution of $\bar{X}$ has μ as its mean. This does not mean, however, that we can expect that any particular value of $\bar{X}$ will equal μ, nor will we ever know in any realistic problem whether or not our sample mean does in fact equal the population mean. You should keep clearly in mind that the term *bias, as used* in this sense, refers to long-run results. In practical research you may be accustomed to using the term to refer to properties of the particular sample which you have drawn.

It was mentioned in the previous chapter that the sample standard deviation s is a slightly biased estimate of σ. The statistic s has a sampling distribution as does $\bar{X}$. In other words, sample standard deviations will be distributed about the true population standard deviation just as sample means are distributed about μ. It can be shown mathematically, however, that the mean of the sampling distribution of s^2 is $[N - 1/N]\,\sigma^2$ and not σ^2. Therefore, s^2 is a biased estimate of σ^2. To find an unbiased estimate of σ^2 we take the quantity

$$\frac{N}{N-1}\,s^2 = \frac{N}{N-1}\,\frac{\displaystyle\sum_{i=1}^{N}(X_i - \bar{X})^2}{N}$$

$$= \frac{\displaystyle\sum_{i=1}^{N}(X_i - \bar{X})^2}{N-1} = \hat{\sigma}^2$$

Since the mean of the sampling distribution of s^2 is $[N - 1/N]\,\sigma^2$, we see that $\hat{\sigma}^2$ has a sampling distribution with mean exactly equal to

$$\frac{N}{N-1}\left[\left(\frac{N-1}{N}\right)\sigma^2\right] = \sigma^2$$

Although the basic reason why $\hat{\sigma}^2$ (and not s^2) is the unbiased estimate is that the mathematics works out that way, an intuitive explanation is sometimes given in terms of the concept *degrees of freedom*. The number of degrees of freedom is *equal to the number of quantities which are unknown minus the number of independent equations linking these unknowns*. You will recall that in order to arrive at a unique solution to a set of simultaneous algebraic equations, it was necessary to have the same number of equations as unknowns. Thus in order to solve for X, Y, and Z there must be three equations linking these variables. Had there been only two equations, we could have assigned any value we pleased to one variable, say Z. The values of the other two variables could then be determined by means of the two simultaneous equations. If there were five unknowns and only three equations to be solved simultaneously, we could assign arbitrary values to any two of the unknowns and then the values of the remaining unknowns would be determined. There would thus be 2 degrees of freedom in this case since we are free to assign values to any two variables.

In computing a standard deviation from sample values, we must make use of an equation linking the N variable X's with the sample mean, i.e., the equation $\displaystyle\sum_{i=1}^{N} X_i/N = \bar{X}$. Given the value of $\bar{X}$, we can assign arbitrary values to $N - 1$ of the X_i's, but the last will then be determined from this equation. Since we have lost 1 degree of freedom in determining the value of the sample mean about which deviations have been taken, we must divide by $N - 1$ rather than N to obtain our unbiased estimate of σ^2. If you prefer to think of it this way, you can consider that we have adjusted the number of cases slightly in order to compensate for the fact that we have taken deviations about the sample mean rather than the true population mean. We have essentially used up one case in computing the mean for the sample.

Efficiency. The *efficiency* of an estimate refers to the *degree to which the sampling distribution is clustered about the true value of the parameter*. If the estimate is unbiased, this clustering can be measured by means of the standard error of the estimate: the smaller the standard error, the greater the efficiency of the estimate. Efficiency is always relative.

Fig. 12.1. Comparison of sampling distributions of a biased estimate with high efficiency and an unbiased estimate with lower efficiency.

No estimate can be completely efficient since this would imply no sampling error whatsoever. We can compare two estimates and say that one is more efficient than the other, however. Suppose, for example, that we have a normal population. Then for random sampling the standard error of the mean is $\sigma/\sqrt{N}$. If the sample median were used to estimate the population mean, the standard error of the median would be $1.253\sigma/\sqrt{N}$.[1] Therefore, since the standard error of the mean is smaller than that of the median, the mean is the more efficient estimate. This, of course, is the reason the mean is usually used in preference to the median. We say that the mean is less subject to sampling fluctuations, i.e., it is more efficient.[2]

Of the two criteria we have discussed, efficiency is the more important. If two estimates have the same efficiency we would of course select the

[1] Here the population mean and median would be identical.

[2] It is not always true that the mean is the more efficient estimate, although for most populations, especially if departure from normality is not too great, this will be the case. Notice that the question of relative efficiency is an entirely different question from that of which measure is the more appropriate descriptive measure of central tendency. The latter concerns only the problem of finding the best single measure to represent the *sample* data.

one which is least biased. This is why $\hat{\sigma}$ is used in preference to s. But an efficient estimate which is slightly biased would be preferable to an unbiased estimate which is less efficient. A simple diagram should help you see why this is the case. In Fig. 12.1 the peaked curve with a slight bias would be preferable since, even though in the long run we would tend to underestimate the parameter by a slight amount, we are more likely on any given trial to obtain a sample estimate which is fairly close to the parameter. Knowledge that estimates will average out to the correct figure in the long run is little consolation if, for any given sample, the estimate is likely to be quite far from the parameter.

12.2. Interval Estimation

You may recall that when you took elementary physics you were taught to weigh a block of wood several times and then to take the mean value and indicate a possible range of error. Thus you might have indicated that the weight of the wood was 102 ± 2 grams, meaning that you would estimate that the true weight was somewhere between 100 and 104 grams. In so doing, you were admitting the fallibility of the measurement procedure and indicating just about how much faith you had in the accuracy obtained. Although at the time it may not have been brought explicitly to your attention, you would also have admitted that you were not absolutely certain that the true value was actually in the interval obtained. If it were made wider, however, you would have been even more sure that it was in the interval. Thus you might have been almost positive that the true value was between 98 and 106 grams and willing to bet your last dollar that it was between 2 and 202 grams. In obtaining interval estimates for parameters, we do essentially the same thing as does the physicist except that we shall be in a position to evaluate the exact probability of error.

The actual procedure used in obtaining an interval estimate, or what is referred to as a *confidence interval*, is quite simple and involves no really new basic ideas. We shall first merely state how the interval is obtained, and then we can examine why it is constructed in this manner. One first decides on the risk he is willing to take of making the error of stating that the parameter is somewhere in the interval when in fact it is not. Let us say that he decides he is willing to be wrong .05 of the time or that he uses what is referred to as the 95 per cent confidence interval.[3] The interval is obtained by going out in both directions from the point estimate (e.g., the sample mean) a certain multiple of standard

[3] Notice that we refer in the case of confidence intervals to one minus the probability of error. This indicates that we have "confidence" of being correct, say, 95 per cent of the time.

errors corresponding to the confidence level selected. Thus, to estimate the population mean μ we obtain an interval as follows (using the 95 per cent level):

$$\bar{X} \pm 1.96\,\sigma_{\bar{X}} = \bar{X} \pm 1.96\,\frac{\sigma}{\sqrt{N}}$$

where the value 1.96 corresponds to the critical region for the normal curve, using the .05 level and a two-tailed test. If $\bar{X} = 15$, $\sigma = 5$, and $N = 100$, the confidence interval would be

$$15 \pm 1.96\,\frac{5}{\sqrt{100}} = 15 \pm 0.98$$

In other words, the interval would run from 14.02 to 15.98.[4]

In order to interpret intervals obtained by this method we need to return to what we know about sampling distributions, in this case the

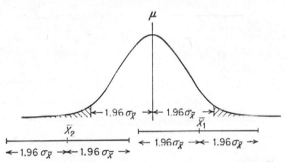

Fig. 12.2. Comparison of confidence intervals with the sampling distribution of the mean, showing why 95 per cent confidence intervals include μ 95 per cent of the time.

sampling distribution of the mean. Let us suppose we have a normal sampling distribution with mean μ and standard deviation $\sigma/\sqrt{N}$. For our purposes there are two kinds of sample means: (1) those which do not fall within the critical region, and (2) those which do fall within this area. Let us first suppose that we have obtained an $\bar{X}$ ($\bar{X}_1$ in Fig. 12.2) which does not fall within the critical region. We know that such an $\bar{X}$ must be within $1.96\sigma_{\bar{X}}$ of μ. If we place an interval on either side of this $\bar{X}$ by going distances equal to $1.96\sigma_{\bar{X}}$ we therefore must cross past μ, the mean of the sampling distribution, no matter whether $\bar{X}$ is to the right or left of μ. Similarly, if the $\bar{X}$ obtained lies within the critical region (see $\bar{X}_2$ in Fig. 12.2), then this $\bar{X}$ will be further than 1.96 standard errors from μ and the confidence interval will not extend as far as μ. But we also know that 95 per cent of the time we shall obtain $\bar{X}$'s which do not lie in the critical region whereas only 5 per cent of the time will

[4] These end points of the interval are sometimes referred to as *confidence limits*.

they fall within this area.   In other words, we know that *only 5 per cent of the time would we get intervals by this procedure which would not include the parameter* (e.g., μ).   The remaining 95 per cent of the time the procedure will yield sample means close enough to the parameter that the confidence intervals obtained will actually include the parameter.

Several words of caution are necessary in interpreting confidence intervals.   The beginning student is likely to use vague phrases such as, "I

Fig. 12.3. Distribution of variable confidence intervals about fixed value of parameter μ.

am 95 per cent confident that the interval contains the parameter," or "the probability is .95 that the parameter is in the interval."   In so doing he may not clearly recognize that the parameter is a fixed value and that it is the intervals which vary from sample to sample.   According to our definition of probability, the probability of the parameter being in any given interval is either zero or one since the parameter either is or is not within the specific interval obtained.   A simple diagram indicating the fixed value of the parameter, in this case μ, and the variability of the intervals may help you understand the correct interpretation more clearly.   Figure 12.3 emphasizes that one's faith is in the procedure used rather than in any particular interval.   We can say that *the procedure* is such that in the long run 95 per cent of the intervals obtained will include the true (fixed) parameter.   You should be careful not to imply or assume that the particular interval you have obtained has any special property not possessed by comparable intervals which would be obtained from other samples. Sometimes it is stated that if repeated samples were drawn, 95 per cent of the means from these samples would fall within the confidence interval one has actually computed. This implies, of course, that the $\bar{X}$ obtained in the researcher's sample exactly equals μ or at least that it is a very close approximation to μ. Actually, the particular interval obtained may be so far out of line that very few $\bar{X}$'s would fall within it. As is always the case in statistical inference, our confidence is not in any particular sample result but in the procedure used.

It is possible to set the risk of error at any desired level by using the proper multiple of the standard error. You should notice, however, that in reducing the risk of error one necessarily increases the width of the interval unless he simultaneously increases the number of cases. The wider the interval, the less he is really saying about the parameter. To say that the median income of New York families is somewhere between $1,000 and $10,000 is to claim the obvious. Thus, the researcher is faced with a dilemma. He can state that the parameter lies within a very narrow interval, but the probability of error will be large. On the other hand, he can make a very weak statement and be virtually certain of being correct. Exactly what he chooses to do will depend upon the nature of the situation. Although 95 and 99 per cent confidence intervals are conventionally used, it should be emphasized that there is nothing sacred about these levels.

Confidence Intervals and Tests of Hypotheses. Although the explicit purpose of placing a confidence interval about an estimate is to indicate the degree of accuracy of the estimate, confidence intervals are also implicit tests of a whole range of hypotheses.[5] They are implicit tests in the sense that specific hypotheses are not actually stated but only implied. In a confidence interval we have an implicit test for every possible value of μ which might be hypothesized. Figure 12.4 indicates how confidence intervals are related to tests of hypotheses.

Focus on the confidence interval drawn about $\bar{X}$. Suppose that, instead of having obtained such an interval, we had hypothesized several alternative values for μ and proceeded to test these hypotheses. Assume, for simplicity, that the value of σ was given and that the .05 significance level was used. First suppose that we had hypothesized a value such as μ_1 (Fig. 12.4a) actually falling within this confidence interval. Then the sample mean $\bar{X}$ would clearly not fall within the critical region, and the hypothesis would not have been rejected at the .05 level. On the other hand, had we hypothesized a value outside the interval such as μ_2 (Fig. 12.4b), the distance between the hypothesized μ and $\bar{X}$ would be greater than $1.96\sigma_{\bar{x}}$, and this second hypothesis would have been rejected.

[5] It should be emphasized that although interval estimation and hypothesis testing involve closely interrelated ideas, they are distinct procedures.

Clearly, then, if we were to hypothesize values for μ which fell anywhere within the confidence interval we would not reject these hypotheses at the appropriate level of significance. Were we to hypothesize values for μ falling outside the interval we know that these hypotheses would be rejected.

Thus, having obtained a confidence interval we can tell at a glance what the results would have been had we tested any particular hypothesis. If the nature of our problem were such that no particular hypothesis were

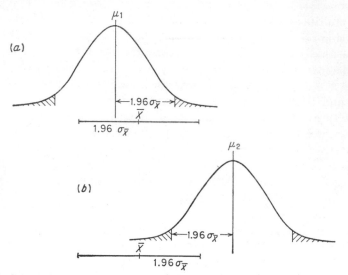

Fig. 12.4. Comparison of 95 per cent confidence interval with tests of hypotheses at the .05 level, showing nonrejection of hypothesized mean μ_1 lying within the interval but rejection of hypothesized mean μ_2 lying outside the interval.

suggested as being preferable to the others, then obviously the practical alternative to a whole series of tests would be to obtain a single confidence interval. You should satisfy yourself that examples taken up in the previous chapter could just as easily have been handled by the confidence-interval method.

Assumptions Made for Confidence Intervals. The use of confidence intervals does not free us from the necessity of making assumptions about the nature of the population and the sampling method used. Basically, the assumptions for a confidence-interval problem are the same as those required for any tests which are being implicitly made except that it is of course unnecessary to hypothesize a particular value for the parameter being estimated. Random sampling will always be assumed in this text. Also, if a normal sampling distribution is being used we must either assume a normal population or have a sufficiently large sample. If the t

distribution or some other sampling distribution is to be used, the usual assumptions required in comparable tests would have to be made.

12.3. Confidence Intervals for Other Types of Problems

The discussion of confidence intervals has so far involved only instances where the parameter being estimated is a population mean and σ is known. If the problem is altered, procedural modifications are completely straightforward, and the basic interpretation of confidence intervals and their relationship to tests of hypotheses remains the same.   A confidence interval for a parameter is always obtained by taking the estimate of the parameter and enclosing it in an interval the length of which is a function of the standard error of the estimate.[6]

If the t distribution must be used because σ is unknown, we simply make use of the estimate of the standard error and replace the multiple obtained using the normal table by the comparable figure in the t table. Thus, for a 99 per cent confidence interval for the mean and 24 degrees of freedom we would get

$$\bar{X} \pm 2.797 \hat{\sigma}_{\bar{X}} = \bar{X} \pm 2.797 \frac{s}{\sqrt{N-1}}$$

Had the example in Sec. 11.3 of the previous chapter been worked by means of a 99 per cent confidence interval, the result would have been

$$52 \pm 2.797 \left(\frac{12}{\sqrt{24}} \right) = 52 \pm 6.85$$

Therefore the 99 per cent confidence interval goes from 45.15 to 58.85. We see that the above result is consistent with that previously obtained (i.e., $.001 < p < .01$) in that the hypothesized μ of 60 is actually outside the interval computed, and therefore we know that the hypothesis should have been rejected at the .01 level (for two-tailed test).

Similarly, we can obtain confidence intervals for proportions.   Replacing $\bar{X}$ by p_s and $\sigma/\sqrt{N}$ by $\sqrt{p_u q_u/N}$, the 95 per cent confidence interval would be

$$p_s \pm 1.96 \sqrt{\frac{p_u q_u}{N}}$$

We encounter a difficulty here which did not occur when a particular value for p_u could be hypothesized. Since p_u will obviously not be known, it becomes necessary to estimate the standard error. Two

---

[6] In some instances, however, such as in the case of confidence intervals for correlation coefficients, the point estimate may not be exactly at the center of the interval.

simple procedures, one of which is more conservative than the other, can be recommended.[7] First, since the sample size must be large in order to justify the use of normal tables, p_s will ordinarily be a reasonably good estimate of p_u. Therefore if we simply substitute p_s for p_u (and q_s for q_u) we can obtain an interval which will usually be a close approximation to the correct one. Thus, in the example in Sec. 11.4 of the previous chapter, we would have obtained the 98 per cent confidence interval as follows:

$$p_s \pm 2.33 \sqrt{\frac{p_s q_s}{N}} = .55 \pm 2.33 \sqrt{\frac{(.55)(.45)}{125}} = .55 \pm 0.1037$$

If one objects to the use of an estimate of the standard error without in some manner correcting for the additional sampling error thereby introduced, he may prefer a more conservative method of obtaining the interval. Since the product pq reaches a maximum value when $p = q = .5$, it follows that the widest possible confidence interval will be obtained when the value .5 is used as an estimate of p_u.[8] Since a narrow interval is ordinarily desired, we are being conservative by obtaining an interval which is as large as it could possibly be regardless of the value of p_u. Using this more conservative method we obtain a somewhat different interval

$$.55 \pm 2.33 \sqrt{\frac{(.5)(.5)}{125}} = .55 \pm 0.1042$$

Notice that this second interval is only slightly wider than the first. Whenever $.3 \le p \le .7$ the two methods will yield approximately the same results.

*If p_s turns out to be either very large or very small, the conservative method may give an interval which is far too wide. If one hesitates to use the first method in which p_u is estimated by p_s, it is possible to combine the two methods in order to obtain a more reasonable interval which is nevertheless a conservative one. We first make use of the more conservative method to obtain an approximate confidence interval. Suppose this interval runs from .10 to .25 with p_s being .175. We would then be reasonably sure that the actual value of p_u is somewhere within this approximate (and conservative) interval. In computing the more exact interval, we now take as our estimate of p_u the value within the approximate interval which is closest to .5. In the above numerical example, we would select the value .25 since the use of this value in the formula for the standard error will result in a wider interval than will

---

[7] For a third and somewhat more accurate procedure see [2], p. 231.

[8] You should convince yourself that this is true.

any other value within the interval .10 to .25. In other words, instead of using our actual p_s (i.e., .175), we select the largest value which we think p_u is likely to have. We therefore compute the 95 per cent confidence interval as follows:

$$.175 \pm 1.96 \sqrt{\frac{(.25)(.75)}{N}}$$

The above interval will be wider and therefore more conservative than that obtained by using p_s under the radical, and yet it does not involve the use of the value .5, which we suspect is far too large.

Confidence intervals are commonly used in several other types of problems which will be taken up subsequently. As will be indicated in the next chapter, however, there are a number of problems involving two or more samples where there seem to be relatively few practical sociological applications in which confidence intervals are used. Therefore, confidence intervals will not be discussed in connection with every test taken up in the following chapters. You should be alert, however, for possible uses of confidence intervals in your own field of interest.

12.4. Determining the Sample Size

In keeping with the practice of introducing a few new ideas at a time, we have postponed the question of how it is that one's sample size can be determined in advance of data collection. One of the most frequent questions asked of the statistician is, "How many cases do I need?" The answer depends, of course, on what one wishes to do with the sample results. More specifically, there are several facts which must be determined before an adequate answer can be given. Generally, what we must do is to work backwards from the data we expect to get in order to determine the unknown sample size. Thus far we have been taking the sample size as a known quantity. Statistics such as the sample mean and standard deviation can be obtained from the sample results. Once we have decided on the significance level of a test or the desired confidence level, we can then put all of these values into a formula and determine the width of the confidence interval or whether or not to reject a null hypothesis. In the kind of problem we are considering in this section, however, the sample size will be unknown. This means that in order to solve our equation for N we must know each of the other quantities in the formula. Once we have put these values into the equation, solving for N becomes a straightforward problem of algebra. We shall make use of a confidence-interval problem in order to illustrate the process.

Suppose we wish to know how many cases will be required to estimate the mean number of years of schooling completed by persons of foreign-born parentage. Before we can determine the answer to this question, we shall need to have the following pieces of information: (1) the confidence level to be used, (2) the degree of accuracy within which we wish to estimate the parameter, and (3) some reasonable estimate of the values of any parameters which may appear in the formula. For example, we may wish to estimate the mean to within an accuracy of $\pm.1$ year of schooling and to make use of a 95 per cent confidence interval. Notice that both of these quantities must be specified since, for example, we can always obtain accuracy to within $\pm.1$ year if we permit ourselves a high risk of error. We now make use of these values in the formula for a confidence interval

$$\bar{X} \pm \underbrace{1.96 \frac{\sigma}{\sqrt{N}}}_{.1}$$

Knowledge of the level of confidence desired has enabled us to insert the value 1.96. Since we wish accuracy of $\pm.1$, or a total interval width of .2, we know that the quantity $1.96 \, \sigma/\sqrt{N}$ must equal .1. Although the value of $\bar{X}$ will be unknown, we see immediately that it is irrelevant in this problem since we wish to obtain an interval of a certain width regardless of the value of $\bar{X}$.

Suppose we now try to solve the equation

$$.1 = 1.96 \frac{\sigma}{\sqrt{N}}$$

for N. There is still one unknown quantity, the value of σ. But how can we obtain σ before the data have been gathered? Clearly, its value must be estimated by some method which in a sense goes beyond the data we shall collect. Essentially, we have to make an enlightened guess as to its value by using either expert knowledge, the results of previous studies, or conceivably a pilot study of some sort. Usually a pilot study will be too expensive and reliance must be placed on either of the remaining methods. Admittedly, the most satisfactory procedure would be to determine σ exactly, but if this could be done there would probably be no point in drawing a sample at all. Notice that the type of estimation necessary in this kind of problem is completely different from that used in estimating σ from *sample* data. Therefore there is no point in estimating σ with $\hat{\sigma}$ or in using the t distribution. If we are going to guess anyway, we might as well guess the value of σ rather than that of $\hat{\sigma}$ or s. In this example suppose that on the basis of the best available information we estimate that σ will be approximately 2.5 years. Making use of this value and solving for the required sample size we get

$$.1 = 1.96 \frac{2.5}{\sqrt{N}}$$

or

$$\sqrt{N} = \frac{1.96(2.5)}{.1} = 49$$

and

$$N = 2,401$$

Notice that we solved for N by placing all quantities except $\sqrt{N}$ on one side of the equation and then simplifying. Finally, we squared both sides of the equation in order to get rid of the radical.

To be sure, we can only obtain an approximate value for the desired sample size since parameters will have to be estimated. There would certainly be no point in taking exactly 2,401 cases, for example. Nevertheless, such an approximation will usually give far better results than some intuitive hunch about the number of cases necessary. In practical applications we usually study more than one variable at a time, a fact which may complicate the picture considerably. We are also ordinarily limited by available funds and often have to settle for whatever degree of accuracy we can get. Even so, it will often be helpful to compute the needed sample size as a guide to one's research design.

Although the question of determining sample size will not be discussed in subsequent chapters in connection with other statistical procedures, you will find several exercises which require you to estimate N for other kinds of problems. In all cases, extensions are straightforward although the algebra may at times become fairly involved.

GLOSSARY

Confidence interval
Degrees of freedom
Efficiency of an estimate
Interval estimate
Point estimate
Unbiased estimate

EXERCISES

1. Obtain confidence intervals for Exercises 3, 4, and 5 of Chap. 11. Are your results consistent with those of these previous exercises? How do you know?

2. You take a random sample of 200 families within a community and find that in 36 per cent of these families the husband makes over half of the financial decisions. What is the 99 per cent confidence interval for the percentage of families in which the husband makes over half of such decisions? In what specific sense does your interval give you implicit tests of hypotheses?

3. How many cases will you need to establish a 99.9 per cent confidence interval for the mean, if the total width of the confidence interval is to be no more than $500 and

if the standard deviation is estimated to be $1,300? What would you have to assume in obtaining such an interval?

4. If you suspect that the proportion of homeowners in a certain residential community is approximately .75, how many cases will you need in order to obtain a 95 per cent confidence interval which will be no wider than .03 when you express the width in terms of proportions? Suppose the proportion of homeowners were estimated to be .5. How many cases would then be needed?

5. Using the fact that for normal populations the sampling distribution of the median has a standard error of $1.253\sigma/\sqrt{N}$, we can place a confidence interval about the sample median. Suppose in Exercise 3 above that you wished to place an interval of the same width about the sample median. Using the same estimate of the standard deviation, how many cases would you need? What does your result show about the relative efficiencies of the mean and median?

*6. It has been argued that a 95 per cent confidence interval represents a series of implicit *two-tailed* tests at the .05 level. Explain why a 95 per cent confidence interval does not represent implicit *one-tailed* tests at the .05 level.

REFERENCES

1. Freund, J. E.: *Modern Elementary Statistics*, Prentice-Hall, Inc., Englewood Cliffs, N.J., 1952, chap. 9.

2. Hagood, M. J., and D. O. Price: *Statistics for Sociologists*, Henry Holt and Company, Inc., New York, 1952, chaps. 15 and 16.

3. Wallis, W. A., and H. V. Roberts: *Statistics: A New Approach*, Free Press, Glencoe, Ill., 1956, chap. 14.

Chapter 13

TWO-SAMPLE TESTS: DIFFERENCE OF MEANS AND PROPORTIONS

In Chap. 11 tests involving a single sample were discussed. It was found that such tests were not very practical to the social scientist because it is not usually possible to find an hypothesis which is specific enough to predict a value for μ or p_u. When interest is focused on *comparisons* between several categories or samples, however, it becomes unnecessary to specify the absolute levels for either group. Instead, one can simply test the null hypothesis that there are no differences between them. For example, it would be extremely difficult to predict the income level of Negroes in Detroit or the prejudice level of whites in that city. But suppose one were interested in testing the hypothesis that the average income of Negroes is the same as that of foreign-born whites or that Jews have the same amount of prejudice toward Negroes as gentiles. It is this latter type of hypothesis which will be considered in this chapter.

In a social science such as sociology, interest is likely to be focused on establishing *relationships* between variables. This is in contrast to the fact-finding type of survey in which, as we have seen, point and interval estimation of a single parameter may be of primary concern. Whenever comparisons are made between two samples, we have the most simple kind of problem in which two variables can be related. Up to this point we have been concerned with only one variable at a time. This is perhaps the main reason why the tests discussed so far have not been too useful to sociologists. In this chapter we shall be taking up tests in which a simple dichotomized variable can be related to a second variable. For example, in comparing Jews and gentiles with respect to prejudice we are relating religion to prejudice. Similarly, one might wish to compare the two sexes with respect to "other directedness" or various other personality characteristics. Comparisons may also be made between

169

a control group and an experimental group into which some variable has been introduced. In subsequent chapters tests involving more than two samples will be discussed.

13.1. Difference-of-means Test

In order to extend the single-sample means test to a test in which a comparison can be made between the means of two samples, we must again make use of the central-limit theorem and the law of large numbers. An important theorem, derivable from the central-limit theorem, can be stated as follows: *If independent random samples of sizes N_1 and N_2, respectively, are drawn from populations which are $Nor(\mu_1,\sigma_1{}^2)$ and $Nor(\mu_2,\sigma_2{}^2)$, respectively, then the sampling distribution of the difference between the two sample means $(\bar{X}_1 - \bar{X}_2)$ will be $Nor(\mu_1 - \mu_2, \sigma_1{}^2/N_1 + \sigma_2{}^2/N_2)$.* As was true in the case of single samples, this theorem can be generalized in the case of large samples to cover any populations with means of μ_1 and μ_2 and variances $\sigma_1{}^2$ and $\sigma_2{}^2$ respectively. As N_1 and N_2 become large, the sampling distribution of $\bar{X}_1 - \bar{X}_2$ approaches normality as before. Let us now examine the above theorem more closely.

Reference is made to independent random samples. This means that samples must be selected *independently of each other*. The fact that a sample is random assures independence *within* the sample in the sense that knowledge of the score of the first individual selected does not help us predict the score of the second. This is *not* what is meant by the phrase "independent random samples." Not only must there be independence within each sample (assured by randomness), but there must be independence *between* samples. For example, the samples cannot be matched, as might be the case in comparison between control and experimental groups. If the two sexes were being compared, one could not use the difference-of-means test on samples composed of husband and wife pairs. This requirement that samples be independent of each other is extremely important but often overlooked in applied research. If one is comparing two subsamples drawn from a single larger random sample, this assumption of independence between subsamples will be met since all cases in the total sample will have been selected independently of each other. Usually in social research we draw a single larger sample although for purposes of analysis we may conceptualize the data as having come from several distinct and independent samples. In most instances the problem of independence between samples will not arise unless we have deliberately matched the samples or unless we have made use of a sampling design which does not yield random samples.

In the above theorem we are told that if we were to continue sampling indefinitely, each time selecting two samples and plotting the difference between their means, the sampling distribution of this *difference* between means would be normal or approximately normal. You should attempt to picture exactly what is occurring here. Keep in mind that as a social scientist you will actually obtain only two samples and a single difference but that here we are dealing with a hypothetical distribution of all possible differences. Since the sampling distribution is for a *difference* between sample means, the mean of the sampling distribution is given by the difference between two population means rather than either of them separately. In the special case where μ_1 and μ_2 are equal, the mean of the sampling distribution will be zero. If $\mu_1 > \mu_2$, we expect that most $\bar{X}_1$'s will be larger than the comparable $\bar{X}_2$'s and the mean of the sampling distribution will therefore be positive. For example, if $\mu_1 = 60$ and $\mu_2 = 40$, the distribution of $\bar{X}_1 - \bar{X}_2$ will have 20 as its mean value.

It is not quite so easy to see why the variance should be $\sigma_1^2/N_1 + \sigma_2^2/N_2$, or the *sum* of the variances of the sampling distributions for the separate means. Obviously, a difference of variances $\sigma_1^2/N_1 - \sigma_2^2/N_2$ could not be used since it would then be possible to obtain a zero or negative variance for the sampling distribution. But the variance $\sigma_1^2/N_1 + \sigma_2^2/N_2$ is *larger* than either of the variances σ_1^2/N_1 or σ_2^2/N_2. Why should this be the case? Although a complete justification for the formula cannot be given without resorting to mathematical reasoning, some sort of intuitive explanation is possible. In essence, we expect the standard error for the difference of means to be larger than either of the separate standard errors because there are now two sources of error, one in each sample. Thus about half the time the two $\bar{X}$'s will be in error in opposite directions. For simplicity let us assume that $\mu_1 = \mu_2$. Then if $\bar{X}_1$ is larger than μ_1 and $\bar{X}_2$ smaller than μ_2, a large positive number will result on subtraction because the errors are in opposite directions. For example, if $\bar{X}_1$ is 20 greater than μ_1 whereas $\bar{X}_2$ is 15 less than μ_2, the resulting difference $\bar{X}_1 - \bar{X}_2$ will differ from $\mu_1 - \mu_2$ by 35, thus compounding the errors involved. Similarly if $\bar{X}_1$ is small and $\bar{X}_2$ large, a substantial negative difference may occur. In other words, we shall get relatively large differences between sample means quite frequently since each mean will vary independently of the other. Therefore the sampling distribution of a difference will have a larger standard deviation than either of the separate sampling distributions. It is interesting to note that the sampling distribution of the *sum* of sample means has exactly the same standard deviation as does that for differences. Why should this be the case?

We shall now take up an example illustrating the use of the difference-of-means test. The case in which the σ's are known will not be treated since this problem is straightforward and rather impractical. Instead,

it will be presumed that the σ's are unknown. Two special cases will
be considered. In model 1 it will be assumed that $\sigma_1 = \sigma_2$; in model 2
the two σ's will be assumed to be unequal. Obviously, these two models
cover all possible alternatives.

Problem. A comparison is made between two types of counties,
those which are predominantly urban and those which are primarily
rural. The counties are compared with respect to the percentage of
persons voting Democratic in a presidential election with the following results:

Urban counties	Rural counties
$N_1 = 33$	$N_2 = 19$
$\bar{X}_1 = 57\%$	$\bar{X}_2 = 52\%$
$s_1 = 11\%$	$s_2 = 14\%$

Do the data give reasonable grounds for concluding that there is a
significant difference in voting preference between these two types
of counties? Assume that the counties have been randomly selected
from a list of all counties in the Far West.

Model 1: $\sigma_1 = \sigma_2$

1. *Assumptions.*

   Level of Measurement: Percentage of Democratic vote an interval
   scale
   Model: Independent random samples
   Normal populations, $\sigma_1 = \sigma_2 = \sigma$
   Hypothesis: $\mu_1 = \mu_2$

The normality assumption can be relaxed whenever the N's are large.
The assumption that $\sigma_1 = \sigma_2$ actually can be tested separately by means
of the F test which will be discussed in Chap. 16. This test involves a
comparison of the two sample standard deviations. If s_1 and s_2 do not
differ markedly, one cannot reject the hypothesis that $\sigma_1 = \sigma_2$. If the
assumption of equal standard deviations appears to be reasonable according to the results of the F test, it will be more efficient to take advantage
of it in estimating the common value of σ. Given the assumption that
both populations are normal, the additional assumptions of equal means
and equal standard deviations amount to postulating that the two populations are identical.

Since we are interested in seeing whether or not there is a difference
between the two types of counties, our null hypothesis will be that there
is no difference. Presumably, we suspect that there will actually be a
difference and therefore set up an hypothesis which we wish to reject.

In this instance, we can legitimately refer to the hypothesis as being a "null" hypothesis indicating no relationship between the variables "type of county" and "voting preference." It is conceivable that we might have been in a position to specify that the difference between population means could be expected to be some constant other than zero. For example, the hypothesis might have taken the form $\mu_1 - \mu_2 = 10$ if it had been predicted that the Democratic vote would be 10 per cent higher in urban counties. In the social sciences we are seldom in a position to be this specific, however.

2. *Sampling Distribution.* The t distribution will be used since the σ's are unknown and since the total number of cases is much less than 120.

3. *Significance Level and Critical Region.* Let us select the .01 level and a two-tailed test.

4. *Computing the Test Statistic.* It will be remembered that t is computed by taking the difference between the obtained sample value and the mean of the sampling distribution and then dividing by an estimate of the standard error of the sampling distribution. We are here concerned with the *difference* between sample means $\bar{X}_1 - \bar{X}_2$. Since the mean of the sampling distribution is $\mu_1 - \mu_2$ we obtain the following expression for t:

$$ t = \frac{(\bar{X}_1 - \bar{X}_2) - (\mu_1 - \mu_2)}{\hat{\sigma}_{\bar{X}_1 - \bar{X}_2}} \tag{13.1} $$

where $\hat{\sigma}_{\bar{X}_1 - \bar{X}_2}$ is an estimate of the standard error of the difference between sample means. Since under the null hypothesis it has been assumed that $\mu_1 = \mu_2$, the expression for t in this *special case* reduces to

$$ t = \frac{\bar{X}_1 - \bar{X}_2}{\hat{\sigma}_{\bar{X}_1 - \bar{X}_2}} $$

The resemblance between the above numerator and the one used in the single-sample test is more or less coincidental, a result of the fact that the μ's dropped out under the null hypothesis. You should *not* draw the conclusion that the μ in the first type of problem has simply been replaced by the *sample* mean of the second sample. Actually, the expression $(\bar{X}_1 - \bar{X}_2)$ has replaced $\bar{X}$, $(\mu_1 - \mu_2)$ has replaced μ, and $\hat{\sigma}_{\bar{X}_1 - \bar{X}_2}$ has replaced $\hat{\sigma}_{\bar{X}}$.

It now remains to evaluate $\hat{\sigma}_{\bar{X}_1 - \bar{X}_2}$. We know, of course, that

$$ \sigma_{\bar{X}_1 - \bar{X}_2} = \sqrt{\frac{\sigma_1^2}{N_1} + \frac{\sigma_2^2}{N_2}} $$

Since in this case $\sigma_1 = \sigma_2$ we can indicate their common value as σ and simplify the expression for $\sigma_{\bar{X}_1 - \bar{X}_2}$ as follows:

$$\sigma_{\bar{X}_1 - \bar{X}_2} = \sqrt{\frac{\sigma^2}{N_1} + \frac{\sigma^2}{N_2}} = \sigma \sqrt{\frac{1}{N_1} + \frac{1}{N_2}} = \sigma \sqrt{\frac{N_1 + N_2}{N_1 N_2}} \qquad (13.2)$$

The common variance σ^2 can now be estimated by obtaining a *pooled estimate* from both samples. Since the two sample variances will ordinarily be based on different numbers of cases, we can obtain an estimate of σ^2 by taking a weighted average of the sample variances, being careful to divide by the proper degrees of freedom in order to obtain an unbiased estimate. Taking the square root we get an estimate $\hat{\sigma}$ as follows:

$$\hat{\sigma} = \sqrt{\frac{N_1 s_1^2 + N_2 s_2^2}{N_1 + N_2 - 2}} \qquad \text{weighted for } N. \qquad (13.3)$$

Since $N_1 s_1^2 = \sum_{i=1}^{N_1} (X_i - \bar{X}_1)^2$ we may replace $N_1 s_1^2$ by $\sum_{i=1}^{N_1} x_1^2$. If we do the same for $N_2 s_2^2$ we get

$$\hat{\sigma} = \sqrt{\frac{\sum_{i=1}^{N_1} x_1^2 + \sum_{i=1}^{N_2} x_2^2}{N_1 + N_2 - 2}}$$

Thus if we take the sum of squares about the mean of the first sample and add to this the sum of the squared deviations about the second sample mean, finally dividing by $N_1 + N_2 - 2$, we obtain a pooled estimate of the common variance.

Notice that the symbol $\hat{\sigma}$ is now being used to represent a different estimate from that discussed in the previous two chapters. The symbol "^" is often used in the statistical literature to indicate an unbiased estimate. Since we have lost 2 degrees of freedom, one each in computing s_1 and s_2 from $\bar{X}_1$ and $\bar{X}_2$, the total degrees of freedom becomes $N_1 + N_2 - 2$. We have used both samples in obtaining our estimate, having given greater weight to the variance from the larger of the two samples. Such a pooled estimate will be more efficient than estimates based on either sample alone. As a computational check, the numerical value of $\hat{\sigma}$ will ordinarily be between that of s_1 and s_2.

Finally, we obtain an estimate of $\sigma_{\bar{X}_1 - \bar{X}_2}$ by taking our estimate of σ and multiplying by $\sqrt{\frac{N_1 + N_2}{N_1 N_2}}$

$$\hat{\sigma}_{\bar{X}_1 - \bar{X}_2} = \sqrt{\frac{N_1 s_1^2 + N_2 s_2^2}{N_1 + N_2 - 2}} \sqrt{\frac{N_1 + N_2}{N_1 N_2}} \qquad (13.4)$$

At this point the formula seems quite formidable. You should review the algebraic steps discussed above in order to convince yourself that the formula is not as complicated as it first appears.

In our numerical example we obtain the following results:

$$\hat{\sigma}_{\bar{X}_1-\bar{X}_2} = \sqrt{\frac{33(121) + 19(196)}{33 + 19 - 2}} \sqrt{\frac{33 + 19}{33(19)}} = (12.42)(.288) = 3.58$$

Therefore,
$$t = \frac{(\bar{X}_1 - \bar{X}_2) - 0}{\hat{\sigma}_{\bar{X}_1-\bar{X}_2}} = \frac{57 - 52}{3.58} = 1.40$$

5. *Decision.* Since a pooled estimate of the common standard deviation was used, the degrees of freedom associated with t will be $N_1 + N_2 - 2$, or 50. We found that $t = 1.40$, the probability of which would be considerably greater than .01 if all the assumptions were correct. We therefore decide not to reject the null hypothesis at the .01 level, and we conclude that there is no significant difference in voting preferences in Far West urban and rural counties.

Model 2: $\sigma_1 \neq \sigma_2$. Now let us see what modifications are necessary when it is impossible to assume that the two populations have the same standard deviations. Presumably, we have tested and rejected the hypothesis that $\sigma_1 = \sigma_2$. It is now no longer possible to simplify the formula for $\sigma_{\bar{X}_1-\bar{X}_2}$ by introducing a common value for σ, nor is it possible to form a pooled estimate. In this instance we estimate the two (different) standard deviations separately. We estimate σ_1^2/N_1 with $s_1^2/(N_1 - 1)$ and σ_2^2/N_2 with $s_2^2/(N_2 - 1)$, obtaining

$$\hat{\sigma}_{\bar{X}_1-\bar{X}_2} = \sqrt{\frac{s_1^2}{N_1 - 1} + \frac{s_2^2}{N_2 - 1}} \tag{13.5}$$

In the example used above

$$\hat{\sigma}_{\bar{X}_1-\bar{X}_2} = \sqrt{121/32 + 196/18} = \sqrt{3.78 + 10.89} = \sqrt{14.67} = 3.83$$

Therefore,
$$t = \frac{57 - 52}{3.83} = 1.31$$

Thus, the results obtained in the two different models are not greatly different.

Although the procedure used in model 2 is both conceptually and computationally simpler, the estimate of $\sigma_{\bar{X}_1-\bar{X}_2}$ is not quite as efficient as the one previously obtained. Also, even if we assume normal populations, model 2 is somewhat questionable in instances where the N's are not too large or where the sample sizes are very different. For example, if the first sample were unusually small it would be highly misleading to use $N_1 + N_2 - 2$ as the degrees of freedom since s_1 would be a very poor estimate of σ_1 and since the value of $s_1^2/(N_1 - 1)$ would ordinarily be much larger than that of $s_2^2/(N_2 - 1)$. It has been sug-

gested that unless the N's are large the following expression be used to
obtain an approximation to the correct degrees of freedom.

$$df = \frac{[s_1^2/(N_1 - 1) + s_2^2/(N_2 - 1)]^2}{[s_1^2/(N_1 - 1)]^2 \, 1/(N_1 + 1) + [s_2^2/(N_2 - 1)]^2 \, 1/(N_2 + 1)} - 2$$

$$(13.6)$$

In the above example, therefore, we obtain

$$df = \frac{(14.67)^2}{(3.78)^2(\frac{1}{34}) + (10.89)^2(\frac{1}{20})} - 2 = 33.89 - 2 = 31.89 \simeq 32$$

Notice that some of the quantities in the formula for degrees of freedom
have already been computed. From the t table, using 32 degrees of
freedom, we see that the null hypothesis should not be rejected at the
.01 level.

As far as assumptions are concerned, the only difference between
model 1 and model 2 is the assumption that $\sigma_1 = \sigma_2$. Notice that there
is nothing in the second procedure which *requires* that the standard
deviations be unequal. If they happen to be equal (or nearly so), the
second model will simply be less efficient. It might seem as though the
second procedure is generally preferable since it does not require the
assumption that $\sigma_1 = \sigma_2$. But this second model, as we have seen,
requires approximations for the degrees of freedom. For large samples,
the two methods will usually yield similar results *if the standard deviations are in fact equal* since both sample standard deviations will ordinarily be good estimates of the common σ.

If the σ's for both populations happen to be known, their values can
be placed directly in the formula for $\sigma_{\bar{x}_1-\bar{x}_2}$ since no estimation will be
necessary. Z can then be computed and the normal table used. With
known σ's there will of course be no need to distinguish between models
1 and 2. Needless to say, instances in which both σ's are known will be
exceedingly rare in practical research.

13.2. Difference of Proportions

As was true in the case of tests involving single-sample proportions, a
difference between two proportions can be treated as a special case of a
difference between two means. If we are comparing two independent
random samples with respect to the proportion of prejudiced persons, we
can formulate the null hypothesis that the proportions, p_{u_1} and p_{u_2}, respectively, of prejudiced persons in the two populations are equal. Since
it has already been shown in the case of proportions that $\sigma_1 = \sqrt{p_{u_1}q_{u_1}}$
and $\sigma_2 = \sqrt{p_{u_2}q_{u_2}}$, it follows that the two population standard deviations
must also be equal. The following example therefore makes use of

essentially the same procedures as used for the first model in the case of the difference-of-means test.

Problem. Suppose a comparison of recreational habits is made between assembly-line workers and persons whose work is non-repetitive and not paced by the machine. Let us assume that the researcher suspects that assembly-line workers will be more inclined to select "passive" spectator-type forms of recreation. Among a random sample of 150 assembly-line workers at a given plant it is found that 57 per cent list passive forms of recreation as their favorites. In the second sample, also selected randomly, 46 per cent of the 120 workers list passive forms as favorites. Is there a significant difference at the .05 level?

1. *Assumptions.*

Level of Measurement: Type of recreation is a dichotomy
Model: Independent random samples
Hypothesis: $p_{u_1} = p_{u_2}$ (Implies $\sigma_1 = \sigma_2$)

2. *Sampling Distribution.* Since the N's are both relatively large the sampling distribution of the difference between proportions will be approximately normal with mean $p_{u_1} - p_{u_2} = 0$ and a standard deviation of

$$\sigma_{p_{s_1}-p_{s_2}} = \sqrt{\frac{\sigma_1^2}{N_1} + \frac{\sigma_2^2}{N_2}} = \sqrt{\frac{p_{u_1}q_{u_1}}{N_1} + \frac{p_{u_2}q_{u_2}}{N_2}} \qquad (13.7)$$

where q_{u_1} and q_{u_2} are equal to $1 - p_{u_1}$ and $1 - p_{u_2}$, respectively.[1]

3. *Significance Level and Critical Region.* The problem specifies that we are to use the .05 level. A one-tailed test is indicated since the direction of the difference is predicted ahead of time. Therefore any positive value of Z greater than 1.65 will indicate that results are so improbable under the assumptions that the null hypothesis may be rejected.

4. *Computing the Test Statistic.* Since by hypothesis $p_{u_1} = p_{u_2}$ it follows that $\sigma_1 = \sigma_2 = \sigma$, and the special formula

$$\sigma_{p_{s_1}-p_{s_2}} = \sigma \sqrt{\frac{N_1 + N_2}{N_1 N_2}}$$

can be used. Previously in the single-sample test for proportions it was possible to avoid estimating σ since the actual value of p_u was hypothesized. This time, however, the hypothesis merely states that $p_{u_1} = p_{u_2}$ without specifying what the numerical value of either of these proportions actually is. For this reason we need a pooled estimate of the standard error. Rather than directly obtaining a weighted average of the two

[1] If samples are small, we use Fisher's exact test described in Chap. 15.

sample variances, which is what we did before, we can obtain a slightly better estimate by computing a pooled estimate $(\hat{p}_u)$ of p_u. We then obtain $\hat{q}_u$ by subtraction. Since

$$\sigma = \sqrt{p_u q_u}$$

we can set
$$\hat{\sigma} = \sqrt{\hat{p}_u \hat{q}_u}$$

Thus
$$\hat{\sigma}_{p_{s_1}-p_{s_2}} = \hat{\sigma}\sqrt{\frac{N_1 + N_2}{N_1 N_2}} = \sqrt{\hat{p}_u \hat{q}_u}\sqrt{\frac{N_1 + N_2}{N_1 N_2}} \tag{13.8}$$

In order to obtain $\hat{p}_u$, a weighted average of the sample proportions is taken as follows:

$$\hat{p}_u = \frac{N_1 p_{s_1} + N_2 p_{s_2}}{N_1 + N_2} \tag{13.9}$$

Notice that the numerator of the above expression is simply the total *number* of individuals in both samples preferring passive forms of recreation. Here we do not lose 2 degrees of freedom as was the case with the comparable difference-of-means test. In the latter test we lost 1 degree of freedom in computing each s since deviations were taken about the sample means, whereas the p's and q's can be computed without having to make use of other sample statistics. We therefore get

$$\hat{p}_u = \frac{150(.57) + 120(.46)}{150 + 120} = .521$$

and
$$\hat{\sigma}_{p_{s_1}-p_{s_2}} = \sqrt{(.521)(.479)} \sqrt{\frac{150 + 120}{(150)(120)}}$$
$$= (.4996)(.1225) = .0612$$

Hence
$$Z = \frac{(p_{s_1} - p_{s_2}) - 0}{\hat{\sigma}_{p_{s_1}-p_{s_2}}} = \frac{.57 - .46}{.0612} = 1.80$$

5. *Decision.* Since with a one-tailed test the probability of obtaining a value of Z as large or larger than 1.80 is .036 if the null hypothesis is actually correct, we may reject the null hypothesis at the .05 level. We conclude that there is a significant difference with respect to preferences for passive forms of recreation between the two types of employees at this plant.

It should be mentioned at this point that there are several alternative kinds of tests, the most important of which is the chi-square test to be discussed in Chap. 15, which can be used in place of the difference-of-proportions test. Since the use of the difference-of-proportions test is restricted to two samples and to a dichotomized variable, it is not as practical as the chi-square test which can be employed on three or more samples as well. One advantage of the difference-of-proportions test, however, is that with suitable modifications it can be used when cluster or area samples have been selected. These modifications required for cluster samples are unfortunately beyond the scope of this text.

13.3. Confidence Intervals

In the case of single-sample problems we saw that the construction of confidence intervals is often a much more useful procedure than is the testing of hypotheses. In sociological research, confidence intervals are seldom used as alternatives to two-sample tests, however. The reason for this is that we are usually interested in establishing the existence of a relationship between two variables, i.e., a significant difference. There is less concern with estimating the actual magnitude of the difference. Seldom does a social scientist attempt to conclude that the difference between two means is probably between 17 and 28, for example. He is usually satisfied when he finds any significant difference at all. This state of affairs undoubtedly reflects the immaturity of the social sciences and the preponderance of exploratory studies. Perhaps as hypotheses become more precise there will be a greater need for confidence intervals in two-sample problems.

The procedure used in establishing confidence intervals is a straightforward extension of that previously discussed. One simply takes the sample results, in this case a *difference* between sample means, and places an interval about $\bar{X}_1 - \bar{X}_2$ which is an appropriate multiple of the standard error. For example, if a 95 per cent confidence interval were desired we would obtain an interval as follows:

$$(\bar{X}_1 - \bar{X}_2) \pm 1.96\sigma_{\bar{X}_1 - \bar{X}_2}$$

If an estimate of the standard error and the t distribution were required, the formula would be modified in the usual manner.

13.4. Dependent Samples: Matched Pairs

Sometimes it is advantageous to design a study in which samples are not independent of each other. One of the most common types of problems of this sort is one in which cases in the two samples have been matched pair by pair. There may be experimental and control groups, members of which have been matched on relevant characteristics. Or a simple "before-after" design may be used in which the same persons are compared before and after an experimental variable has been introduced. In this latter instance the "two" samples consist of the very same individuals. Obviously such samples are not independent of each other; knowing the scores of the first members of each pair (first sample) would help to predict the scores of the second members. In fact the whole aim of matching, or of using the same individuals twice, is to control as many variables as possible other than the experimental variable. The attempt is made to make the two samples as much alike as possible, much more alike than if they had been selected independently.

A researcher might be tempted to use a difference-of-means test in such problems.   But it should be quite apparent that this procedure would be unjustified since we do not have $2N$ cases (N in each sample) which have been independently selected.   Since samples have been deliberately matched, any peculiarities in one sample are most likely to occur in the other as well.   In reality there are only N independent cases, each "case" being a *pair* of individuals, one from each sample.   Therefore if we treat each pair as a single case, we can legitimately make statistical tests provided other required assumptions are met.   Instead of making a difference-of-means test we can make a direct pair-by-pair comparison by obtaining a difference score for each pair.   If we use the null hypothesis that there is no difference between the two populations, thereby assuming that the experimental variable has no effect, we can simply hypothesize that the mean of the pair-by-pair *differences* in the population (μ_D) is zero.   The problem then reduces to a single-sample test of the hypothesis that $\mu_D = 0$.

Problem.   Suppose an action group is interested in influencing urban voters to vote in favor of fluoridation proposals in the coming elections.   Cities within the state are carefully matched on variables thought to be relevant, and two different techniques for influencing the voters are attempted.   The technique for group A involves an indirect approach through influencing city leaders but making no direct mass appeal.   In cities of group B the organization acts as a pressure group and makes a direct appeal to the voter as an outside organization.   The following figures indicate the percentages of voters favoring fluoridation.   Is either technique superior?

Pair no.	Group A, %	Group B, %	Difference, %
1	63	68	5
2	41	49	8
3	54	53	−1
4	71	75	4
5	39	49	10
6	44	41	−3
7	67	75	8
8	56	58	2
9	46	52	6
10	37	49	12
11	61	55	−6
12	68	69	1
13	51	57	6
			52

1. *Assumptions.*

  Level of Measurement: Per cent voting is an interval scale
  Model: Random sampling
         Population differences distributed normally
  Hypothesis: $\mu_D = 0$

It must be assumed that the pairs appearing in the samples have been selected randomly from some population of pairs. As will be discussed below, this assumption sometimes causes a difficult problem of interpretation. Since it is the differences for each pair in which we are directly interested, it must be assumed that the population of all possible differences is normally distributed. If N were large this assumption could be relaxed.

  2. *Sampling Distribution.* Since the population standard deviation of differences is not given, it will be necessary to use the t distribution with $N - 1$ or 12 degrees of freedom. Notice that this is half the degrees of freedom that would have been used had a difference-of-means test been possible.

  3. *Significance Level and Critical Region.* Let us use the .05 level and a two-tailed test. Therefore, for 12 degrees of freedom, if $|t| \geq 2.179$ we shall reject the null hypothesis.

  4. *Computing the Test Statistic.* First we find the mean of the sample differences by adding the difference column and dividing by N (= 13). The sample standard deviation of differences is also obtained.

$$\bar{X}_D = {}^{52}\!/_{13} = 4.0$$

$$s_D = \sqrt{\frac{\Sigma(X_D - \bar{X}_D)^2}{N}} = \sqrt{\frac{328}{13}} = 5.023$$

Therefore $$t = \frac{\bar{X}_D - \mu_D}{s_D/\sqrt{N-1}} = \frac{4.0 - 0}{5.023/\sqrt{12}} = 2.76$$

  5. *Decision.* With 12 degrees of freedom, a probability of .02 corresponds to a t of 2.681. We therefore decide to reject the null hypothesis, and noting the direction of the difference we conclude that method B is superior to method A.

*13.5. Comments on Experimental Designs

Although it is not possible in a general text such as this to go very deeply into questions of design of experiments, a few comments are in order.[2] You may have asked yourself why it is that one would ever want to make use of matched samples in preference to independent

---

[2] For further discussion of experimental designs, see any standard text on research methods. In particular, see [2], chap. 4.

samples. Clearly, degrees of freedom are sacrificed. Since the use of matched samples requires cutting the number of cases in half (as far as the test is concerned), don't we lose more than we gain? This all depends on how successful we have been in matching cases. The purpose of matching is, of course, to minimize differences due to extraneous variables. What this means is that careful matching should reduce considerably each of the pair-by-pair differences. In other words, the better the matching, the smaller the standard deviation of differences. Thus although the number of cases is reduced, s_D should also be reduced. If there is a large reduction in the standard deviation of differences relative to the loss in cases, then we gain by matching. Since cases will ordinarily be lost in the matching process (see below), the moral is this: don't match unless you are quite sure you have located the important relevant variables. If you are studying delinquency and match according to hair color, you will probably be worse off than if you didn't match at all.

Methods texts usually mention the fact that there is likely to be considerable loss of cases due to the matching process. That is, a large number of cases will have to be eliminated because there are no similar cases with which they can be paired. Such an attenuation of cases can play havoc with the randomness assumption. A social scientist may start with a random sample of 1,000 cases, ending up with 200 which are matchable. In so doing, he is probably biasing his final sample considerably since he is undoubtedly eliminating many of the more extreme or unusual cases which cannot be matched. Thus it is often difficult to determine the nature of the population to which one is generalizing. For this reason, extreme caution should be used in generalizing results. This type of design is therefore likely to be most useful in studies in which there is minimal interest in generalizing to a specific finite population such as native whites in Chicago.

In connection with such an attenuation of cases and the resulting difficulties in generalizing to a specific population, it is sometimes claimed that there is no real interest in the population itself since the researcher's concern is primarily with establishing "relationships between variables." For example, a social psychologist may begin by using only those white male college freshmen taking introductory psychology who volunteer as subjects for study. Still further selectivity may occur as some subjects are eliminated in the matching process. Suppose a relationship is then found between the experimental variable and some dependent variable. It would be tempting to conclude that the same relationship would-hold regardless of the population studied, i.e., that it is a universal relationship. If this should indeed prove to be the case, the social scientist may very well assert that he has no interest in generalizing to any particular finite population. But on what basis can he assume that the relationship found for such a very restricted population will hold for other populations as well? Obviously, the experiment must be performed on a large number of very different populations before such an assertion can legitimately be made. Although one may gain control over a number of variables in a carefully designed experiment, there is practically always a comparable loss in the degree to which results can be generalized to more inclusive populations. It is naive in the extreme to expect that one can be interested only in relating variables without having to specify the nature of the population within which such relationships can be expected to hold.

In pair-by-pair matching it is desirable to randomize within each pair by flipping a coin to decide which member of the pair should be assigned to the experimental group and which to the control group. This procedure makes interpretation of results more meaningful in the sense that possible self-selection can be ruled out. For example, in the attempt to influence voters on the fluoridation issue, suppose community leaders were permitted to choose which of the two types of influences they preferred or which they thought would be most effective in their particular community. It is possible that all or most communities with a certain type of leadership might receive the indirect approach, whereas those with another type of leadership would receive the direct method. We would then have an uncontrolled variable (leadership type) the effects of which would be hopelessly confounded with those of the experimental variable. Specifically, suppose group B turned out to have the higher percentage of favorable votes but also the more democratic leadership because of the fact that democratic leaders tended to favor this approach for their communities. How would we know whether or not the difference in vote was actually due to the superiority of method B or to the leadership differences between the two communities?

It might be argued that leadership type should have been controlled in the matching process so that two communities in any given pair would have the same type of leadership. But it is obviously impossible to control for all relevant variables in the matching process, not only because of practical difficulties but also because of our limited knowledge of which variables are actually the most important. At some point we must admit that there may be important variables, many of which are unknown to the researcher, which have not been controlled in the matching process. It is precisely at this point that we rely on randomization, i.e., on the laws of probability, in the expectation that the effects of uncontrolled variables will be neutralized. For example, we expect with a fairly large N that roughly half of the communities with the more democratic leadership will fall into group A and half into group B. The same will also be true for other uncontrolled variables.

In ex post facto experimental designs, in which the researcher comes on the scene *after* the experiment has taken place and consequently has had no opportunity to make such random assignments, the possibility of self-selection can never be ruled out.   Nor can the laws of probability be used to help one evaluate the effects of the experimental variable as contrasted with possible effects of variables for which the groups have not been matched.   One of the major advantages of laboratory experiments over so-called "natural" or ex post facto experiments is this randomization control over possible self-selection.

Other methods of matching samples are often suggested as alternatives to pair-by-pair matching.   These alternative methods usually have the advantage of reducing the attenuation of cases but lead to difficulties when it comes to statistical analysis.   One such method involves matching by frequency distributions.   For example, care may be taken that the two groups are similar with respect to mean income, mean age, general income distribution, and so forth.   The groups are thus comparable with respect to these summarizing measures even though a given individual may have no exact counterpart in the other group with whom he can be paired.   In this type of design we are again clearly violating the independence assumption, but to the writer's knowledge there is no simple way to make use of a statistical test which is at the same time efficient and also does not involve dubious assumptions.   One could pair cases as well as possible and proceed as above, but pairing would undoubtedly lead to an inefficient design.   Certainly it would not be legitimate to use a difference of means test with $N_1 + N_2 - 2$ degrees of freedom.

EXERCISES

1. Fifty census tracts in a city are selected at random.   It is found that twenty of these are serviced by community centers, the remainder are not.   You compare the delinquency rates for these two types of tracts and obtain the following delinquency rates (given in terms of the number of delinquents per 1,000 adolescents):

Measure	With center	Without center
Sample size	20	30
Mean	27	31
Standard deviation (s)	6	8

Test for the significance of the difference between these two types of tracts (.01 level) using (a) model 1, and (b) model 2.   How do the two results compare?

2. A random sample of married women still living with their husbands is selected, and the women are classified as being either "satisfied" or "unsatisfied" with their marital lives.   The two groups of women are then compared with respect to the duration of their marriages with the following results:

Duration of marriage (nearest whole year)	Satisfied f_1	Unsatisfied f_2
0–2	34	10
3–4	41	16
5–9	50	23
10–14	39	25
15–19	18	14
20–39	15	16
Total	197	104

Is there a significant difference between the two groups at the .01 level?

3. Suppose you expect to find the difference between the mean annual incomes of samples of doctors and dentists to be about $500 (i.e., $\bar{X}_1 - \bar{X}_2 = 500$). You estimate the standard deviations to be $1,900 and $1,600 respectively. You plan to take the same number of doctors and dentists in the total sample. How many cases would you need in order to establish significance at the .05 level? Suppose you intended to take twice as many doctors as dentists. How many cases would you then need?

4. You have classified a random sample of college students as either "other-directed" or "inner-directed." You find that 58 per cent of the males are other-directed, whereas 73 per cent of the females belong to this category. There are 117 males and 171 females in the total sample. Is this difference significant at the .001 level?

*5. Suppose you have designed a before-after experiment with control group. In other words, you have matched two groups, pair by pair, and have before and after measures on both groups. Make use of the t test to test for the effectiveness of your experimental variable (a) using only the "after" scores, ignoring the "before" scores, (b) using the "before" and "after" scores of the experimental group only, and (c) using all four sets of scores. (Hint: How can you use all four scores to separate out the effects of the experimental variable from extraneous factors which might have affected both groups?) Contrast the advantages and disadvantages of methods (a) and (b). What are the advantages of (c) over both (a) and (b)?

Pair	Control group Before	After	Experimental group Before	After
A	72	75	66	77
B	61	60	61	65
C	48	37	43	49
D	55	64	55	53
E	81	76	76	91
F	50	59	52	68
G	42	49	40	51
H	64	55	65	74
I	77	75	67	79
J	69	78	64	63

REFERENCES

1. Hagood, M. J., and D. O. Price: *Statistics for Sociologists*, Henry Holt and Company, Inc., New York, 1952, chap. 19.

2. Selltiz, C., M. Jahoda, M. Deutsch, and S. W. Cook: *Research Methods in Social Relations*, Henry Holt and Company, Inc., New York, 1959, chap. 4.

3. Walker, H. M., and J. Lev: *Statistical Inference*, Henry Holt and Company, Inc., New York, 1953, chaps. 3 and 7.

Chapter 14

ORDINAL SCALES: TWO-SAMPLE NONPARAMETRIC TESTS

As yet we have not had occasion to discuss significance tests involving ordinal scales, although it was pointed out in Chap. 2 that ordinal scales are very frequently used in social science research. In the present chapter we shall take up certain two-sample tests that can be used with ordinal scales, tests which are directly comparable to tests involving differences of means and proportions discussed in the previous chapter. Tests taken up in this chapter can therefore be used in relating ordinal-scale variables to variables involving a dichotomized nominal scale. In subsequent chapters we shall take up tests which permit one to relate an ordinal scale to a nominal scale with any number of categories or to another ordinal scale.

The tests discussed in this chapter are often referred to as *nonparametric* or *distribution-free* tests in that they do not require the assumption of a normal population. Actually, both the terms *nonparametric* and *distribution-free* are somewhat misleading. We do not imply that such tests involve distributions which do not have parameters. Nor can a population be "distribution-free." Both terms are actually used to refer to a large category of tests which do not require the normality assumption or any assumption which specifies the exact form of the population. Some assumptions about the nature of the population are required in all nonparametric tests, but these assumptions are generally weaker and less restrictive than those required in parametric tests. We have already come across certain nonparametric tests. The binomial, sign, and difference-of-proportions tests, for example, do not require the assumption of normality since they all refer to dichotomized nominal scales. In contrast with these particular nonparametric tests, the tests taken up in this chapter all involve ordinal scales, thus making it possible to use a somewhat higher level of measurement. In the following chapter two additional nonparametric tests will be considered, both involving only nominal scales.

What is the advantage of nonparametric tests as compared with a test such as the difference-of-means test? In using the t test for a difference of means, we saw that it was necessary to assume not only an interval scale but normal populations as well. The assumption of normality could of course be relaxed in the case of large samples, but it was argued that it is precisely when samples are small that the normality assumption is most questionable. Therefore we would expect to find that nonparametric alternatives to the difference-of-means test will be most useful whenever either of two conditions is met: (1) we cannot legitimately use an interval scale but ordering of scores is justified, or (2) the sample is small and normality cannot be assumed. Since these nonparametric tests involve weaker assumptions than the difference-of-means test, they may not take advantage of all the available information. Thus if an interval scale can legitimately be used and if the normality assumption can be either made in the case of small samples or relaxed in the case of larger ones, a difference-of-means test will ordinarily be preferable to one of the nonparametric tests.

In what sense can we speak of one test being preferable to another? What criteria are used in making such a decision? First, as we have already implied above, if a test requires us to make certain dubious assumptions which cannot themselves be tested, it will not be as satisfactory as one which does not require such assumptions. If everything else were equal, which is practically never the case, we would always select that test which required the weakest assumptions. If the results of the test called for rejection, we could more readily turn to the null hypothesis as the single faulty assumption. Unfortunately, however, the problem is not quite so simple. If it were, we would always make use of nonparametric procedures. It usually turns out that a test which requires stronger assumptions is a more powerful test in the sense that its use will involve a lower risk of a type II error. We thus have two criteria which work in opposite directions and which must be evaluated accordingly. Nonparametric tests require weaker assumptions but they are less powerful. We shall get a better idea of what is meant by "strong" and "weak" assumptions when we come to the specific nonparametric tests which can be used as alternatives to the difference-of-means test. First, however, we must consider the question of how the relative power of a test is evaluated.

*14.1. Power and Power Efficiency

The *power* of a test is defined as $1 -$ (probability of a type II error) or as $1 - \beta$. Thus the power of a test is inversely related to the risk of

failing to reject a false hypothesis.   The greater the ability of a test to
eliminate false hypotheses, the greater is its relative power.   As we have
already indicated, it is much more difficult to evaluate the risk of type II
than type I errors.   Not only must we know the exact form of the population, but we must also know the degree to which the hypothesized
parameter differs from the true value.   In other words, the probability
of a type II error, and therefore the power of the test, depends upon
which alternative hypothesis is actually correct.   For these reasons, we
seldom actually compute the probabilities of type II errors in applied
research.   As implied earlier, however, the power of a test must be used

Fig. 14.1. Power functions for two-tailed tests, with $\alpha = .05$, for samples of varying
size.   (*By permission from W. J. Dixon and F. J. Massey, Introduction to Statistical
Analysis, McGraw-Hill Book Company, Inc., New York, 1957, fig. 14.6, p. 252.*)

in evaluating its relative efficiency.   Several alternative tests may be
made to involve the same risk of a type I error.   We then use the relative
risks of making type II errors to select the test which will be most appropriate under a given set of conditions.   Although the problem of determining the power of a test is fairly complex and beyond the scope of this
text, we can indicate in a general way what is involved in making such
comparisons.   In order to do so, we must introduce the notion of a
power function.

   The general form of a power function for a two-tailed test is given in
Fig. 14.1.   Such a function gives us the power of a test for the various
possible correct alternatives to H_0.   To be specific, let us assume that we
have hypothesized a particular value μ_0 for the population mean.   Suppose, however, that the true population mean is actually two standard
errors away from the hypothesized mean.   Clearly, then, H_0 is false and
should be rejected.   Since the power of a test is $1 - \beta$, the power of the
test actually gives us the probability of *rejecting H_0* when it is false.   This
latter probability, rather than the probability of error, is given by the
height of the curve.   If the true mean is two standard errors from μ_0,
the probability of rejecting H_0 can be determined by finding the height

of the curve at this point on the X axis.   Thus the values along the X axis indicate the possible *correct* values of μ whereas those on the Y axis indicate the probabilities of rejecting H_0.

Notice that when the correct value of the mean is actually μ_0 (and therefore we would be making an error in rejecting H_0), the height of the power function is given by the significance level of the test. Why?

Notice also that if the correct value of μ is not too distant from μ_0, the power of the test, as indicated by the height of the curve, will be less than will be the case if the true value is quite different from μ_0.   This tells us that our risk of a type II error is relatively large whenever the hypothesized value is not too far from the correct value, but that if we have missed the mark by a considerable amount we shall have a much higher probability of rejecting our false hypothesis.   This is consistent with the intuitive argument we developed earlier in connection with the binomial.   It is also in line with our practical interests.   If the null hypothesis is almost correct we are not too bothered if we fail to reject it, even though technically we are in error in so doing.   It is when H_0 is substantially incorrect that we are really interested in rejecting it.

In order to give a better indication of how power functions are actually used, we can compare the power function of a two-tailed test (Fig. 14.1) with those of some one-tailed tests.   Again let us suppose that H_0 predicts that the true mean is μ_0.   Consider the one-tailed test in which we have used the upper or positive tail as our critical region.   If the true value of μ is actually greater than μ_0, most of the sample means drawn from the population will also be greater than μ_0 and we have a better chance of ending up in this one-tailed critical region than would have been the case had we used a two-tailed test at the same significance level. In other words, if μ is actually to the right of μ_0 we have a better chance of rejecting H_0 with a one-tailed test in this direction.   This means, of course, that the power of this particular one-tailed test will be greater for values of μ in the positive direction.   But suppose the true value of μ is actually to the left of μ_0.   Then most of the $\bar{X}$'s will fall to the left of μ_0 and very few will fall into the critical region at the opposite (or positive) end of the continuum.   In this case, therefore, we shall practically never be able to reject H_0, and the power of the one-tailed test will be very weak indeed.   The opposite kind of pattern will obviously hold in the case of one-tailed tests with critical regions in the lower or negative tails.

The power functions of one- and two-tailed tests can be compared as in Fig. 14.2.   In summary, we see that a one-tailed test will be more powerful than its two-tailed counterpart (using the same significance level) for alternatives which are in the direction of the critical region, but it will be much less powerful than a two-tailed test if the parameter actually lies in

the direction opposite to that predicted.   The risk of a type II error is
therefore considerable if one makes a one-tailed test and happens to
predict the wrong direction.   In such an event the data cannot be used
to support the theory anyway.   Therefore one would probably have no
interest in proceeding with the test unless, for exploratory purposes, he
wanted to ascertain whether or not a completely opposing theory would
have any merits.

We have seen in comparing one- and two-tailed tests that one test may
be more powerful for certain alternatives but less powerful for others.   In

Fig. 14.2. Comparison of power functions for one- and two-tailed tests, with $\alpha = .05$.
(a) Reject if $Z > 1.645$.   (b) Reject if $Z < -1.645$.   (c) Reject if $Z > 1.96$ or if
$Z < -1.96$.   (*By permission from W. J. Dixon and F. J. Massey, Introduction to
Statistical Analysis, McGraw-Hill Book Company, Inc., New York, 1957, fig. 14.5,
p. 249.*)

general, this may also occur in comparing two very different kinds of tests.
For example, we shall soon see that one particular nonparametric test
may be more powerful than a second under one set of circumstances but
less so under another.   It is this fact which makes it difficult to develop
relatively simple generalizations concerning the superiority of one test
over another.   The situation is further complicated by the fact that one
test may be powerful for small samples but relatively less so for larger
samples.   The power of any given test will of course increase with the
sample size since for any given significance level an increase in sample
size essentially makes it possible to reject the null hypothesis with smaller
deviations from hypothesized values.   We have seen, for example, that
the standard error of the mean decreases as N increases and that therefore as N increases the sample mean must be closer to the hypothesized
value if we are to retain H_0.   What we are saying, then, is that we can

more easily reject a false hypothesis when N is large. But although the power of a test may increase with N, the *rate* of increase in power may not be the same for all tests. A test which has relatively weak power for small N's may therefore "catch up" with another test so that the former test is actually more powerful for large samples. It is no wonder that we have put off a consideration of type II errors until this point.

In order to compare the relative powers of two tests we can ask ourselves how many cases would be needed with the first test in order to get the same power as with a given number of cases using the second test. Usually we compare the power of a given test with that of the most powerful alternative. In the case of the first three nonparametric tests considered in this chapter, the most powerful alternative will be the t test for the difference of means. The term *power efficiency* is usually used to refer to the power of a certain test relative to that of its most powerful alternative. If we refer to the power efficiency of one of these nonparametric tests as 95 per cent, we mean that the power of the nonparametric test using 100 cases is the same as that of the t test using 95 cases *if the model used in the t test is correct.*

Since it is necessary to assume a particular form for the population in order to evalaute the power of a test, we imagine in the above illustration that we actually have an interval-scale level of measurement and that the populations are both normal in form. In determining the power efficiency of the nonparametric test, we are essentially asking ourselves how much our failure to accept the normality assumption will cost us if in fact such an assumption were actually legitimate. Here we see that the failure to accept this assumption and our consequent use of the nonparametric test would cost us an extra five cases above the 95 used in the difference-of-means test. With such a small loss in efficiency we would probably go ahead with the nonparametric test if we were at all in doubt about the assumptions required by the difference-of-means test. On the other hand, if the power efficiency were only 60 per cent and if departures from normality were not too great (or if N were large), we would probably use the difference-of-means test.

As indicated in the previous chapter, it is when samples are small that we need to be most concerned about the normality assumption. For small N's it will not in general be possible to translate power efficiency statements into comparisons of exact sample sizes since the latter quantities must always be integers. Thus with 95 per cent efficiency, a sample of size 10 using the nonparametric test would be equivalent to one of 9.5 using the t test. Although such a statement is operationally meaningless, it is at least helpful for comparative purposes.

Before closing this section, it is again necessary to remind you that the power efficiency of a given test may depend upon the sample size selected;

it may be highly efficient for large samples but much less so for smaller ones.

14.2. The Wald-Wolfowitz Runs Test

In the runs test and also in the following two tests to be considered in this chapter, we assume that we have two independent random samples and that the level of measurement is at least an ordinal scale. In all three tests our null hypothesis will be that the two samples have been drawn from the same continuous population (or identical populations). The underlying dimension will be assumed to be continuous rather than discrete, although we recognize that tied scores may result because of the crudity of the measuring instrument.   The hypothesis that the two samples have been drawn from the same population is actually very similar in nature to our assumptions in the difference-of-means test.   As previously indicated, when we put together the assumptions of normality, equal variances, and equal means we are in effect assuming the two populations to be identical.   In the case of the runs test we are hypothesizing that the two populations have exactly the same form and hence can be thought of as identical.   We do not have to specify the nature of this form, however.   It might be normal or it might not.   We are therefore making a weaker set of assumptions than required in the difference-of-means test, weaker in the sense that the difference-of-means test (with equal σ's) requires all of the assumptions of the runs test *plus* the assumption of normality and the use of an interval scale.

In the difference-of-means test our interest centered on differences in central tendency rather than differences in dispersion or differences in form.   The runs test essentially tests for all of these possible differences simultaneously.   As we shall see presently, its main use is in testing for differences in dispersion or form since there are more powerful nonparametric tests available for testing for differences in central tendency. Notice, incidentally, that the null hypothesis has not been stated in terms of means or standard deviations but rather in terms of any differences whatsoever.   This will also be the case for other nonparametric tests discussed in this chapter.   With ordinal scales, it is of course meaningless to think in terms of means and standard deviations.

The basic principle involved in the runs test is very simple, as are the computations.   We first take the data from both samples and rank the scores from high to low, ignoring the fact that they come from two different samples.   If the null hypothesis is correct, we would expect that the two samples will be well mixed.   In other words, we would not expect a long run of cases from the first sample followed by a run of cases from the second.   For example, if we refer to the samples as A and B we expect that the rank ordering will be more or less as follows:

ABBABAAABABBABBAAABAAB

rather than

AAAAAAAAABABBBBBBBBBBB

In order to test to see how well the two samples are mixed when ranked, we can simply count the number of runs that occur. A run is defined as any sequence of scores from the same sample. In the first example above we have a "run" of a single A, followed by a run of two B's, then a single A, a single B, a run of three A's, and so on. The total number of runs is therefore 14. In the second example, however, the A's are bunched toward the lower end of the continuum and we have only four runs. The procedure of counting runs will usually be simplified and errors reduced by drawing a line under all scores in the first sample and a line above those in the second. We then only need to count the number of separate lines. If the number of runs turns out to be quite large, as in the first case, the two samples will be well enough mixed that we shall not be able to reject the null hypothesis. On the other hand, a small number of runs probably means that the hypothesis is incorrect and therefore should be rejected. The sampling distribution of runs can be used to establish the critical region used in rejecting the null hypothesis.

Problem. Suppose that judges have ranked 19 women's organizations according to their prestige, giving a score of 1 to the group with the highest standing and 19 to that with the lowest. Ten of these groups restrict their membership to gentiles, whereas the remaining nine admit Jewish women. Assuming that these women's organizations have been selected randomly from a list of all such organizations in the community, can we conclude that in the population there is a significant difference in the prestige of restrictive and nonrestrictive women's organizations?

Restrictive membership: Ranks 1, 2, 4, 5, 6, 7, 9, 11, 14, 17 ($N_1 = 10$)
Nonrestrictive membership: Ranks 3, 8, 10, 12, 13, 15, 16, 18, 19

$$(N_2 = 9)$$

1. *Assumptions.*

   Level of measurement: Prestige is an ordinal scale
   Model: Independent random samples
   Hypothesis: Samples have been drawn from populations having the same continuous distributions

2. *Sampling Distribution.* If both N_1 and N_2 are less than or equal to 20, the exact sampling distribution of the number of runs r is given in Table E of Appendix 2. For larger N's the sampling distribution of r is

approximately normal with

mean of runs

$$\text{Mean} = \mu_r = \frac{2N_1N_2}{N_1 + N_2} + 1 \qquad (14.1)$$

Std Dev of runs

and   Standard deviation $= \sigma_r = \sqrt{\dfrac{2N_1N_2(2N_1N_2 - N_1 - N_2)}{(N_1 + N_2)^2(N_1 + N_2 - 1)}}$ (14.2)

Notice that although normality of the population is not assumed, the sampling distribution of r will be approximately normal even with small N's. As we shall presently see, a number of other nonparametric test statistics also have this property. Note also that the formulas for the mean and standard error involve only the sample sizes and therefore do not require us to estimate population parameters as was necessary for the difference-of-means test. The comparative simplicity of formulas for the sampling distributions of nonparametric statistics is in part due to the fact that since scores have been ranked and therefore must always take on the numerical values 1, 2, 3, . . . , N, such quantities as the sum and standard deviation of ranks depend only on the number of cases used.

3. *Significance Level and Critical Region.* Since Table E, Appendix 2, gives only the number of runs necessary for rejection at the .05 level, for small samples we are restricted to this level of significance, although more complete tables can be found in [5]. Notice that the runs test does not take into consideration the direction of the relationship between prestige and restriction of membership. On the other hand, when we make use of the sampling distribution of r we are interested in only one tail since we can reject the null hypothesis only when there is a small number of runs (regardless of the direction of the difference).[1] Strictly speaking, therefore, we are using the runs test as a one-tailed test even though direction of relationship has not been predicted. The same sort of situation will occur in the Mann-Whitney test discussed in the next section and in several important tests to be taken up in subsequent chapters. In order to avoid ambiguities we shall therefore distinguish between one-tailed tests and situations in which direction has been predicted. Up to this point, such a distinction has been unnecessary since all one-tailed tests have involved predictions as to direction. Numbers in the body of the table give us the number of runs which will yield significance at the .05 level. Therefore any value of r which is equal to or less than the figure in the table will indicate that we have so few runs that we may reject the null hypothesis at this level. Since the numbers of cases in the two samples are ten and nine respectively, we see that we may reject if we get six or fewer runs.

---

[1] There are other applications of the runs test, however, in which both tails may be used. For example, there may be too many runs if the samples have been artificially rather than randomly mixed, and this fact may be used in a test for randomness.

4. *Computing the Test Statistic.* Arranging the organizations in order of prestige, drawing lines under the scores of the first sample and above those of the second, we see that there are 12 runs.

$$1\ 2\ \overline{3}\ \underline{4\ 5\ 6\ 7}\ \overline{8}\ \underline{9}\ \overline{10}\ \underline{11}\ \overline{12\ 13}\ \underline{14}\ \overline{15\ 16}\ \underline{17}\ \overline{18\ 19}$$

Although the number of cases is somewhat too small for the normal approximation to hold, we can go ahead with the computations using this approximation in order to illustrate its use and to compare results with those obtained using Table E, Appendix 2. As usual, we compute the value of Z, which will tell us how many standard deviations the obtained number of runs is from the mean or expected number of runs under the null hypothesis. Thus,

$$\mu_r = \frac{2(10)(9)}{10+9} + 1 = 10.47$$

and

$$\sigma_r = \sqrt{\frac{2(10)(9)[2(10)(9)-10-9]}{(19)^2(18)}} = 2.11$$

We therefore get

$$Z = \frac{r - \mu_r}{\sigma_r} = \frac{12 - 10.47}{2.11} = .725$$

Since the number of runs obtained actually exceeds the mean or expected number, we need go no further since small numbers of runs are needed for rejection. Had the number of runs been less than the expected number, we would have looked up the Z value in the normal table, using a one-tailed test since we are only interested in small numbers of runs and hence negative Z's.

5. *Decision.* Since the number of runs turned out to be greater than six, the figure given in Table E, we decide not to reject the null hypothesis at the .05 level. As we have just seen, the use of the normal approximation also leads us to this same conclusion. On the basis of our data we therefore do not conclude that there is a significant difference between the two types of organizations with respect to prestige.

Ties. In the above data there were no two organizations which received tied scores. The assumption of underlying continuity theoretically rules out the possibility of ties since no two scores would ever be exactly the same. But owing to crudities of measurement, and such crudities will almost certainly exist in most social research, ties do arise in practice. Notice that if two organizations within the same sample had been tied with respect to prestige scores, the runs test would have been unaffected. But suppose ties occurred across samples. Then the number of runs can be considerably affected depending on how the ties are broken. Suppose, for example, that two organizations (from different samples) had been tied for eighth and ninth positions. Had the positions of these two groups been switched from the order previously used, we would have obtained

10 runs instead of 12.   In other words, we would get either 10 or 12 runs depending on the order used.   Since this order would be completely arbitrary, we might find ourselves sometimes rejecting and other times failing to reject the null hypothesis.   The safest procedure we can use in the case of ties is to compute the number of runs using all possible ways of breaking the ties.   If all orderings lead to the same decision (rejection or nonrejection), we may safely adhere to this decision.   If they lead to different decisions, it will be possible to resolve the problem by flipping a coin, but perhaps the safest procedure is to withhold judgment. Obviously, then, if there are a large number of tied ranks the runs test cannot be used.

14.3. The Mann-Whitney or Wilcoxon Test

Another nonparametric test which can be used in situations where the runs test is appropriate is a test which seems to have been invented independently by a number of persons and which is commonly known as either the Mann-Whitney or Wilcoxon test.   This test requires exactly the same assumptions as the runs test and, like the latter test, involves a very simple procedure.   We again combine the scores of both samples and rank them from 1 to 19.   We then focus on the scores in the second sample (or whichever sample is the smaller).   Taking each score in the second sample, we count the number of scores in the first sample which have larger ranks.   Having done this for each of the scores in the second sample, we then add the results to give us the statistic U.   The sampling distribution of U can then be obtained exactly if the N's are small, or it can be approximated by a normal curve in the case of larger samples.   If U is either unusually small or unusually large we can reject the assumption that the two samples have been drawn from the same population.

An alternative form of exactly the same test may be used with the normal approximation.   Instead of obtaining U directly, we can compute the sum of the ranks for each of the samples.   We then go through a procedure which is analogous to that used in the difference-of-means test. We take a difference of the sums of the ranks for each sample, subtracting from this difference a quantity representing the expected difference under the null hypothesis.   This difference of differences, which is analogous to $(\bar{X}_1 - \bar{X}_2) - (\mu_1 - \mu_2)$, is then divided by the standard error in order to obtain Z.   The analogy is not perfect since we are dealing with sums of ranks rather than means of ranks, but the parallel with the difference-of-means test is quite clear.   Again, a large numerical value of Z will lead to rejection.   We shall now proceed to illustrate the Mann-Whitney test by making use of the same example as used above.   We shall then compare the power efficiency of this test with that of the runs test.

Problem.   Same as used for runs test.

Restrictive membership: ranks 1, 2, 4, 5, 6, 7, 9, 11, 14, 17

$$(N_1 = 10)$$

Nonrestrictive membership: ranks 3, 8, 10, 12, 13, 15, 16, 18, 19

$$(N_2 = 9)$$

1. *Assumptions.*   Same as those required in runs test.

2. *Sampling Distribution.*   The sampling distribution of U will be found in Table F of Appendix 2 if neither N_1 nor N_2 is larger than eight, and in Table G if one of the N's is between 9 and 20 and the other between 1 and 20.   For larger N's the sampling distribution of U will be approximately normal with

$$\text{Mean} = \mu_U = \frac{N_1 N_2}{2} \qquad (14.3)$$

and $$\text{Standard deviation} = \sigma_U = \sqrt{\frac{N_1 N_2 (N_1 + N_2 + 1)}{12}} \qquad (14.4)$$

3. *Significance Level and Critical Region.*   For comparative purposes we shall continue to use the .05 level without predicting the direction of relationship although the Mann-Whitney test can be used to take advantage of such predictions.

4. *Computing the Test Statistic.*   The statistic U can be computed by either of two methods.   With small N's it will be relatively simple to compute U by carrying out the procedure implied in the definitional formula.   Focusing on each of the nine groups in the second sample, let us count the number of cases in the first sample which have lower prestige and therefore larger rank scores.   Since the first organization in the second sample has been ranked third in prestige, there are eight groups in the first sample having lower prestige scores.   Similarly, the second group in sample 2 is ranked eighth, and therefore there are four groups in the other sample with lower prestige scores.   Continuing the process for each of the remaining organizations in sample 2, and then summing, we get

$$U = 8 + 4 + 3 + 2 + 2 + 1 + 1 + 0 + 0 = 21$$

Notice that had we carried out the same procedure but focusing on the groups within the first sample we would have gotten

$$U' = 9 + 9 + 8 + 8 + 8 + 8 + 7 + 6 + 4 + 2 = 69$$

Either of these quantities could be used to test for the significance of the relationship, but since the tables have been set up in terms of the *smaller* U value, we always make use of the lesser of these two quantities.   It will not be necessary to compute both U and U' since once either value has been obtained, the other can be computed from the formula

$$U = N_1N_2 - U' \quad \text{or} \quad U' = N_1N_2 - U \quad\quad (14.5)$$

In this case we would use the value 21 as our test statistic.

If the number of cases is relatively large or if ties occur, it will probably be more convenient to obtain U by summing the ranks of the separate samples, calling these sums of ranks R_1 and R_2, and then using the formulas

$$U = N_1N_2 + \frac{N_2(N_2 + 1)}{2} - R_2 \quad\quad (14.6)$$

or

$$U' = N_1N_2 + \frac{N_1(N_1 + 1)}{2} - R_1 \qu\quad (14.7)$$

whichever is the more convenient.   Summing the ranks we thus get

1	3
2	8
4	10
5	12
6	13
7	15
9	16
11	18
14	19
17	
$R_1 = 76$	$R_2 = 114$

As a check, we should have

$$R_1 + R_2 = \frac{N(N + 1)}{2} \qquad ck. \ \ R_1 + R_2$$

or

$$76 + 114 = \frac{19(20)}{2} = 190$$

where N represents the total number of cases in *both* samples.   Therefore

$$U = 10(9) + \frac{9(10)}{2} - 114 = 90 + 45 - 114 = 21$$

*The sums of ranks R_1 and R_2 could have been used directly in making the test, making it unnecessary to compute U. Since exact tables for small N's are usually given in terms of U, you will ordinarily find it advantageous to think in terms of the U statistic. The use of the sums of ranks can be used heuristically to point up the similarity of the Mann-Whitney test to the difference-of-means test, however. The use of a little algebra will convince you that we can take equations (14.3) to (14.7) and obtain the result that for the normal approximation the statistic

$$Z = \frac{R_1 - R_2 - (N_1 - N_2)(N + 1)/2}{\sqrt{N_1 N_2 (N + 1)/3}} \qquad (14.8)$$

will be approximately $Nor(0,1)$. Expressing Z in this form, we notice that the numerator consists of the difference $R_1 - R_2$ together with a term which turns out to be the expected or long-run value of this difference under the null hypothesis. This correction factor is of course necessary since we are dealing with a difference of *sums* rather than means, requiring us to take into consideration the fact that the two N's will not ordinarily be equal. If N_1 and N_2 are the same we note that this second factor becomes zero, and we are left with a numerator of $R_1 - R_2$. Thus we see the similarity with the difference-of-means test in which the numerator reduced to $\bar{X}_1 - \bar{X}_2$ in the case of the null hypothesis of no differences. The Mann-Whitney test may therefore be thought of as a *difference-of-summed-ranks* test.

5. *Decision.* Making use of Table G, Appendix 2, we see that at the .05 level we need a U of 20 or *smaller* in order to reject the null hypothesis if direction has not been predicted. Therefore we barely fail to reject the hypothesis that there is no difference between the two types of organizations. Notice, however, that had direction been predicted in advance, we would have needed a U of 24 or less at the .05 level. We see, incidentally, that although the same decision was reached in using both the runs and Mann-Whitney tests, we came much closer to rejecting when the latter test was used. If H_0 were really false, we therefore in this instance would have less of a risk of a type II error than with the runs test.

Had our N's been larger we could have made use of the normal approximation. In order to illustrate the procedure used, we can compute Z for the above data. We get

$$Z = \frac{U - N_1 N_2/2}{\sqrt{N_1 N_2 (N_1 + N_2 + 1)/12}} = \frac{21 - 45}{\sqrt{10(9)(20)/12}} = -1.96$$

*Had we used equation (14.8) we would also have gotten

$$Z = \frac{76 - 114 - (10 - 9)(20)/2}{\sqrt{10(9)(20)/3}} = -1.96$$

The use of the normal approximation thus yields the conclusion that we may just barely reject at the .05 level. We see that the exact tables are slightly more conservative than the approximation and should therefore always be used when the N's are sufficiently small.

Ties. If ties occur, we must again assume that they are due to crudities of measurement and that the underlying distributions are really continuous. If ties occur within classes there will of course be no effect on U, and we can proceed as before. If ties occur across classes, we give each of the cases the average of the scores they would have had if no ties existed. Thus if two organizations are tied for eighth and ninth, each receives a score of $(8 + 9)/2$ or 8.5. Had the tenth organization also been tied with these two groups, each would have received the rank $(8 + 9 + 10)/3$ or 9.0. In computing U it will now probably be less confusing to use the sum-of-ranks method. The correction factor involves the standard error of U and therefore appears in the denominator of Z. The revised formula becomes

$$Z = \frac{U - N_1 N_2 / 2}{\sqrt{[N_1 N_2 / N(N-1)][(N^3 - N)/12 - \Sigma T_i]}} \tag{14.9}$$

where $N = N_1 + N_2$ and $T_i = (t_i^3 - t_i)/12$, where t is the *number* of observations tied for a given rank.

In computing ΣT_i we first note all of the instances in which ties occur. Perhaps two groups are tied for eighth and ninth, and three for the lowest honors. Thus we have one t of two, and another of three. Therefore

$$\sum T_i = T_1 + T_2 = \frac{t_1^3 - t_1}{12} + \frac{t_2^3 - t_2}{12}$$

$$= \frac{2^3 - 2}{12} + \frac{3^3 - 3}{12} = \frac{6}{12} + \frac{24}{12} = 2.5$$

and

$$Z = \frac{21 - 45}{\sqrt{\frac{10(9)}{19(18)}\left(\frac{19^3 - 19}{12} - 2.5\right)}} = -1.964$$

This correction for ties can be used only with the normal approximation since the exact tables have not been computed allowing for ties. The correction factor will ordinarily have negligible effect unless the number of ties is quite large. Its effect is to produce a larger Z value. If one wishes to reject the null hypothesis, the failure to correct for ties will therefore lead to conservative results. This is all the more reason why it will ordinarily not be necessary to correct for ties. If the number of ties is extremely large, the Smirnov test (see below) should probably be used as an alternative to the Mann-Whitney test.

Comparison of the Mann-Whitney and Runs Tests. The null hypothesis for both tests is that the two samples have been drawn from identical populations. Usually our interest centers on differences in central tendency, as was true in the difference-of-means test. Occasionally, however, we may be more interested in differences in dispersion or form. As a general proposition, we can say that the Mann-Whitney test will be more powerful than the runs test whenever the major differences between the two populations are with respect to central tendency, whereas the runs test will be more powerful in situations in which the populations differ only slightly in central tendency but substantially in dispersion or form.

A simple example can be used to illustrate this point. Suppose we had two populations with identical medians but in the one case with a very homogeneous distribution and in the other a very heterogeneous one. We then might expect results such as the following:

Sample 1	Sample 2
5	1
6	2
7	3
8	4
9	13
10	14
11	15
12	16
$R_1 = 68$	$R_2 = 68$

In this extreme example, the Mann-Whitney test would not lead to rejection of the null hypothesis (which is obviously false) because R_1 is exactly equal to R_2. Using the runs test, on the other hand, we would obviously be able to reject since there would be only three runs. Since failing to reject would mean making a type II error, we see that the power of the runs test is greater than that of the Mann-Whitney test. In most instances, however, we are more likely to find differences in central tendency with relatively minor differences in dispersion. You should convince yourself that for populations of this sort we are likely to obtain a fairly large number of runs toward the center of the distribution. For such data the runs test will turn out to be much less powerful than the Mann-Whitney test. For most sociological applications the Mann-Whitney test seems to be the more useful of the two tests.

*If an interval-scale level of measurement has been attained and normal populations legitimately assumed, the t test for the difference between means could have been made. Under such conditions how much would we lose by using the Mann-Whitney test, thereby dropping back in level of measurement and using a weaker model? The evidence is that for moderate and large samples, the power efficiency of the Mann-Whitney test is approximately 95 per cent as compared with the t test. The power efficiency for small samples is also quite high, although exact numerical values are not easily obtainable. The Mann-Whitney test is thus a very powerful alternative to the t test. In view of the fact that it requires much weaker assumptions, it should therefore be used in instances where there is reasonable doubt of the legitimacy of either the interval scale or normality. Less is known about the power efficiency of the runs test. Smith [4] has found efficiencies of approximately 75 per cent in several empirical examples where sample sizes were about 20 and where the normal populations had equal standard deviations.

14.4. The Kolmogorov-Smirnov Test

The Kolmogorov-Smirnov test, which we shall refer to simply as the Smirnov test, is another two-sample nonparametric test requiring the same assumptions as the runs and Mann-Whitney tests and having a power efficiency comparable with that of the Mann-Whitney test ([3], page 136). Unlike the first two tests, however, the Smirnov test can conveniently be used in instances where there are large numbers of ties. Quite frequently in sociological research we make use of variables which are actually ordinal scales but for which data have been grouped into three or more large categories. If there are four or more such ordered categories the Smirnov test will be especially useful, whereas the number of ties involved would prohibit the use of the Mann-Whitney test. A sociologist may have divided community residents into six social classes, treating all persons within one class as tied with the other members of the class with respect to over-all status. Or occupations may have been ranked according to status, with all persons within the same occupational class receiving tie scores. Perhaps an attitudinal variable has been found to yield a Guttman scale with seven response types. In all of these examples we may wish to conceptualize the variable as being continuous in nature but the measuring instrument as being exceedingly crude so as to yield data which are grouped into a relatively small number of ordered categories. As was true in the case of interval scales, the finer the distinctions made and the larger the number of categories used, the less information lost. What we need is a test statistic which takes advantage of the ordering of categories without being either invalidated or made unusually cumbersome by the presence of large numbers of ties. The Smirnov test has been designed to meet this requirement.

The principle behind the Smirnov test is also a very simple one. If the null hypothesis that independent random samples have been drawn from identical populations is correct, then we would expect the cumulative frequency distributions for the two samples to be essentially similar. The test statistic used in the Smirnov test is the maximum difference between the two cumulative distributions. If the maximum difference is larger than would be expected by chance under the null hypothesis, this means that the gap between the distributions has become so large that we decide to reject the hypothesis. We can take either the maximum difference in one direction only (if direction has been predicted) or the maximum difference in both directions.

Problem. Suppose we have divided a random sample of adult males in a community into six social classes and have also classified them as having either low or high mobility aspirations. The latter two categories can be considered to be independent random samples from the larger populations of adult males with low and high aspirations respectively since a completely random total sample assures independence between any subsamples we might select. Let us suppose that we have predicted that those with high mobility aspirations will tend to have higher class standing than those with low aspirations. Can we conclude that the results are significant at the .01 level?

Class	Low aspirations	High aspirations
Lower-lower	58	31
Upper-lower	51	46
Lower-middle	47	53
Upper-middle	44	73
Lower-upper	22	51
Upper-upper	14	20
Total	236	274

1. *Assumptions.* Same as required for Mann-Whitney and runs tests.
2. *Sampling Distribution.* The sampling distribution of D, the maximum difference between the two cumulative distributions, can be given exactly in the case of small N's (≤ 40) when $N_1 = N_2$ ([3], page 129). This case will not be treated since with relatively small N's the Mann-Whitney test may be used instead of the Smirnov test and since in most sociological examples we ordinarily do not obtain samples of exactly the same size. If both samples are larger than 40 and if direction has not been predicted, we shall need a value of D at least as large as

$$1.36 \sqrt{\frac{N_1 + N_2}{N_1 N_2}}$$

in order to reject at the .05 level. For the .01 and .001 levels, the coefficient 1.36 can be replaced by 1.63 and 1.95 respectively. In the case of the .10 level, the comparable coefficient is 1.22.

If direction has been predicted we may use a chi-square approximation. The chi-square test statistic (χ^2) will be considered in the following chapter, and the chi-square table will become more familiar at that time.[2] The approximation formula, however, is as follows:

$$\chi^2 = 4D^2 \frac{N_1 N_2}{N_1 + N_2}$$ (14.10)

where the degrees of freedom associated with chi square are two. Although continuous population distributions are assumed in using the chi-square approximation, if data are actually discrete and therefore result in large numbers of ties, the probabilities obtained will be in the conservative direction if rejection is desired. In other words, the true probabilities will be less than those computed.

Table 14.1. Computations for Smirnov Two-sample Test

Class	Mobility aspirations				Difference $F_1 - F_2$
	Low F_1		High F_2		
Below upper-lower	58	.246	31	.113	.133
Below lower-middle	109	.462	77	.281	.181
Below upper-middle	156	.661	130	.474	.187 ←
Below lower-upper	200	.847	203	.741	.106
Below upper-upper	222	.941	254	.927	.014
Total	236	1.000	274	1.000	

$$\chi^2 = 4D^2 \frac{N_1 N_2}{N_1 + N_2} = 4(.187)^2 \frac{236(274)}{236 + 274} = 17.74$$

3. *Significance Level and Critical Region.* The problem calls for the .01 level of significance. Since direction has been predicted, we shall use the chi-square approximation.

4. *Computing the Test Statistic.* We first obtain the cumulative frequency distributions for each of the samples (see Table 14.1), expressing the F values as *proportions* of the total sample sizes. Thus the first value entered in the F column for sample 1 will be $58/236$ or .246; the second will be $109/236$ or .462, and so on. The last entries in both columns will of course be unity. We now form a difference column $F_1 - F_2$ and locate the largest difference with a positive sign since we predicted higher percentages of lower-class persons with low aspirations, i.e., higher F_1 values. This value of D turns out to be .187, as indicated by the arrow. Next, we compute the value of chi square, using equation (14.10).

[2] For this reason, you may prefer to postpone consideration of the Smirnov test until after you have read Chap. 15.

5. *Decision.* Note that the larger the value of D, the larger will be the chi square. Therefore, we need to determine just how large chi square must be in order to reject the null hypothesis. Referring to the chi-square table (Table I, Appendix 2), locating the degrees of freedom down the left-hand margin and the significance level across the top, we see that for 2 degrees of freedom the value 9.210 corresponds to the .01 level. This means that if the null hypothesis were actually true, we would get a chi square this large or larger by chance less than 1 per cent of the time. Since we obtained a chi square of 17.74 we see that we can reject the null hypothesis. This same chi-square test can be used for small samples when direction has been predicted, and if one is interested in rejecting the null hypothesis the chi-square approximation will actually be conservative. In other words, the probabilities obtained by this method will be larger than the true probabilities.

Had direction not been predicted, we would need a value of D which is at least as large as

$$1.63 \sqrt{\frac{N_1 + N_2}{N_1 N_2}} = 1.63 \sqrt{\frac{236 + 274}{236(274)}} = 1.63(.0888) = .145$$

in order to reach significance at the .01 level. In this case we obtain D by taking the largest difference regardless of sign. Since this value is the same as the D previously used (.187), we see that we may again reject the null hypothesis.

14.5. The Wilcoxon Matched-pairs Signed-ranks Test

All three nonparametric tests discussed up to this point in the chapter have required that the two samples be selected independently of each other. It will be remembered that when pairs were matched we could not use the ordinary difference-of-means test. Instead, we treated each matched pair as a single case and obtained a difference score for each pair. We then went ahead as though we had a single sample and tested the null hypothesis that $\mu_D = 0$. In addition you will recall that in using the sign test we also could have made use of matched pairs, considering only the sign of the difference score and testing the null hypothesis by using the binomial distribution. In the sign test we had to throw away any information we might have had about the magnitude of the differences involved. On the other hand, the most powerful test, the t test, required not only an interval scale but also the assumption of a normal population of difference scores. The Wilcoxon matched-pairs signed-ranks test combines some of the features of both these tests and lies between them with respect to power efficiency.

As we shall presently see, the Wilcoxon test requires slightly higher than an ordinal-scale level of measurement. It will be necessary to assume an ordered-metric scale in which it is possible not only to rank the original scores themselves but to rank the *differences* between such scores. Since ordered-metric scales are seldom found in sociological research, this requirement essentially amounts to our needing an interval scale. Since the Wilcoxon test does not assume a normal population, however, it will be considered along with the other two-sample nonparametric tests in this chapter. The power efficiency of this test is substantially higher than that of the sign test, a fact which is not surprising since the sign test takes advantage of so little information. When the assumptions of the *t* test are actually true, the power efficiency of the Wilcoxon test is approximately 95 per cent for both small and large samples. It is therefore especially useful in situations where we have an interval-scale level of measurement but where the sample size is too small to justify the normality assumption.

The Wilcoxon test involves essentially the same null hypothesis as used in the sign test and also the *t* test for paired samples. The null hypothesis states that there are no differences between the scores of the two populations. In making use of this test we first obtain the difference scores for each pair. These differences are then ranked, ignoring the sign of the difference. Thus a difference of -6 would receive a higher rank than a difference of $+3$. Having ranked the absolute values of the differences, we then go back and record the signs. Finally, we obtain the sums of the ranks of both the positive and negative differences. If the null hypothesis is correct, we expect that the sum of the ranks of the positive differences will be approximately the same as the sum of the ranks for negative differences. If these sums are quite different in magnitude, the null hypothesis may be rejected. We form the statistic T which is the *smaller* of these two sums. We can then make use of exact tables for the sampling distribution of T when N is small and a normal approximation when N is large.

For comparative purposes let us use the same data as were used in the case of the comparable *t* test. Table 14.2 repeats these data and also gives the necessary computations for the Wilcoxon test. Notice that when we ignore sign, several of the difference scores are tied as to magnitude. In such an instance we again give the tied scores the average of the ranks they would have received had the scores not been tied. Thus there are two differences of size 1. Since we are here giving the smallest differences the lowest ranks, each of these differences has received a rank score of 1.5. In the fifth column we have indicated the sign associated with each rank in parentheses to the left of the rank. By inspection we see that the sum of the negative ranks will be less than that of the positive

Table 14.2. Computations for Wilcoxon Matched-pairs Test

Pair no.	Group A	Group B	Difference	Rank of difference	Negative ranks
1	63	68	5	(+) 6	
2	41	49	8	(+) 10.5	
3	54	53	−1	(−) 1.5	1.5
4	71	75	4	(+) 5	
5	39	49	10	(+) 12	
6	44	41	−3	(−) 4	4
7	67	75	8	(+) 10.5	
8	56	58	2	(+) 3	
9	46	52	6	(+) 8	
10	37	49	12	(+) 13	
11	61	55	−6	(−) 8	8
12	68	69	1	(+) 1.5	
13	51	57	6	(+) 8	
Total					13.5

ranks.   Therefore we obtain T by adding these negative ranks.   It is not necessary to keep the negative signs in looking up the value of T in the table since T values will always be given as positive.   Thus

$$T = 1.5 + 4 + 8 = 13.5$$

Let us now formalize what we have done by listing the steps in the usual manner.

1. *Assumptions.*

    Level of Measurement: Ordered-metric scale (difference scores can be ranked)

    Model: Random sampling

    Hypothesis: Sum of positive ranks = sum of negative ranks in population

2. *Sampling Distribution.*   The sampling distribution of T for $N \leq 25$ is given in Table H, Appendix 2.   For larger samples, T is approximately normally distributed with

$$\text{Mean} = \mu_T = \frac{N(N + 1)}{4} \tag{14.11}$$

and $\text{Standard deviation} = \sigma_T = \sqrt{\dfrac{N(N + 1)(2N + 1)}{24}} \tag{14.12}$

3. *Significance Level and Critical Region.*   As in the case of the t test we shall use the .05 level without predicting the direction of the outcome.

4. *Computing the Test Statistic.*   The value of T has already been computed from Table 14.2.   We obtained a T of 13.5.

5. *Decision.* Table H of Appendix 2 gives critical values of T for $N \leq 25$. Since T represents the smaller of the two sums of ranks, we need small numerical values of T in order to reject the null hypothesis. Thus we may reject H_0 whenever T is equal to or less than the values given in the body of the table. We see that for an N of 13 we need a T of 17 or smaller in order to reject at the .05 level. We also see that a T of 13 or less would be required for rejection at the .02 level. In using the t test in the previous chapter you will note that we just barely rejected at the .02 level; here we are slightly above the .02 level, but the results of the two tests are quite similar.

Although our N is quite small we can make use of the normal approximation for illustrative purposes. We get

$$Z = \frac{T - N(N+1)/4}{\sqrt{N(N+1)(2N+1)/24}}$$

$$= \frac{13.5 - 13(14)/4}{\sqrt{13(14)(27)/24}} = \frac{13.5 - 45.5}{\sqrt{204.75}} = -2.24$$

Since a Z of -2.24 corresponds to $p = .025$, we again reach the same conclusion. The value of T is much smaller than we would expect by chance, and we may reject the null hypothesis.

14.6. Summary

In the present chapter we have discussed four different nonparametric tests. Others will be taken up in later chapters. You have undoubtedly noted that all of the nonparametric tests we have discussed so far involve very simple ideas and considerably fewer computations than, say, the difference-of-means test. This is a further reason why we may predict that in the future sociologists will make much more frequent use of these nonparametric tests. It is unfortunately impossible in a general text to do much more than discuss a few such tests very briefly. Some of the tests taken up in this chapter have other kinds of applications which have not been discussed. For example, the runs test can be used as a test for randomness. The Smirnov test can be used as a one-sample test to compare observed frequencies with those predicted theoretically. In some cases, confidence intervals can be obtained using nonparametric procedures. Once you have gained a certain familiarity with the tests covered in this text, you may therefore want to consult more specialized sources. Fortunately, a good many of these nonparametric procedures can be easily understood by the reader who is not mathematically trained. It is also fortunate that a number of these procedures have been summarized in a recent text by Siegel [3]. You may also want to refer to an extensive bibliography of nonparametric methods compiled by Savage [2].

GLOSSARY

*Power efficiency
*Power function
*Power of a test

EXERCISES

1. A number of Protestant churches in a community have been classified as being (1) predominantly upper or upper-middle class, or (2) predominantly lower-middle or lower class. They are ranked according to how formal their services are, with the following results:

Upper and upper-middle: Ranks 1, 2, 3, 6, 7, 8, 11, 13, 14, 15, 17, 21, 25
Lower-middle and lower: Ranks 4, 5, 9, 10, 12, 16, 18, 19, 20, 22, 23, 24, 26, 27

Using the .05 level, can you establish a significant difference (a) with the runs test, and (b) with the Mann-Whitney test? Which test would you prefer? Why?

2. In Table 18.3, p. 318, data are given on the popularity rankings of the members of a summer work-camp group. Consider persons with participation ranks 1 to 8 as being "active" in group discussions, with the remainder of the group being placed in the "inactive" category. Is there a significant difference at the .05 level between the "actives" and "inactives" with respect to popularity? Use both the runs and Mann-Whitney tests.

3. Suppose you have been able to rank urban occupations from high to low, using the general categories of professional and managerial, clerical, skilled, semiskilled, and unskilled. You have asked every head of the household whether or not he favors increasing social security benefits at the taxpayer's expense. The results are as follows:

Occupational level	Favors	Opposes
Professional and managerial	46	97
Clerical	81	143
Skilled	93	88
Semiskilled	241	136
Unskilled	131	38
Total	592	502

Is there a significant relationship between occupation and attitude at the .001 level?

4. Work Exercise 2, Chap. 13, using the Smirnov test. Compare results with those of the t test.

5. Work all parts of Exercise 5, Chap. 13, using the Wilcoxon matched-pairs signed-ranks test. How do the results of the two tests compare?

*6. Verify that equation (14.8) is algebraically equivalent to the other formula for Z given on p. 200.

REFERENCES

1. Dixon, W. J., and F. J. Massey: *Introduction to Statistical Analysis*, 2d ed., McGraw-Hill Book Company, Inc., New York, 1957, chap. 14.

2. Savage, I. R.: "Bibliography of Nonparametric Statistics and Related Topics," *Journal of the American Statistical Association*, vol. 48, pp. 844–906, 1953.

3. Siegel, S.: *Nonparametric Statistics for the Behavioral Sciences*, McGraw-Hill Book Company, Inc., New York, 1956, chaps. 5 and 6.

4. Smith, K.: "Distribution-free Statistical Methods and the Concept of Power Efficiency," in L. Festinger and D. Katz (eds.), *Research Methods in the Behavioral Sciences*, The Dryden Press, New York, 1953, pp. 536–577.

5. Swed, F. S., and C. Eisenhart: "Tables for Testing Randomness of Grouping in a Sequence of Alternatives," *Annals of Mathematical Statistics*, vol. 14, pp. 66–87, 1943.

6. Walker, H. M., and J. Lev: *Statistical Inference*, Henry Holt and Company, Inc., New York, 1953, chap. 18.

Chapter 15

NOMINAL SCALES: CONTINGENCY PROBLEMS

In this chapter we shall study the relationships between two or more nominal scales. We have already seen that the case of two dichotomized nominal scales can be handled as a problem involving a difference of proportions. It is often desirable to make use of a more general test procedure which enables us to test for differences among three or more samples or to compare two (or more) samples with respect to a variable which has more than two categories. The chi-square test discussed in the next section enables us to interrelate nominal scales with any number of categories. Several new ideas will also be introduced. So far we have only been concerned with tests for the *existence* of a relationship between two variables. Some measures indicating the *strength* or degree of relationship will be presented in this chapter. Procedures used in controlling for one or more variables will also be discussed.

15.1. The Chi-square Test

The chi-square test is a very general test which can be used whenever we wish to evaluate whether or not frequencies which have been empirically obtained differ significantly from those which would be expected under a certain set of theoretical assumptions. The test has many applications, the most common of which in the social sciences are "contingency" problems in which two nominal-scale variables have been cross-classified.[1] For example, suppose religious affiliation and voting preference have been interrelated and the data summarized in the following 3 × 3 contingency table:

Party	Protestants	Catholics	Jews	Total
Republicans	126	61	38	225
Democrats	71	93	69	233
Independents	19	14	27	60
Total	216	168	134	518

[1] For another use of chi square, see Exercise 3 at the end of the chapter.

Notice that if frequencies were converted to percentages we could say that whereas 58.3 per cent of the Protestants are Republican, only 36.3 per cent of the Catholics and 28.4 per cent of the Jews prefer this political party.   We would then want to ask whether or not these differences were statistically significant.   Since there are three religious denominations and three categories of political preference, a single difference-of-proportions test cannot be used.   In using the chi-square test we can make essentially the same kind of null hypothesis as before, however.   We can assume that there are no differences among the three religious populations. This amounts to saying that the proportions of Republicans, Democrats, and Independents should be the same in each of the three groups.   Proceeding under the assumption that the null hypothesis is correct and that the samples are random and independently selected, we can then compute a set of frequencies that would be expected given these marginal totals. In other words, we can compute the number of Protestants whom we would expect to be Republicans and compare this figure with that actually obtained.   If these and comparable differences for other cells are quite large, we are likely to be suspicious of the null hypothesis.

Some measure of the difference between observed and expected frequencies must be obtained.   There are, of course, a large number of possible measures, but we need one for which the sampling distribution is known and tabulated.   For this reason, we make use of a measure referred to as chi square (χ^2) which is defined as follows:

$$\chi^2 = \sum \frac{(f_0 - f_e)^2}{f_e} \tag{15.1}$$

where f_o and f_e refer respectively to the observed and expected frequencies for each cell.[2]   In words, chi square is obtained by first taking the square of the difference between the observed and expected frequencies in each cell.   We divide this figure by the *expected* number of cases in each cell in order to standardize it so that the biggest contributions do not always come from the largest cells.   The sum of these nonnegative quantities for all cells is the value of chi square.

Notice that the larger the differences between observed and expected frequencies, the larger the value of chi square.   Chi square will be zero only when all observed and expected frequencies are identical.   We can now perform a test of the null hypothesis by looking at the sampling distribution of chi square.   We would hardly expect observed and expected frequencies to be exactly the same.   If the value of chi square turns out to be larger than that expected by chance, however, we shall be in a position to reject the null hypothesis under the usual procedures.

[2] In order to reduce confusion we have dropped the subscript i, it being assumed that we are summing over all the cells.

Problem. We can make use of the example given above but simplified so as to give a 2 × 2 table. The extension to the general case will turn out to be straightforward. Let us assume that Catholics and Jews have been combined and the Independents omitted. We then have the following table:

Party	Protestants	Catholics and Jews	Total
Republicans	126	99	225
Democrats	71	162	233
Total	197	261	458

It is important to note that the figures in each cell are actual frequencies rather than percentages. If figures given are percentages, they must be converted into frequencies, since the chi-square test statistic involves a comparison of frequencies rather than percentages.

1. *Assumptions.*

Level of Measurement: Two nominal scales
Model: Independent random samples
Hypothesis: No differences among religious populations with respect to political preference

The level of measurement *can*, of course, be higher. Chi-square tests are frequently used with ordinal scales and sometimes even interval scales. As we have seen in previous chapters, however, more powerful tests are available in such instances and would ordinarily be used in preference to chi square unless ease of computation were an overwhelming consideration. Again, it is necessary to assume independence between samples in order to make use of the chi-square test. The sample size must be relatively large because chi square, as defined by the formula, has a sampling distribution which approximates the distribution given in the table only when N is large.[3]

The null hypothesis can be stated in a number of equivalent ways. Saying that there is no difference among religious groups with respect to political preference is essentially saying that there is no relationship between religious affiliation and voting preference. It must be realized, however, that such a statement would apply only to these variables as they have been operationally defined: in this case political preference and religion would be defined as dichotomized variables. One could also state the null hypothesis by listing the various proportions which are assumed equal. Although this last method is perhaps the most precise, it can become quite cumbersome in the general case.

[3] See pages 220–221 for a more complete discussion of this problem.

2. *Significance Level.* Let us suppose that we want to demonstrate a difference and that we wish to be extremely conservative. We shall therefore use the .001 level. Suppose, also, that the direction of the difference is not predicted.

3. *Sampling Distribution.* The sampling distributions for chi square are given in Table I, Appendix 2. Notice that distributions differ according to the degrees of freedom involved. The determination of degrees of freedom will be discussed below. Since regardless of the direction of the relationship between religion and political preference, our interest is in whether or not the obtained chi square is *larger* than would be expected by chance, we are concerned only with the upper tail of the distribution. The lower tail, consisting of very small values of chi square, is not ordinarily used in contingency problems.

4. *Computation of Test Statistic.* Our first task in the computation of chi square is to obtain the expected frequencies. The null hypothesis states that there are no population differences as to voting preference. Therefore, regardless of what the true percentage of Republicans in each religious *population* may be, we would expect that in the long run there would be the same proportion of Republicans in both of the *samples*. Since the proportion of Republicans in the combined sample is $^{225}/_{458}$ or .4913, we would expect this same figure in each of the two religious samples. Each sample would thus be expected to have the same percentage of Republicans and the same percentage of Democrats. We can then obtain the expected *number* of Republicans among the Protestants by multiplying .4913 by the total number of Protestants in the sample. Thus the expected number of Republican Protestants would be $(.4913)(197) = 96.8$. The other expected frequencies can be computed in a similar manner. It is generally advisable to keep at least one decimal place in computing expected frequencies. Thus we would not round up to 97.

Before going on, it should be noted that expected frequencies can also be obtained by reasoning the other way around, i.e., in terms of the proportion of Republicans we would expect to be Protestant. Since the proportion of Protestants in the combined sample is $^{197}/_{458}$ or .4301, we can get the expected frequency of Protestant Republicans as follows: $(.4301)(225) = 96.8$. You should learn to obtain expected frequencies both ways as a check on your computations.

After the procedure has become a familiar one, you will then probably find it more convenient to make use of a simple formula described below. If we label the cells and marginal totals as

a	b	$a + b$
c	d	$c + d$
$a + c$	$b + d$	N

the expected frequency for any cell can be obtained by multiplying the two marginals corresponding to the cell in question and dividing by N. For example, the expected figure for cell a would be

$$(a + b)(a + c)/N = (225)(197)/458 = 96.8$$

The use of this last procedure reduces any rounding errors which may be introduced by first dividing (to obtain a proportion) and then multiplying. By convention, we usually place the expected frequencies in parentheses beneath the frequencies actually obtained for each cell as indicated below.

Party	Protestants	Catholics and Jews	Total
Republicans	126 (96.8)	99 (128.2)	225
Democrats	71 (100.2)	162 (132.8)	233
Total	197	261	458

Computations for chi square can then be summarized in a table such as Table 15.1. Notice that the quantity $f_o - f_e$ has the same numerical

Table 15.1. Computations for Chi Square

Cell	f_o	f_e	$f_o - f_e$	$(f_o - f_e)^2$	$(f_o - f_e)^2/f_e$
a	126	96.8	29.2	852.64	8.808
b	99	128.2	−29.2	852.64	6.651
c	71	100.2	−29.2	852.64	8.509
d	162	132.8	29.2	852.64	6.420
Total	458	458.0			30.388

value for each cell. You should convince yourself that this will always be the case in 2×2 tables but that it will not hold generally. Squaring this value has the effect of getting rid of the negative quantities. It is important that the *expected* frequencies, rather than the observed ones, be used in the denominators. The observed frequencies will vary from sample to sample and some might even be equal to zero.

It is often more convenient to make use of a computing formula which does not actually require subtraction of each expected frequency from each observed frequency. Expanding the numerator in the expression for chi square and then collecting terms we get

$$\chi^2 = \sum \frac{(f_o - f_e)^2}{f_e} = \sum \frac{f_o{}^2 - 2f_of_e + f_e{}^2}{f_e}$$

$$= \sum \frac{f_o{}^2}{f_e} - 2 \sum f_o + \sum f_e$$

But since both Σf_o and Σf_e are equal to N we obtain

$$\chi^2 = \sum \frac{f_o{}^2}{f_e} - N \tag{15.2}$$

Using this formula, which involves only a single subtraction, we get the same result as before (see Table 15.2).

Table 15.2. Computations for Chi Square, Using Computing Formula

Cell	$f_o{}^2$	$f_o{}^2/f_e$
a	15,876	164.008
b	9,801	76.451
c	5,041	50.309
d	26,244	197.620
Total		488.388

$$\chi^2 = 488.388 - 458$$
$$= 30.388$$

In the case of the 2×2 table only, it is possible to express chi square as a simple function of the cell frequencies and marginal totals. If the table is labeled as before we get

$$\chi^2 = \frac{N(ad - bc)^2}{(a + b)(c + d)(a + c)(b + d)} \tag{15.3}$$

Although this computing form requires the multiplication of large numbers, the use of logarithms may simplify considerably the computations involved. Incidentally, we see from equation (15.3) that chi square will be zero when the diagonal product ad is exactly equal to the product bc. This fact can be used as a quick method to determine whether or not it will be necessary to go ahead with a test for significance. If the diagonal products are almost equal, chi square will be too small to yield significance. These diagonal products can also be used to determine the direction of the relationship without bothering to compute percentages. The larger of the two products indicates which diagonal contains the bulk of the cases.

5. *Decision.* Before using the chi-square table we must first determine the degrees of freedom associated with this test statistic. In previous problems the degrees of freedom have always depended on the number of cases sampled. For contingency problems, however, the degrees of freedom depend only on the number of *cells* in the table. In computing expected frequencies you may have noticed that it is not necessary to compute values for each cell since most could have been obtained by subtraction. In fact in the 2 × 2 table we need to compute only one expected frequency and the others will all be determined. This is true because we make use of our sample marginal totals to compute expected frequencies. In other words, if we fill in a value for any one cell the other values are completely determined since expected frequencies must have the same marginal totals as observed frequencies. We therefore have only 1 degree of freedom. *for* 2 × 2

Having determined that there is only 1 degree of freedom in the 2 × 2 table, we look across the row corresponding to 1 degree of freedom in the chi-square table until we come to the desired level of significance. Corresponding to the .001 level we find a chi square of 10.827. This means that if all assumptions were in fact correct, we would obtain a value for chi square this large or larger only one time in a thousand. In other words, only very seldom will observed and expected frequencies differ by such an amount as to yield a chi square ≥ 10.827 *if* there were no relationship between religious affiliation and voting preference (as operationally defined in this problem). Since we actually obtained a value for chi square equal to 30.388 we conclude that the null hypothesis can be rejected at the .001 level. We see incidentally that when N is large it is not at all difficult to obtain significance at the .001 level.

Even though we were concerned only with large values of chi square, the direction of the relationship was not predicted in the above example. Regardless of whether Protestants were more likely to be Republicans or Democrats, the result would have been a large chi square if differences in percentages were also large. In other words, the test statistic is insensitive to the direction of relationship since it involves the squares of deviations and cannot be negative. We can take advantage of predictions as to direction simply by halving the significance level obtained. If chi square is large enough to yield significance at the .10 level without predicting direction, the result will be significant at the .05 level provided, of course, that the direction of the relationship was predicted beforehand. If the desired significance level cannot be obtained exactly from the chi-square table, a good approximation can be made by taking the square root of chi square and entering the normal table. For example, we know that a chi square of 3.841 with 1 degree of freedom corresponds to the .05 level when direction has not been predicted. The square root of this figure is 1.96 which is the Z value necessary for significance with the normal table. The normal table can be used only in the case of 2×2 contingency problems.

General Case. In the general case of the contingency table with r rows and c columns the assumptions and computations for chi square require only slight modification. The null hypothesis of "no difference" or "no relationship" now implies that each population will have the same proportions for each of the categories of the second variable. The expected frequencies can be obtained in exactly the same way as before, but there will now be rc cells and the degrees of freedom will be different.

Suppose we make use of the same example as before but in its original form, that of a 3×3 table. Incidentally, this table supplies us with more information than in the 2×2 case in which Catholics and Jews were combined into a single category. We therefore can expect results which may differ somewhat from those obtained above. Computing expected frequencies by any of the methods previously suggested, we obtain

Party	Protestants	Catholics	Jews	Total
Republicans	126 (93.8)	61 (73.0)	38 (58.2)	225
Democrats	71 (97.2)	93 (75.6)	69 (60.2)	233
Independents	19 (25.0)	14 (19.4)	27 (15.6)	60
Total	216	168	134	518

A computing table can be constructed as before (see Table 15.3).

Table 15.3. Computations for Chi Square for 3×3 Contingency Table

Cell	f_o	f_e	f_o^2	f_o^2/f_e
a	126	93.8	15,876	169.254
b	61	73.0	3,721	50.973
c	38	58.2	1,444	24.811
d	71	97.2	5,041	51.862
e	93	75.6	8,649	114.405
f	69	60.2	4,761	79.086
g	19	25.0	361	14.440
h	14	19.4	196	10.103
i	27	15.6	729	46.731
Total	518	518.0		561.665

$$\chi^2 = 561.665 - 518 = 43.665$$

To determine the proper degrees of freedom we notice that once the first two expected frequencies have been filled in for the first column, the third is determined by subtraction. The same will be true for the second column. All the expected frequencies in the third column will then be determined from the row totals. Generally, for each of the first $c - 1$ columns it will be possible to fill in all but one, or $r - 1$, of the cells. The final column will then always be completely determined. Therefore the number of degrees of freedom for the $r \times c$ contingency table can be given by the formula

$$\text{df} = (r - 1)(c - 1)$$

Notice that this formula gives 1 degree of freedom in the special case where $r = c = 2$.

Since there are 4 degrees of freedom associated with our 3×3 table, we see that a chi square of 18.465 is required for rejection at the .001 level. We therefore reject the null hypothesis. Notice that although a larger value of chi square is required for rejection, there are many more cells contributing to its value. Since chi square represents a sum rather than an average, we would expect that, other things being equal, the greater the number of cells the larger the chi square. The fact that the value of chi square needed for significance increases with the degrees of freedom shouldn't surprise us.[4]

Correction for Continuity. It has been indicated that the chi-square test requires a relatively large N because of the fact that the sampling distribution of the test statistic approximates the sampling distribution given in the chi-square table only when N is large. The question naturally arises, then, as to how large N has to be in order to make use of this test. The answer depends on the number of cells and the marginal totals. Generally, the smaller the number of cells and the more nearly equal are all marginal totals, the smaller the total N can be. The criteria usually used for deciding whether or not the number of cases is sufficient involve the *expected* frequencies in each cell. Whenever any of the expected frequencies are in the neighborhood of 5 or smaller, it is advisable to make some kind of modification as indicated below.

The chi-square distribution is assumed to be a continuous one. Actually, however, when the number of cases is relatively small it is impossible for the computed value of chi square to take on very many different values. This is true because observed frequencies must always be integers. In correcting for continuity we imagine that observed frequencies actually can take on all possible values, and we make use of those values within a distance of half a unit on either side of the integer obtained which will give the most conservative results. In the case of

[4] Note that the opposite was true in the case of the t distribution. Why?

he 2 × 2 table a correction for continuity can very easily be made.
his correction consists of either adding or subtracting .5 from the
observed frequencies in order to reduce the magnitude of chi square.
To see the effect of correcting for continuity we can take the following
ables:

	(A)	7	13	20		(B)	7.5	12.5	20
		(10)	(10)				(10)	(10)	
		8	2	10			7.5	2.5	10
		(5)	(5)				(5)	(5)	
		15	15	30			15	15	30
		$\chi^2 = 5.40$					$\chi^2 = 3.75$		

n Table B we have corrected for continuity by reducing the differences
etween observed and expected frequencies in each cell by .5. We have
nagined that there are between 6.5 and 7.5 cases in the top left-hand
ell and have used the number 7.5 since it is the closest value within this
nterval to the expected frequency of 10.0. In this example, correcting
or continuity reduces the significance level from approximately .02 to
omewhat greater than .05. Obviously, corrections for continuity will
ave less effect when expected frequencies are larger. Since making such
 correction actually involves very little additional effort, and since one
s on the conservative side in so doing, it is recommended that the correc-
ion be made whenever the expected frequency in any cell falls below 10.
With very small samples even this correction produces misleading results.
n alternative test discussed in the next section is available for 2 × 2
ables.
   Corrections for continuity cannot easily be made in the case of the
eneral contingency table. If the number of cells is relatively large and
f only one or two cells have expected frequencies of 5 or less, then it is
enerally advisable to go ahead with chi-square tests without worrying
bout such corrections. If there are a large number of small cells, how-
ver, the only practical alternative may be to combine categories in such
 manner as to eliminate these cells. Of course categories can only be
ombined if it makes sense to do so theoretically. Thus if there were an
other religions" category consisting of such a wide range of religious
roups as to make the category theoretically meaningless, it would
perhaps be better to exclude these persons from the analysis altogether.

*15.2. Fisher's Exact Test

   In the case of 2 × 2 tables where N is small it is possible to make use
f a test developed by R. A. Fisher which gives us exact rather than

approximate probabilities. If we label the cells and marginals of a 2 × 2 table as

$$
\begin{array}{cc|c}
a & b & a+b \\
c & d & c+d \\
\hline
a+c & b+d & N
\end{array}
$$

we can obtain the probability of getting *exactly* these frequencies under the null hypothesis that there are no differences in the population proportions. This probability is given by the formula

$$
P = \frac{(a+b)!(c+d)!(a+c)!(b+d)!}{N!a!b!c!d!}
$$

Notice that there are nine factorials in this formula for P. The task of directly evaluating the formula would therefore be quite formidable. Furthermore, since one is ordinarily interested in the entire tail of the sampling distribution rather than the probability of getting exactly the results obtained, he will then have to add to this first probability the probabilities of getting even more unusual outcomes in the same direction.

A simple numerical example can be used to illustrate what is involved. Suppose we have obtained the following 2 × 2 table:

$$
\begin{array}{cc|c}
3 & 9 & 12 \\
12 & 5 & 17 \\
\hline
15 & 14 & 29
\end{array}
$$

If we assume that the marginals remain fixed, we immediately see that there are three outcomes (in the same direction) which are even more unlikely than the one obtained. They are as follows:

$$
\begin{array}{cc|c}
2 & 10 & 12 \\
13 & 4 & 17 \\
\hline
15 & 14 & 29
\end{array}
\qquad
\begin{array}{cc|c}
1 & 11 & 12 \\
14 & 3 & 17 \\
\hline
15 & 14 & 29
\end{array}
\qquad
\begin{array}{cc|c}
0 & 12 & 12 \\
15 & 2 & 17 \\
\hline
15 & 14 & 29
\end{array}
$$

Notice that we can arrive at the successive tables by each time reducing by one the cells a and d, and increasing by one the cells b and c, until we reach the final table in which cell a is empty.

We shall suppose that it is always cell a which contains the smallest number of cases since it will always be possible to arrange the tables in this fashion. Let us use the symbol P_0 to denote the probability of getting exactly no cases in cell a (given these marginals) under the null hypothesis let P_1 represent the probability of getting exactly one case in cell a, P_2 the probability of getting exactly two, etc. Then in this particular problem we must obtain the sum of the probabilities

$$
P_0 + P_1 + P_2 + P_3
$$

in order to compute the probability of getting three or fewer cases in cell a. Since we are making use of a one-tailed test, we shall have to double the significance level obtained if we were unable to predict direction beforehand.

Rather than compute each of the P_i from the above formula involving products of factorials, it will be much more convenient to obtain P_0 directly and then to obtain the remaining probabilities as simple functions of P_0. In order to distinguish between the various possible combinations of numerical values of a, b, c, and d for fixed marginals, let us make use of the subscript k to denote the magnitude of the smallest cell a. Thus if there are k individuals in cell a, we shall refer to the quantities in the various cells as a_k ($= k$), b_k, c_k, and d_k. Since the marginals are assumed to remain fixed, if we decrease a_k and d_k by 1 we must increase b_k and c_k by 1. We can now simplify the formula for P_0 since $a_0 = 0$ and therefore $a_0! = 1$ (by definition), $(a_0 + b_0)! = b_0!$ and $(a_0 + c_0)! = c_0!$. A number of the factorials therefore cancel out, leaving us with

$$P_0 = \frac{(c_0 + d_0)!(b_0 + d_0)!}{N!d_0!}$$

The numerator now consists of the factorials of just two of the marginals rather than all four, and the denominator involves only $N!$ and $d_0!$. The value of d_0 can be obtained from the last of the four tables given above. In this example, therefore, $(c_0 + d_0) = 17$, $(b_0 + d_0) = 14$, $N = 29$, and $d_0 = 2$. P_0 can now be evaluated by using a table of logarithms of factorials or by writing out the factorials and simplifying.

In order to compute the values of P_1, P_2, and P_3 we now need a general formula for P_{k+1} in terms of P_k. Since marginals are assumed fixed, we have

$$P_{k+1} = \frac{(a + b)!(c + d)!(a + c)!(b + d)!}{N!(a_k + 1)!(b_k - 1)!(c_k - 1)!(d_k + 1)!}$$

because of the fact that when we add 1 to the a cell we also add 1 to d and subtract 1 from both b and c. If we now divide P_{k+1} by P_k practically all terms will vanish. The numerators for both probabilities are identical since they involve the same marginals. The factorial N's cancel. We are then left with

$$\frac{P_{k+1}}{P_k} = \frac{a_k!b_k!c_k!d_k!}{(a_k + 1)!(b_k - 1)!(c_k - 1)!(d_k + 1)!}$$

But $a_k!/(a_k + 1)!$ is just $1/(a_k + 1)$ and similarly for $d_k!/(d_k + 1)!$. Also, $b_k!/(b_k - 1)! = b_k$ and $c_k!/(c_k - 1)! = c_k$.

Therefore,
$$\frac{P_{k+1}}{P_k} = \frac{b_k c_k}{(a_k + 1)(d_k + 1)}$$

or
$$P_{k+1} = \frac{b_k c_k}{(a_k + 1)(d_k + 1)} P_k$$

and the troublesome factorials have disappeared. Therefore, we can make use of this formula to obtain P_1 from P_0. Having computed P_1 we can then get P_2 and so on.

Returning to our numerical example, we obtain P_0 as follows:

$$P_0 = \frac{14!17!}{29!2!} = .17535 \times 10^{-5}$$

Therefore,

$$P_1 = \frac{b_0 c_0}{(a_0 + 1)(d_0 + 1)} P_0 = \frac{12(15)}{1(3)}(.17535 \times 10^{-5}) = 10.521 \times 10^{-5}$$

In computing P_2 we must be careful to make use of a_1, b_1, c_1, and d_1 rather than the figures used in obtaining P_1. We get

$$P_2 = \frac{b_1 c_1}{(a_1 + 1)(d_1 + 1)} P_1 = \frac{11(14)}{2(4)}(10.521 \times 10^{-5}) = 202.529 \times 10^{-5}$$

Similarly,

$$P_3 = \frac{b_2 c_2}{(a_2 + 1)(d_2 + 1)} P_2 = \frac{10(13)}{3(5)}(202.529 \times 10^{-5}) = 1{,}755.252 \times 10^{-5}$$

Notice that each of the factors in the numerator is decreased by 1 as we compute P_{k+1} from P_k, whereas the factors in the denominators are each increased by unity. Adding the probabilities we thus get

$$P_0 + P_1 + P_2 + P_3 = [.175 + 10.521 + 202.529 + 1{,}755.252] \times 10^{-5}$$
$$= 1{,}968.48 \times 10^{-5} = .0197$$

Therefore the probability of getting three or fewer individuals in cell a under the null hypothesis is .02, and we would make our decision whether or not to reject the null hypothesis accordingly.

Because the Fisher test is an exact test it is to be preferred over the chi-square test corrected for continuity. Since the chi-square test will ordinarily yield somewhat lower probabilities than the Fisher test, one will be on the conservative side in using this exact test if he actually wants to reject the null hypothesis. In other words, in using the chi-square test we may arrive at probabilities which are actually too small, possibly leading us to the conclusion that the null hypothesis should be rejected when actually it shouldn't. If the smallest expected frequency is quite a bit larger than 5 and if the correction for continuity is used, the two tests will give approximately the same results. Even though we may avoid the use of factorials in the case of the Fisher test, it can be seen that if the smallest cell frequency is greater than 5, the computations involved will become quite tedious. Therefore, the Fisher test will be found to be most useful in the case of very small N's or whenever the total sample size is moderate but one or more of the marginals very small. In cases where $N \leq 30$, tables are available in [5] which make this exact test extremely simple to use.

To HERE

15.3. Measures of Strength of Relationship

Up to this point we have only been concerned with the question of whether or not a relationship between two variables exists. We have set up null hypotheses to the effect that there is no relationship and have then tried to reject these hypotheses. But just how much have we accomplished when we are able to reject? We refer to a relationship as being statistically significant when we have established, subject to the risk of a type I error, that *there is* a relationship between the two variables. But does this mean that the relationship is significant in the sense of being a strong relationship or an important one? Not necessarily. The question of the strength of a relationship is a completely different question from that of whether or not a relationship exists. In this section we shall take up several measures of degree of association which can be used to help answer this second kind of question.

It would seem reasonable, on first thought, to attempt to assess the strength of a relationship by simply noting the significance level attained in a test. For example, it might be reasoned that if one test were significant at the .001 level and another at the .05 level, the former relationship would be the stronger of the two. But is this necessarily the case? Looking at the two significance levels can tell us in which case we can have more faith that a relationship exists. Thus, we would be almost certain of the *existence* of a relationship in the first case but not so sure in the second. We must remember, however, that the significance level attained depends on the size of the samples used. As indicated previously, if the samples are very large it is generally very easy to establish significance for even a very slight relationship. This means, in effect, that when samples are large we are saying very little when we have established a "significant" relationship. For large samples, a much more important question is, "Given that a relationship exists, how strong is it?"

In order to illustrate the above argument, let us take a closer look at a property of chi square. In doing so, you should keep in mind that exactly the same principles apply for other kinds of significance tests. Let us ask ourselves what happens to chi square when the number of cases is increased. For illustrative purposes we can take the following 2 × 2 table:

30	20	50
20	30	50
50	50	100

Chi square for this table turns out to be exactly 4.0. Now suppose we were to double the sample sizes, keeping the same proportions in each cell. We would then obtain

60	40	100
40	60	100
100	100	200

and chi square would be 8.0, a figure which is exactly double the previous one. By examining the formula for chi square it is very easy to prove that if proportions in the cells remain unchanged, chi square varies directly with the number of cases. If we double the number of cases, we double chi square; if we triple them we triple chi square. Suppose the original number of cases is multiplied by a factor k. Then since proportions in the cells remain unchanged, each new observed frequency will be exactly k times the old one, and similarly for the expected frequencies. The new chi square can thus be expressed as

$$(\chi^2)' = \sum \frac{(kf_o - kf_e)^2}{kf_e} = \sum \frac{k^2(f_o - f_e)^2}{kf_e} = k \sum \frac{(f_o - f_e)^2}{f_e}$$

Thus the value of the new chi square is exactly k times that of the original one.

The implications of this fact can be brought out by means of another illustration. Suppose we obtain the following results when we relate sex differences to tolerance of deviant behavior:

Tolerance	Males	Females
High	26	24
Low	24	26

In this case chi square is 0.16, and we would rightly report that the relationship is not a significant one. Suppose, however, that the survey had been a very ambitious one and that data had been collected on 10,000 cases with the following results:

Tolerance	Males	Females
High	2,600	2,400
Low	2,400	2,600

Chi square is now 16.0, a value which is highly significant statistically. Had we expressed the results in terms of percentages, however, they would have looked much less interesting. If we said that 52 per cent of the males were highly tolerant whereas "only" 48 per cent of the females were in this category, we would rightly be criticised for emphasizing differences which seemed trivial from the standpoint of theoretical or practical significance. This example illustrates a very important point. A difference may be statistically significant without being significant in any other sense. In the instance where 10,000 cases were selected, we can be very sure that there is some slight relationship. Had we used census data with an N of some 180 million we probably could have established statistical significance between any two variables we happened to choose! We can see that when a sample is small it requires a much more striking relationship in order to obtain significance. Therefore, with small samples significance tests are far more important. In such cases we may be saying quite a bit when we can establish significance. The significance level depends on two factors: the strength or degree of relationship and the size of the samples. Significance can be obtained with a very strong relationship and very small samples or with a very weak relationship and large samples. In most social research our primary interest is not so much in finding variables that are interrelated but in locating the important relationships. Although it should be emphasized that not all strong relationships are important (e.g., the relationship between age of husband and age of wife), in order for a relationship to be of some practical importance it must be at least moderately strong. Having first established the existence of a relationship, the researcher should always ask himself, "How strong is it?"

How is strength of relationship measured, then? We are seeking a descriptive measure which can help us summarize the relationship in such a manner that we can compare several relationships and reach a conclusion as to which is the strongest. Ideally, we would also like to have some kind of operational interpretation for the measure which has intuitive appeal. By convention, statisticians have adopted the custom of designing measures which have unity as an upper limit and either zero or −1.0 as a lower limit. Most measures can attain their limit of 1.0 (or

−1.0) only when the relationship is a perfect one, and they take on the value zero when there is no relationship at all between the variables, i.e., they are independent. Several measures which can be used with contingency tables will presently be discussed and their properties evaluated.

Before taking up various measures of association which can be used with contingency tables, we should at least mention the rather simple and obvious procedure of reporting differences in terms of percentages. It is certainly possible to get a very good indication of the degree of relationship between two dichotomized variables by comparing percentages. For example, if 60 per cent of the males sampled are classed as highly tolerant whereas only 30 per cent of the females are so categorized, there is a 30 per cent difference between the two groups. Why not use such a figure as a measure of strength of relationship? If, for example, we compare middle- and lower-class individuals with respect to tolerance, obtaining only a 20 per cent difference, we can then claim a stronger relationship between sex and tolerance than between class and tolerance.

In the special case of the 2×2 table percentages can easily be compared in such a manner, and the widespread familiarity with percentages as contrasted with other types of measures would certainly argue for such comparisons of percentages. But what about the general $r \times c$ table? Here the use of percentages may make it difficult for the reader to see at a glance how strong the relationship may be. For example, suppose three social classes were used with the following results: upper class, 70 per cent highly tolerant; middle class, 50 per cent highly tolerant; and lower class, 30 per cent highly tolerant. We now have a spread of 40 per cent between the upper and lower classes, a difference which is numerically larger than that between males and females. On the other hand, we would ordinarily expect a larger difference when only the extremes are used. Suppose there had been five classes. What kind of percentage differences would we now expect, and how would we compare the results with those of a 2×2 table? To introduce a further complication, suppose we had used four categories of tolerance. Quite obviously, it becomes difficult to make comparisons from one table to the next. We need a single summarizing measure which will have the same upper and lower limits regardless of the number of cells.

Traditional Measures Based on Chi Square. It has already been noted that chi square is directly proportional to N. We can make use of this fact to construct several measures of association. In the case of the two contingency tables

30	20	50		60	40	100
20	30	50	and	40	60	100
50	50	100		100	100	200

we desire a measure which would have the same value for each table since when we express results in terms of percentages they are the same in both cases. In other words, we would probably say that the degrees or strengths of relationship in the two sets of data are identical, and that the only difference is in the size of the samples. Although the value of chi square for the second table is double that of the first, we notice that if chi square is in each instance divided by the total number of cases the results are identical. This suggests that χ^2/N or some multiple of this expression would give us one of the properties we desire in our measure, that it yield the same result when the proportions in comparable cells are identical.

Notice that the value of χ^2/N, or ϕ^2 as it is commonly denoted, is 0 when there is absolutely no relationship between the two variables. It turns out that in the case of 2 × 2 (or 2 × k) tables, ϕ^2 also has an upper limit of unity when the relationship between the two variables is perfect. Suppose we had obtained the following table:

50	0	50
0	50	50
50	50	100

You can easily verify that in this case chi square is 100 and therefore ϕ^2 is $100/100$ or 1.0. It will always be the case that when two diagonally opposite cells are both empty the value of chi square in a 2 × 2 table will be N, and therefore ϕ^2 will be unity. Obviously, the relationship in the above example is as perfect as it could possibly be. If sex were being related to tolerance we could then say that all males are highly tolerant and all females intolerant. In terminology with which we shall shortly become more familiar, we can say that all of the variation in tolerance is explained by or associated with sex.[5]

In the general r × c table, ϕ^2 can attain a value considerably larger than unity. Therefore, several other measures have been developed which are also simple functions of χ^2/N but which also have unity as their upper limits. The first of these measures, referred to as Tschuprow's T, is fairly commonly used in the literature and is defined as

$$T^2 = \frac{\chi^2}{N\sqrt{(r-1)(c-1)}} = \frac{\phi^2}{\sqrt{(r-1)(c-1)}}$$

Although the upper limit of T is unity, this limit can be attained only when the numbers of rows and columns are equal. In other words, T must always be less than one in a 2 × 3 or 3 × 5 table. If there are considerably more rows than columns (or vice versa) the upper limit of T

[5] This assumes, of course, that tolerance is taken as a dichotomized variable.

may be well below unity. To correct for this fact, we can always divide the obtained value of T by the maximum T possible for given numbers of rows and columns. Since more satisfactory measures are available, however, there is no need to discuss such a correction procedure.

There is another measure, introduced by Cramér and which we shall denote by V, defined as follows

$$V^2 = \frac{\chi^2}{N \operatorname{Min}(r-1, c-1)} = \frac{\phi^2}{\operatorname{Min}(r-1, c-1)}$$

where $\operatorname{Min}(r-1, c-1)$ refers to either $r-1$ or $c-1$, whichever is the smaller (minimum value of $r-1$ and $c-1$). Although V is not commonly used in the social science literature, it seems to be preferable to T in that it can attain unity even when the numbers of rows and columns are not equal. As can easily be verified, V and T are equivalent whenever $r = c$. Otherwise, V will always be somewhat larger than T. Of course both measures become equivalent to ϕ in the 2×2 case. Also, in the $2 \times k$ case we see that V and ϕ will be identical.

Still another measure of association based on chi square is Pearson's contingency coefficient C which is given by

$$C = \sqrt{\frac{\chi^2}{\chi^2 + N}}$$

Like the other measures, C becomes 0 when the variables are independent. The upper limit of C, however, depends on the number of rows and columns. In the 2×2 case the upper limit of C^2 becomes $N/(N + N)$ since χ^2 can reach a maximum value of N. Therefore, the upper limit of C is .707. Although the upper limit increases as the number of rows and columns increases, this upper limit is always less than one. For this reason, C is somewhat more difficult to interpret than the other measures unless a correction is introduced by dividing by the maximum value of C for the particular numbers of rows and columns. In the case of the 2×2 table, for example, the obtained C should be divided by .707.

The above measures of strength of relationship are all based on chi square. Since the value of chi square would ordinarily have been previously calculated in order to test for significance, all of these measures require very little additional computation. On the other hand, there is no particular reason why a measure of association has to be based on the comparable test statistic. In fact it can be shown that all measures based on chi square are somewhat arbitrary in nature, and their interpretations leave a lot to be desired. For example, they all give greater weight to those columns or rows having the smallest marginals rather than to those with the largest marginals [1]. Since both T and C are frequently found in the literature, however, you should be familiar with their properties.

~~Kendall's~~ *YULES* Q. Another commonly used measure is ~~Kendall's~~ *yules* Q. This measure can only be used in a 2 × 2 table and is defined as

$$Q = \frac{ad - bc}{ad + bc}$$

where *a, b, c*, and *d* refer to the cell frequencies. Notice that the numerator, when squared and multiplied by N, is the numerator in the expression for chi square. Like the other measures, Q disappears when the variables are independent, i.e., when diagonal products ad and bc are equal. Unlike ϕ^2, however, Q attains its limits of ± 1.0 whenever any *one* of the cells is zero. In order to understand the nature of the circumstances under which Q can be unity whereas ϕ^2 is less than this value, let us take the following examples:

30	0	30		40	0	40
20	50	70		10	50	60
50	50	100		50	50	100

Although Q takes on the value of unity in both of the above tables, the values of ϕ^2 are .429 and .667 respectively. In both cases it would be impossible to have *two* diagonally opposite cells vanish because of the nature of the marginal totals. Therefore ϕ^2 can take on the value 1 only when certain conditions hold for the marginals. In the 2 × 2 table the marginals for the first variable have to be identical with those of the second.[6] The greater the discrepancy between row and column marginals, the less the upper limit of ϕ^2.

*The question now arises as to whether or not we wish to consider a relationship "perfect" when only one of the cells vanishes. The answer to this question would seem to depend, among other things, upon how the categories of the two variables were formed. Usually it is possible to conceptualize a problem in terms of an independent and a dependent variable. It would then seem reasonable to argue that in order for a relationship to be perfect, the marginals for the dependent variable should naturally "fit" those of the independent variable. Suppose, for example, that there were 60 Protestants and only 40 Catholics and Jews. Then for a perfect relationship we would expect all 60 Protestants to vote Republican and all 40 of the others to vote Democratic. The marginals would

[6] This does not mean that marginals have to involve a 50-50 split. It means that if one marginal is split 70-30 the other must also be split 70-30. Corrections for unequal marginals are also possible, but, as implied in the discussion which follows, one should be cautious in using such corrections.

then be the same for both variables and both ϕ^2 and Q would be unity. On the other hand, if half of the sample voted Republican and half Democrat, then even though all of the Republican votes came from the Protestants, we would not call the relationship a perfect one since 10 of the Protestants must have voted Democratic.   In this case, the marginals for the dependent variable would not coincide with those of the independent variable and ϕ^2 would be less than unity.   Therefore ϕ^2 would seem the more appropriate measure in such an instance since Q would take on the value unity in spite of the imperfect relationship between the two variables.

*Occasionally it so happens that the marginals of the dependent variable are fixed by the method used in categorizing.   If, for example, the dependent variable were actually continuous but had been dichotomized at the median, then the two sets of marginals could not possibly be identical unless the marginals for the independent variables were also split 50-50.   For example, had religious preference been related to political conservatism scores dichotomized at the median, then ϕ^2 could not attain unity (assuming the same religious split as above).   In such a case Q might be a more appropriate measure since it can take into consideration the fact that the marginals for the dependent variable have been completely fixed by the method of research.

Goodman and Kruskal's Tau.   A number of other measures of association which can be used with contingency tables have been presented by Goodman and Kruskal [2].   Most of these measures, only one of which will be discussed in this text, involve what have been referred to as probabilistic interpretations.   Since they have an intuitive meaning enabling one to interpret values intermediate between zero and one, these measures would seem to be superior to those based on chi square.

In order to illustrate one of these measures τ_b, let us take a numerical example.   We shall refer to the nominal scales being related as A and B, and we shall take B as the dependent variable.

	B_1	B_2	B_3	Total
A_1	300	600	300	1,200
A_2	600	100	100	800
Total	900	700	400	2,000

Now let us suppose that we are given a sample (or population) of 2,000 persons and are asked to place them in one of the three categories B_1, B_2, or B_3 in such a manner that we are to end up with exactly 900 cases in B_1, 700 in B_2, and 400 in B_3.   Suppose, first, that we know nothing about the individuals that will aid us in this task.   If the individuals are given to us in a completely random order, we can very easily calculate the number of errors we can expect to make in assigning individuals to one of the three categories.[7]

Since we shall be assigning 900 individuals to B_1, whereas 1,100 out of every 2,000 actually do not belong in this class, we can expect to make $900(1,100/2,000)$ or 495 errors in the long run. Similarly, we must assign 700 individuals to B_2 whereas 1,300 out of 2,000 do not belong there. Therefore we can expect to make $700(1,300/2,000)$ or 455 errors in putting individuals into B_2. In other words, of the 700 we place in this category we can expect that only $700 - 455$ or 245 will be placed correctly. Of course we do not expect to make exactly 455 errors, but this is the figure we would get if we averaged out our errors in the long run. Finally, we would expect to make $400(1,600/2,000)$ or 320 errors in assigning individuals to B_3. Notice that although we make fewer assignments to this smaller category, our risk of error is greater than for the other two categories since only 20 per cent of the individuals actually belong in this class. Therefore, in total, we would expect to make

$$495 + 455 + 320 = 1,270$$

errors in placing these 2,000 individuals. Our batting average would not be very good.

Now suppose we are given some additional information about each individual; we are told whether he is in A_1 or A_2. We now ask ourselves whether knowing the A class will help us reduce the number of errors made in assigning the individuals to B categories. If the variables A and B are independent, we know that knowledge of A will not help us predict B. In this case, then, we would expect to make just as many errors as when we did not use the information about the A class. On the other hand, if the relationship between A and B were perfect, we would be able to predict B with complete accuracy if we knew A. The measure we shall develop tells us the proportional reduction in errors when A is known.

Let us see how we calculate the number of expected errors when A is known. If we are given the fact that the individual belongs in A_1 we can use the top row of figures. We now must place exactly 300 of these 1,200 individuals in B_1, the remaining 600 in B_1 coming from A_2. Since 900 out of the 1,200 individuals in A_1 actually do not belong in B_1, we can expect to make $300(900/1,200)$ or 225 errors. Similarly, out of the 600

---

[7] Notice that the expected number of errors will actually be minimized if we are allowed to place *all* the individuals in B_1, the largest of the B categories, rather than restricting ourselves to 900 cases in this category. Why? A measure λ_b, based on the assignment of all individuals to the largest B category, can be computed in a manner similar to τ_b. See [2] and also Exercise 5, Chap. 9.

individuals in A_1 we place in B_2 we can expect to make 300 errors, and the expected number of errors for B_3 will be 225. We now take the 800 individuals in A_2 and assign 600 to B_1 and 100 each to the remaining two categories. In so doing, we can expect to make 150, 87.5, and 87.5 errors respectively. Adding these quantities for both A_1 and A_2 we see that we can expect to make a total of 1,075 errors when A is known.

We define the measure τ_b to be the proportional reduction of errors. Thus

$$\tau_b = \frac{\text{no. of errors not knowing } A - \text{no. of errors knowing } A}{\text{no. of errors not knowing } A}$$

$$\tau_b = \frac{1,270 - 1,075}{1,270} = \frac{195}{1,270} = .154$$

In other words, we have saved ourselves 195 errors out of an expected number of 1,270 and have reduced our errors by 15.4 per cent. If τ_b had turned out to be .50 we could thus give it the very simple interpretation that knowledge of A would cut the number of errors in half; a value of .75 would mean reducing the number of errors to one-fourth of the original number, and so forth. No such simple interpretation is possible in the case of ϕ^2 (see [1]). Had we wished to predict A classes from B classes, we would denote the comparable measure as τ_a. τ_a and τ_b will not in general have the same numerical values. Why?

15.4. Controlling for Other Variables

Discussions of tests of significance and measures of association have to this point involved only two variables at a time. In most practical problems, however, it is necessary to control for one or more additional variables which may be either obscuring a relationship or creating a spurious one. Although it is often true that generalizations in the social sciences are stated in terms of only two variables, it is practically always implicitly recognized that relevant variables are assumed to be controlled. Frequently the phrase "other things being equal" is used to emphasize this fact. Ideally, an hypothesis should be stated in such a manner that it is clearly understood what variables are to be controlled. As a discipline advances toward maturity, generalizations become qualified so as to indicate the exact conditions under which they can be expected to hold true. In the initial stages of its development, however, it is frequently impossible to know what the relevant variables are which need to be controlled. For this reason, propositions are not usually stated in the social sciences in such a manner as to suggest what variables are to be controlled. Nevertheless, you should develop the habit of always looking for possible control variables even though you may not have been explicitly told to do so.

As we shall see later, there are several possible methods of controlling statistically. The method discussed in this chapter is perhaps the most straightforward and the one most directly analogous to the laboratory experiment in which control variables are actually physically held constant. In this respect it is far superior to the methods used in partial correlation or analysis of covariance which will be discussed in subsequent chapters. Its major shortcoming, however, is that it requires a much larger number of cases.

In laboratory experiments a control variable is held at a constant value while other variables are interrelated. Thus, the temperature may be held at 70°F while the relationship between pressure and volume is investigated. If a relationship is then found between the latter variables, it may be possible to state much more precisely its nature than if temperature were not controlled. But the scientist would not be justified in stating a generalization as if it always applied unless he were to find that exactly the same relationship actually held for all temperatures. He would undoubtedly perform a series of experiments, each at a slightly different temperature. It is quite likely that he would find the relationship to hold only within a certain range of temperatures. He would then have to qualify his generalization to read, "The relationship between pressure and volume is such and such *provided* the temperature is between – 100 and 600° Fahrenheit." Hopefully, he might find a correction factor which would enable him to restate his proposition in a more general form which would apply to a greater range of temperatures. Exactly the same kind of argument would apply to additional control variables. Simultaneous controls could be made for several variables by holding each at a fixed value. Further experiments could then be performed with different *combinations* of values for control variables. With several controls acting simultaneously, a much larger number of replications would be required.

Basically, we can use the same type of controlling in contingency problems or any of the other types of problems discussed in previous chapters. We can physically hold constant variables such as sex or social class while investigating the relationship between religious preference and voting behavior. In order to hold sex constant, for example, we can look only at the male voter. If the relationship is found to hold for males and also separately for females, then we can say that it generally holds controlling for sex since we have examined both categories of the sex variable. Quite possibly, however, the relationship might hold for males but not for females. In this case the generalization would have to be qualified, and attention could be turned to the question of why it should hold for one sex but not the other.   It can be seen that controlling for relevant variables not only provides a more rigorous test of an hypothesis, but it may also lead to additional insights if the relationship is found to differ from one category of the control variable to the next.

Sometimes it may be desirable to control for several variables simultaneously.   Because of a shortage of cases it is frequently necessary to control for relevant variables one at a time, but a certain amount of information may be lost in this manner.   For example, suppose that sex were ignored and a control introduced for the voter's social class.   We would then look separately at each social class to see whether or not the relationship always held.   In contrast to this procedure, we might have

Table 15.4. Master Table for Interrelating Four Variables

Intelli-gence	Effort	High grades		Low grades		Totals
		Middle class	Lower class	Middle class	Lower class	
High	High	60	40	20	16	136
	Low	40	18	24	38	120
Low	High	40	6	24	32	102
	Low	24	2	12	54	92
Totals		164	66	80	140	450

controlled simultaneously for class and sex by taking all possible combinations of the control variables (e.g., male lower class, female lower class, male middle class, etc.) and studying the relationship within each combination of control categories.   Conceivably, the relationship might hold for every combination except that of the female lower-class voter.   If this were the case we would be led to look for any peculiarities of this particular subgroup.

Let us take another concrete example in order to illustrate the process. Suppose we have the following data on school children: their class background, IQ's, school grades, and how hard each child works.   It will be helpful to summarize the data in terms of a master table as in Table 15.4.

Suppose we suspect a middle-class bias on the part of teachers resulting in a tendency to give high grades to middle-class children regardless of ability or effort but to give high grades to lower-class children only when there is evidence of both high ability and high effort.   We would then predict that grades should generally be higher for middle-class children, controlling for both ability and effort, except possibly in the case of children with high ability and effort.   We would also predict that the relationships between grades and both ability and effort would be stronger in the lower class than the middle. In other words, if middle-class children always receive high grades there should be no relationship (or a very slight one) within this class between grades and either effort or ability. Let us concentrate on the relationship between grades and ability and investigate whether or not this relationship is stronger for the lower class. In this case, we shall want to control for effort. In each class there will be both high- and low-effort students. Therefore we can construct four contingency tables as in Table 15.5.

Table 15.5. Series of Contingency Tables Relating Two Variables, with Two Simultaneous Controls

IQ	High effort		Low effort	
	High grades	Low grades	High grades	Low grades
Middle class				
High	60	20	40	24
Low	40	24	24	12
Lower class				
High	40	16	18	38
Low	6	32	2	54

Table 15.6

Class	Effort	Chi square	Significance level	ϕ
Middle	High	2.565	Not significant	.133
	Low	.188	Not significant	.043
Lower	High	28.064	$p < .001$	.546
	Low	15.582	$p < .001$	.373

We now compare the two classes with respect to the existence and strength of relationship, looking separately at high- and low-effort students. The direction of relationship can also be noted in each case by simply computing percentages or by comparing the diagonal products. Computing chi square and ϕ for each table, we get the results shown in Table 15.6. Thus we see that relationships for middle-class children are nonsignificant, but for lower-class children in both effort categories there is a moderately strong positive relationship between ability and grades. We also notice that the relationship is somewhat stronger in the case of the hard-working students.

You have undoubtedly noticed the marked effect that controlling has on the number of cases appearing in each cell. Instead of having only four cells, we have four times this number when we use two dichotomized control variables. Had a third simultaneous control, say sex, been added there would have been 32 cells instead of 16. Had any of the variables involved more than two categories the number of cells would have been further multiplied. Therefore, although simultaneous controls can theoretically be added indefinitely, the number of cases must be very large in order to control by this method. An alternative would simply be to restrict the nature of the population and to generalize only to middle-class males with a college education or some comparable subgroup. A much larger sample of this particular subgroup could then be selected. Usually if simultaneous controlling is to be used, it becomes necessary to select those two or three controls which look most promising. It is, of course, possible to make use of Fisher's exact test when the number of cases in each cell becomes very small, but it should be remembered that it will then be necessary to have a very high degree of relationship in order to obtain significance. Because of this attenuation of cases, the mere fact that a relationship becomes nonsignificant when controls are introduced is not sufficient evidence that the control variable is having an effect. Measures of degree of relationship should always be computed and compared.

*It is sometimes both possible and desirable to pool the separate chi-square tests into a single over-all test. Let us suppose that there are four separate tables as was the case for the data of Table 15.5. In this latter example, only two of the chi squares turned out to be significant and only two of the ϕ's were moderately large. In such a case, it would hardly make sense to pool the results of all four tables since the relationship between IQ and grades was obviously quite different in the two classes. But what if all the ϕ's had been roughly the same size and the direction of the relationship between IQ and grades the same for all tables? We then might reason that basically the same relationship was holding up in all four tables, and it would make sense to ask what would happen if we could pool these results.

*Fortunately, the chi-square statistic has an important property. If a number of chi squares have been computed for independent data (e.g., on completely different sets of people), then we may add the values of chi square and also the degrees of freedom, evaluating the result in the familiar manner. For example, suppose that for four 2×2 tables the resulting chi squares were 2.1, 3.3, 2.7, and 2.9. The sum of these values is 11.0, and the sum of the degrees of freedom is 4. From the table we see that a chi square of 11.0 with 4 degrees of freedom is significant at the .05 level. Thus, although none of the separate chi squares were significant, we were able to take advantage of the fact that it makes theoretical sense to pool the results. In effect, we are saying that if a relationship comes out in the same direction each time but the probabilities of the separate results are each greater than .05, we still may ask ourselves how likely such a combination of outcomes would be if there were no relationships in any of the four tables.

*Notice that the results of such a pooling operation may very well differ from the total relationship between the two variables *without any controls*. We are essentially getting an *average* relationship *within* categories of the control variable(s) when we pool results. Had we simply ignored the control variable(s), the effects of such controls would have been completely obscured. By pooling we are making a single chi-square test of the over-all relationship between two variables, controlling for the additional variables.

*Similarly, we might want to obtain a single measure of association by computing a weighted average of the measures based on the four separate tables. One method which has been suggested for doing this is to use weights which are proportional to the number of cases in each table. Thus we might multiply each r_b by the number of cases in the table, add the results, and finally divide by the total number of cases in all four tables. We would then end up with a single test of significance and a single measure of association representing an average of the results of all four tables.

*In substituting a single measure and test for four separate measures and tests we run into the usual problems involved whenever summarizing statistics are used. We boil down our data so as to obtain fewer statistics. On the other hand, we run the risk of distorting our results. For example, if one of the four tables produced a large chi square and a very high degree of relationship as compared with the rest, then combining the results, thereby obscuring this fact, may prove highly misleading. As always, statistical manipulations can never be a substitute for common sense.

Some of the ideas discussed in the present section, and especially the notion of pooling the results of separate tables, are undoubtedly new and somewhat confusing at this point. It will therefore be helpful to review this section after you have been exposed to some of the material in Chaps. 16 to 20. By that time, several different types of control procedures will have been discussed and compared.

EXERCISES

1. Compute chi square for the data of Exercise 5, Chap. 9. Taking occupational aspirations as the dependent variable B, what is the value of τ_b? How does the value of τ_b compare with that of the measure you computed in part (d) of Exercise 5?

2. In Exercise 3 of Chap. 14 you made use of the Smirnov test. Taking these same data, what conclusion do you reach using the chi-square test? For these particular data, which test would you prefer? Why? Compute ϕ, T, V, C, and τ_b.

*3. The chi-square test can generally be used to compare observed and theoretical frequencies. In particular, it can be used to test the null hypothesis that sample data have been drawn randomly from a normal population. The observed frequencies are compared with those which would be expected if the distribution were actually normal, with the same mean and standard deviation as computed from the sample data. After obtaining the values of $\bar{X}$ and s, you may use the true limits and the normal table to give the expected frequencies within each interval. The degrees of freedom will be $k - 3$, where k represents the number of intervals. One degree of freedom will be lost since the total of the expected frequencies must be N; the remaining two degrees of freedom which have been lost are due to the necessity of using $\bar{X}$ and s as estimates of the actual parameters μ and σ. With these facts in mind, test to see whether or not the following data depart significantly from normality.

Interval	Frequency
0.0– 9.9	7
10.0–19.9	24
20.0–29.9	43
30.0–39.9	56
40.0–49.9	38
50.0–59.9	27
60.0–69.9	13
	208

4. In a recent study, H. L. Wilensky [6] found a general relationship between union activity and both political orientation and voting intentions, controlling for socio-economic status. Data for 15 Negro members with respect to voting intentions tended to support these general findings. Seven of the eight Negroes who were inactive members of the union did not follow the "union line" in their 1948 voting behavior. Of the seven members who were really active in the union, five voted as suggested by the union. Test for the significance of a relationship using (a) Fisher's exact test with direction predicted, (b) Fisher's exact test with no direction predicted, and (c) chi square corrected for continuity with no direction predicted. Compare the results of (b) and (c).

5. Make use of the data given below to obtain information as to the accuracy of statements (a), (b), and (c). Where appropriate, compute measures of the degree of relationship and control for relevant variables.

   a. Females are less prejudiced than males.
   b. The degree of relationship between religion and prejudice toward Negroes will depend on the social class of the "prejudiced" person.
   c. The reason that Jewish persons appear in the table to be less prejudiced than non-Jews is due to the high percentage of women and upper-class persons in the Jewish sample.

Religion	Sex	Amount of prejudice toward Negroes				Totals
		High		Low		
		Upper class	Lower class	Upper class	Lower class	
Non-Jew	Male	14	30	15	16	75
	Female	8	13	9	7	37
Jewish	Male	13	7	22	15	57
	Female	18	9	33	21	81
Total						250

REFERENCES

1. Blalock, H. M.: "Probabilistic Interpretations for the Mean Square Contingency," *Journal of the American Statistical Association*, vol. 53, pp. 102–105, 1958.

2. Goodman, L. A., and W. H. Kruskal: "Measures of Association for Cross Classifications," *Journal of the American Statistical Association*, vol. 49, pp. 732–764, 1954.

3. Hagood, M. J., and D. O. Price: *Statistics for Sociologists*, Henry Holt and Company, Inc., New York, 1952, chap. 21.

4. McCarthy, P. J.: *Introduction to Statistical Reasoning*, McGraw-Hill Book Company, Inc., New York, 1957, chap. 11.

5. Siegel, S.: *Nonparametric Statistics for the Behavioral Sciences*, McGraw-Hill Book Company, Inc., New York, 1956, pp. 96–111.

6. Wilensky, H. L.: "The Labor Vote: A Local Union's Impact on the Political Conduct of its Members," *Social Forces*, vol. 35, pp. 111–120, 1956.

7. Zelditch, M.: *A Basic Course in Sociological Statistics*, Henry Holt and Company, Inc., New York, 1959, chaps. 7 and 10.

Chapter 16

ANALYSIS OF VARIANCE

In Chap. 13 we compared two samples by testing for the significance of the difference between means or proportions. Such tests were capable of handling situations in which one of the two variables being interrelated was a dichotomized nominal scale. In the last chapter we saw how more than two samples could be compared by means of the chi-square test. In the present chapter we shall take up a very important kind of test, analysis of variance, which can be used to test for differences among the means of more than two samples. Analysis of variance thus represents an extension of the difference-of-means test and can generally be used whenever we are testing for a relationship between a nominal (or higher order) scale and an interval scale. We shall also see that under certain circumstances analysis-of-variance tests can be extended to situations in which there is a single interval scale and two or more nominal scales. An analogous nonparametric test will also be considered, as will several measures of degree of association.

16.1. Simple Analysis of Variance

Although analysis of variance can be considered as an extension or generalization of the difference-of-means test, it involves some basically new principles which will require a fairly lengthy explanation. For this reason a brief overview may be helpful so that you will not find yourself becoming lost in the details. The assumptions for analysis of variance are basically the same as required for the difference-of-means test, but the test itself is very different. We shall have to assume normality, independent random samples, and equal population standard deviations, and the null hypothesis will be that population means are equal. The test itself, however, involves working directly with variances rather than means and standard errors.

Suppose the data in Table 16.1 represent murder rates for each of three types of cities: those which are primarily industrial, trade, or political

centers.   We can compute separate means for each of the three categories
or samples, and we can also obtain a grand mean by ignoring the classes
and averaging all scores.   In this example all samples are of the same
size, but this need not always be the case.

Since it is being assumed that all populations have the same standard
deviation, we can form two independent estimates of the common
variance σ^2. One of these estimates will be directly analogous to the
pooled estimate used in the difference-of-means test.   This estimate will

Table 16.1. Data for Analysis of Variance

	Murder rates			Total
	Industrial community	Trade community	Political community	
	4.3	5.1	12.5	
	2.8	6.2	3.1	
	12.3	1.8	1.6	
	16.3	9.5	6.2	
	5.9	4.1	3.8	
	7.7	3.6	7.1	
	9.1	11.2	11.4	
	10.2	3.3	1.9	
Sums	68.6	44.8	47.6	161.0
Means	8.58	5.60	5.95	6.71
No. of cases	8	8	8	24

be a weighted average of the variances *within* each of the separate samples and will always be unbiased even if the sample means differ considerably among themselves.   This is true because each sample variance
will be computed separately and will involve only the deviations from
the mean of that particular sample.

The second estimate of the common variance involves the variance
of the separate sample means treated as individual scores.   In this case,
the deviations of the sample means about the grand mean will be used in
estimating σ^2.   For the data of Table 16.1 we would obtain the variation
of the three sample means 8.58, 5.60, and 5.95 about the total mean of
6.71.   This estimate of σ^2 will be unbiased only if the population means
are in fact equal.   If the population means are equal the sample means
can be expected to differ from one another according to the central-limit
theorem, and we can make use of this law and the actual differences
among sample means to estimate the true variance.   On the other hand,
if the population means are actually different we expect that the sample
means will differ from one another more than would be the case if the
population means were the same.   Therefore, if the null hypothesis is

false the second estimate of σ^2 will ordinarily be too large, and it will be a biased estimate.

The test used in analysis of variance involves a comparison of the two separate estimates of the population variance. Instead of taking the difference between the two estimates, however, we take the *ratio* of the second estimate to the first. If the null hypothesis is correct, then both estimates will be unbiased and the ratio should be approximately unity. If the population means actually differ, however, the second estimate will ordinarily be larger than the first and the ratio greater than unity. Since sampling fluctuations are always a factor, we have to ask ourselves how large a ratio we are willing to tolerate before we become suspicious of the null hypothesis. Fortunately, the ratio of the two estimates F has a known sampling distribution, provided the two estimates of variance are actually independent of each other, and therefore a fairly simple test can be made. This, in essence, is what we do in an analysis-of-variance test. Now let us take a more detailed look at the procedure involved.

Breaking Total Variation into Component Parts. Although our ultimate goal is the formation of two independent estimates of the variance, it will be necessary to introduce a new concept in order to explain how these estimates are obtained. Let us use the term *variation* (as distinct from variance) to refer to the sum of the squared deviations from the mean. The total variation about the grand mean for all samples would be $\sum_{i=1}^{N} (X_i - \bar{X})^2$. The term variation thus will refer to a sum of squares, ignoring the number of cases involved. We shall now proceed to break this total variation into two component parts, each of which will be used in the computation of the two estimates.

Let us represent our data symbolically as in Table 16.2. The individual scores are represented by $X_{11}, X_{21}, \ldots, X_{ij}$, the sample means by $\bar{X}_{\cdot 1}, \bar{X}_{\cdot 2}, \ldots, \bar{X}_{\cdot k}$, and the grand mean by $\bar{X}_{\cdots}$ The dots are used in the subscripts in order to distinguish column means from row means which will be used when we add a second nominal scale. The general symbol X_{ij} represents the score of the ith individual in the jth column. The sum $\sum_{i=1}^{N_1} X_{i1}$ indicates that the N_1 scores in the first column have been summed, and similarly for the remaining columns.[1]

---

[1] Since there are two subscripts, i and j, it is important to distinguish between the symbols $\sum_i$ and $\sum_j$. In the latter case, the j values would be summed for any particular (fixed) i, and we would thus obtain the sum of scores in the ith *row*.

Now we perform some simple algebra.   We can write

$$X_{ij} - \bar{X}.. = (X_{ij} - \bar{X}_{.j}) + (\bar{X}_{.j} - \bar{X}..)$$

or

$$\left(\begin{array}{c}\text{Individual}\\ \text{score}\end{array} - \begin{array}{c}\text{grand}\\ \text{mean}\end{array}\right) = \left(\begin{array}{c}\text{individual}\\ \text{score}\end{array} - \begin{array}{c}\text{category}\\ \text{mean}\end{array}\right)$$
$$+ \left(\begin{array}{c}\text{category}\\ \text{mean}\end{array} - \begin{array}{c}\text{grand}\\ \text{mean}\end{array}\right)$$

having subtracted $\bar{X}_{.j}$ (the mean of the jth column) from X_{ij} and then added it back in immediately.   We have therefore expressed the difference between a single individual's score and the grand mean as a sum of

Table 16.2. Symbolic Representation of Data for Analysis of Variance

	Categories				Total
	A_1	A_2	$\cdots$	A_k	
Scores	X_{11} X_{21} X_{31}	X_{12} X_{22} X_{32}	$\cdots$ $\cdots$ $\cdots$	X_{1k} X_{2k} X_{3k}	
	$X_{N_1 1}$	$X_{N_2 2}$	$\cdots$	$X_{N_k k}$	
Sums	$\sum_{i=1}^{N_1} X_{i1}$	$\sum_{i=1}^{N_2} X_{i2}$	$\cdots$	$\sum_{i=1}^{N_k} X_{ik}$	$\sum_i \sum_j X_{ij}$
Means	$\bar{X}_{.1}$	$\bar{X}_{.2}$	$\cdots$	$\bar{X}_{.k}$	$\bar{X}..$
No. of cases	N_1	N_2	$\cdots$	N_k	N

two quantities: (1) the difference between his score and the mean of the category to which he belongs, and (2) the difference between the category mean and the grand mean.   In the above numerical example we can express the difference between the score of the first individual in the first category and the grand mean as

$$4.3 - 6.71 = (4.3 - 8.58) + (8.58 - 6.71)$$
or
$$-2.41 = -4.28 + 1.87$$

Squaring both sides of the equation we obtain

$$(X_{ij} - \bar{X}..)^2 = (X_{ij} - \bar{X}_{.j})^2 + 2(X_{ij} - \bar{X}_{.j})(\bar{X}_{.j} - \bar{X}..) + (\bar{X}_{.j} - \bar{X}..)^2$$

By summing both sides we obtain the sum of the squared deviations for all individuals. We can first sum down each column and then add the resulting figures for each category. When we do this the middle term becomes zero. In order to see why this is the case, notice that in summing down any particular column the value of j will be constant. Therefore for the jth column the factor $(\bar{X}_{\cdot j} - \bar{X}_{\cdot\cdot})$ will be constant and can be taken outside of the summation. Thus for the sum of the scores in the jth column the middle term becomes

$$2(\bar{X}_{\cdot j} - \bar{X}_{\cdot\cdot}) \sum_i (X_{ij} - \bar{X}_{\cdot j})$$

But since for every column the deviations about the column mean must be zero, we immediately see that the middle term must vanish for each and every column. We thus get

$$\sum_i \sum_j (X_{ij} - \bar{X}_{\cdot\cdot})^2 = \sum_i \sum_j (X_{ij} - \bar{X}_{\cdot j})^2 + \sum_i \sum_j (\bar{X}_{\cdot j} - \bar{X}_{\cdot\cdot})^2 \quad (16.1)$$

$$\text{Total sum of squares} = \frac{\text{within sum}}{\text{of squares}} + \frac{\text{between sum}}{\text{of squares}}$$

In so doing, we obtain a double summation which we write as $\sum_i \sum_j$, indicating that we have summed over both rows and columns.

We have divided the total variation into two parts. The first of these is a sum of squared deviations of the individual scores from their own category means. This is referred to as a *within* sum of squares and will be used to obtain our first estimate of the common variance σ^2. Notice that this sum of squares is obtained essentially the same way that the pooled estimate was formed in the difference-of-means test. If we write the within sum of squares as

$$\sum_{i=1}^{N_1} (X_{i1} - \bar{X}_{\cdot 1})^2 + \sum_{i=1}^{N_2} (X_{i2} - \bar{X}_{\cdot 2})^2 + \cdots + \sum_{i=1}^{N_k} (X_{ik} - \bar{X}_{\cdot k})^2$$

we see that the first term is just $N_1 s_1^2$, where deviations have been taken about the category mean, and similarly for the other terms. Therefore

$$\text{Within SS} = N_1 s_1^2 + N_2 s_2^2 + \cdots + N_k s_k^2$$

When we divide by the proper degrees of freedom, which will turn out to be $N - k$, we obtain a pooled estimate based on all k categories. The second or *between* sum of squares involves the deviations of category means from the grand mean and is therefore a measure of the variability between samples. The second estimate of the variance will be based on this between sum of squares.

The between and within sums of squares are often referred to as *explained* and *unexplained* variations respectively. It is perhaps easier to see why the within variation is referred to as being unexplained since this refers to variation which is left unaccounted for by the categorized variable. If within category A there is still some variability about the category mean, then this variability can certainly not be explained by the category. On the other hand, if the category means differ considerably among themselves a relatively large fraction of the total variation may be attributed to differences among the several categories. Thus, it is the amount of variability within the categories as compared with differences between them which determines how closely the two variables are associated. Homogeneous categories which differ considerably among themselves will explain a high proportion of the variation[2] In the extreme case, if we had completely homogeneous categories the within sum of squares would be zero and all of the variability could be attributed to the categorized variable. Thus if all industrial cities had exactly the same murder rates that differed from those of all trade centers which were also completely homogeneous, etc., then city type could be said to explain all of the variation in murder rates. Knowing the city type would enable us to predict the murder rate exactly.

In order to obtain estimates from these two separate sums of squares it is only necessary to divide by the appropriate degrees of freedom. The degrees of freedom associated with the total sum of squares is $N - 1$ since we have seen that $\hat{\sigma}^2$ is the unbiased estimate of σ^2, 1 degree of freedom having been lost through the computation of the grand mean $\bar{X}...$ Let us now look at the between sum of squares. This quantity represents the sum of squared deviations of the k sample means from the grand mean. In effect, each category mean is being treated as a single case. Therefore there are $k - 1$ degrees of freedom involved, one having been lost because of the fact that the weighted average of the $\bar{X}._j$ must be $\bar{X}...$ In the case of the within-class estimate, 1 degree of freedom will be lost in each column through the computation of the $\bar{X}._j$. Therefore, in all, there will be $N - k$ degrees of freedom associated with the within estimate. Notice that the degrees of freedom add as do the sums of squares. Thus

$$N - 1 = (N - k) + (k - 1)$$
$$\text{Total df} = \text{within df} + \text{between df}$$

---

[2] This does not imply causality, of course.

Our two estimates of the common variance thus become

$$
\text{Within estimate} = \frac{\sum_i \sum_j (X_{ij} - \bar{X}_{.j})^2}{N - k} \tag{16.2}
$$

$$
\text{Between estimate} = \frac{\sum_i \sum_j (\bar{X}_{.j} - \bar{X}_{..})^2}{k - 1} \tag{16.3}
$$

At this point it may have occurred to you that we actually have three separate estimates of the common variance if we include the usual estimate based on the total sum of squares. Why, then, not compare the latter estimate with either of the others since this total estimate may well be a better estimate than either of the other two? It will be recalled that the F test requires that the estimates compared be independent of each other. The estimate based on the total sum of squares is not independent of the others, however, and this is the reason this estimate cannot be used in the F test. Ordinarily, the within and between sums of squares are not independent of each other either. It so happens that the normal distribution has the property that these two quantities are independent in spite of the fact that the same $\bar{X}_{.j}$'s appear in both expressions. It is for this reason that we must assume all populations sampled to be normal. It will be recalled that normality was also required in the case of the t distribution because of the necessity of having the numerator independent of the denominator. As will be seen presently, the t distribution is a special case of the F distribution.

Problem. Let us make use of the above hypothetical data representing murder rates for three types of cities. We wish to find out whether there are significant differences among the means of the three types of cities.

1. *Assumptions.*

   Level of Measurement: Murder rates an interval scale.
                                     City type a nominal scale.
   Model: Independent random sampling.
             Normal populations for each city type.
             Population variances are equal.
             $(\sigma_1{}^2 = \sigma_2{}^2 = \cdots = \sigma_k{}^2 = \sigma^2)$
   Hypothesis: Population means are equal.
             $(\mu_{.1} = \mu_{.2} = \cdots = \mu_{.k})$

As was the case with difference-of-means tests, it must be assumed that samples are selected independently of each other. In other words, cities are not matched in any way. Since all three populations of city types are assumed to be normal with equal means and variances, we are in effect assuming they are identical. The three samples can therefore be conceived as being randomly drawn from the same population. The researcher is usually interested in the assumption of equal means. In this example, he probably would expect differences in murder rates among the three types of cities and would set up the null hypothesis of no differences. It should be noted that large samples are not required because of the normality assumption. Obviously if there were only one case in each category, however, there could be no variability within the categories, and therefore no test is possible.

The F test itself does not test the assumption of equal variances or *homoscedasticity* (as this assumption is referred to in technical language). In instances where sample variances seem to differ considerably among themselves, an independent test for the equality of variances may have to be made (see [1], pp. 141 to 144). If the results of such a test indicate that there are rather extreme departures from homogeneity of variance, then analysis of variance should not be used. Moderate departures from homogeneity can be tolerated, however. Such departures can often be reduced considerably by the transformation of variables.[3] If a single category is either considerably more or less homogeneous than the others, it may be advisable to omit this category from the analysis-of-variance test. Generally speaking, moderate departures from normality and equality of variances can be tolerated without necessitating the use of nonparametric alternatives (see [1], pp. 220 to 223).

2. *Significance Level and Critical Region.* Let us use the .05 level. If the null hypothesis is actually incorrect, then if we always take the ratio of the between to the within estimate we can expect to find the value of F to be larger than unity. We shall therefore use the upper tail of the F distribution as the critical region. If F turns out to be less than unity there will be no point in looking up the probability value in the table since F values of greater than unity will be needed to reject the null hypothesis. An F of less than unity would indicate a greater degree of heterogeneity than would be expected by chance. You should again keep in mind that although we shall use only one tail of the F distribution, this does not imply that we are predicting in advance which of the categories means will be the largest.

3. *Sampling Distribution.* The sampling distribution of F is given in Table J, Appendix 2. The use of the table will be described below.

[3] For example, it sometimes happens that categories having the highest means also are the least homogeneous. In such instances if one takes as his interval scale the logarithm of the original variable, the effect will be to equalize the variances. For an additional discussion of the use of logarithmic transformations, see Sec. 18.2.

4. *Computation of Test Statistic.* In order to obtain a value for F, the ratio of the between and within estimates, it will first be necessary to calculate the total, between, and within sums of squares. Since the total variation is equal to the sum of the other two, we shall only have to compute two of the values, the third being obtained from the other two. The within sum of squares, it will be remembered, involves a pooling operation. This is considerably more work than that required for the other two sums of squares, and therefore we get the within sum of squares by subtracting the between from the total sum of squares.

The computing formula for the total sum of squares is obtained in the same way as the formula for the variance [see equation (6.6)]. Thus,

$$\text{Total sum of squares} = \sum_i \sum_j (X_{ij} - \bar{X}_{..})^2 = \sum_i \sum_j X_{ij}^2 - \frac{\left(\sum_i \sum_j X_{ij}\right)^2}{N}$$

$$(16.4)$$

This is the same formula that we have used in computing standard deviations, but it is now necessary to make use of double summation notation.

The computing formula for the between variation looks considerably more formidable but on inspection is found to involve a relatively simple procedure. It is as follows:

$$\text{Between sum of squares} = \sum_j \frac{\left(\sum_i X_{ij}\right)^2}{N_j} - \frac{\left(\sum_i \sum_j X_{ij}\right)^2}{N} \qquad (16.5)$$

$$= \left[\frac{\left(\sum_i X_{i1}\right)^2}{N_1} + \frac{\left(\sum_i X_{i2}\right)^2}{N_2} + \cdots + \frac{\left(\sum_i X_{ik}\right)^2}{N_k}\right] - \frac{\left(\sum_i \sum_j X_{ij}\right)^2}{N}$$

Notice that the second term in the above expression is the same factor which was subtracted from $\sum_i \sum_j X_{ij}^2$ to obtain the total sum of squares. The first term may confuse some readers, however. Taking this expression apart we see that we first compute each column sum and then square it to obtain $\left(\sum_i X_{ij}\right)^2$. We then divide this expression by the number of cases in the column, which need not always be the same. We then have for the jth column $\left(\sum_i X_{ij}\right)^2/N_j$. Finally, we do the same thing for each column and add the results.

Computations for our numerical problem, given below, should help to make the procedures more clear. The total and between sums of squares are computed as follows:

$$\sum_i \sum_j X_{ij}{}^2 = (4.3)^2 + (2.8)^2 + \cdots + (1.9)^2 = 1,453.58$$

$$\frac{\left(\sum_i \sum_j X_{ij}\right)^2}{N} = \frac{(161.0)^2}{24} = 1,080.042$$

$$\text{Total SS} = 1,453.58 - 1,080.042 = 373.538$$

$$\text{Between SS} = \frac{(68.6)^2}{8} + \frac{(44.8)^2}{8} + \frac{(47.6)^2}{8} - 1,080.042$$

$$= 1,122.345 - 1,080.042 = 42.303$$

To obtain the within sum of squares we simply subtract the second expression from the first, getting

$$\text{Within SS} = \text{total SS} - \text{between SS}$$

or $$331.235 = 373.538 - 42.303$$

The estimates of the common variance can now be computed by dividing by the proper degrees of freedom. Finally, F is computed by dividing the between estimate by the within estimate. Computations are summarized in Table 16.3.

Table 16.3. Computations for Analysis of Variance

	Sums of squares	Degrees of freedom	Estimate of variance	F
Total	373.538	$N - 1 = 23$		
Between	42.303	$k - 1 = 2$	21.152	1.34
Within	331.235	$N - k = 21$	15.773	

5. *Decision.* In order to decide whether or not to reject the null hypothesis we must determine whether the value of F falls within the critical region. It will be noticed that three separate tables for F are given corresponding to the .05, .01, and .001 significance levels respectively. This information cannot be condensed into a single table because two degrees of freedom must be associated with each F, one for the numerator and one for the denominator. The degrees of freedom associated with the numerator, the between estimate, are found across the top of the table. Those for the denominator, the within estimate, are obtained by reading down the table. Notice that all values of F given

in the table are ≥ 1.0, indicating that the table is set up directly for one-tailed tests. In other words, the numerator is always the larger of the two estimates. In our problem we obtained an F with 2 and 21 degrees of freedom (written $F_{2,21}$) equal to 1.34. Using the table for the .05 significance level and locating the proper degrees of freedom, we find the figure 3.47. We therefore know that if the assumptions were correct, we would get a value of F equal to or larger than this value less than 5 per cent of the time. Since the value we actually obtained for F is less than 3.47, we fail to reject the null hypothesis at the .05 level. We decide that there is insufficient evidence for concluding that city types actually differ with respect to murder rates.

Comparison with Difference-of-means Test. It will be noticed that the above problem could have been handled by using difference-of-means tests involving the t distribution. Three separate pair-by-pair comparisons might have been made between industrial and trade, industrial and governmental, and trade and governmental cities. In contrast to this method, analysis of variance offers a *single test* of whether or not all three types differ significantly among themselves or, in other words, whether they all could have come from the same population. The advantage of analysis of variance is that a single test may be used in place of many. Had there been four categories, $4(3)/2$ or 6 difference-of-means tests would have been necessary. With 6 categories 15 tests would be required, whereas with 10 categories 45 would be needed. Suppose 15 tests were required and only 4 turned out to be significant. What would we conclude? It might be difficult to say.

There is an easy way out which, on the surface, appears to be a reasonable procedure. Why not simply perform a difference-of-means test on the two categories having the smallest and largest means respectively? Then if these are significantly different we can conclude that the categories do in fact differ among themselves. But we must remember that we would be selecting the single test most likely to yield significance and ignoring the rest. Since we can expect one test in twenty to yield significance at the .05 level even if all population means are identical, it is apparent that we are loading the dice in favor of rejection. In other words, the significance level actually being used is not the .05 level but perhaps the .5 or .7 level since we are essentially obtaining the probability of getting *at least one* success (significance at the .05 level) in a large number of trials.

It should not be concluded that analysis of variance is always preferable to a series of difference-of-means tests, however. The latter tests, when used cautiously, may yield considerably more information. For example, analysis of variance may lead to significant results primarily because one category is far out of line with the rest. Had this category been excluded the conclusion might have been quite different. A series of difference-of-means tests might indicate this fact more clearly. Especially if one suspects before making the test that one or more categories will differ considerably from the others, a number of one-tailed difference-of-means tests might be appropriate. It is also sometimes possible to predict the order in which category means will fall. Suppose, for example, that it had been predicted that murder rates would be highest in industrial cities and lowest in governmental. In such a case 2 one-tailed difference-of-means tests could have been used—one predicting a difference between industrial and trade cities, and the other a difference between trade and governmental. Generally, it would seem that the more knowledge we have for predicting the relative magnitudes and/or directions of differences, the more likely it is that separate difference-of-means tests will be appropriate. Analysis of variance, on the other hand, seems to be more useful on the exploratory level.

Finally, the relationship between the t and F distributions can be noted. Had there been only two types of cities an analysis-of-variance test might also have been made and the results compared with those of a difference-of-means t test. In this case, the degrees of freedom associated with the numerator of F would have been $2 - 1$ or 1. The degrees of freedom for the denominator would have been $N - 2$, the same as for t in a difference-of-means test. Also, it will be recalled that when we assume $\sigma_1 = \sigma_2$ the denominators of both t and F involve pooled estimates of the variance. It turns out that the t distribution can be considered as a special case of the F distribution. If we were to compute the values of t^2 with $N - 2$ degrees of freedom we would find that they are exactly the same as those for an F with 1 and $N - 2$ degrees of freedom. In other words, t is the square root of an F having 1 degree of freedom associated with its numerator. This means, of course, that exactly the same conclusions will be reached in the two-sample case regardless of whether we use analysis of variance or the difference-of-means test. In this sense analysis of variance is actually an extension of the difference-of-means test.

*16.2. Two-way Analysis of Variance

Under certain circumstances it is possible to extend analysis of variance by adding further nominal-scale variables. Such a procedure is mainly feasible in controlled experiments in which the researcher can assign individuals randomly to several groups, thereby controlling the number of cases in each category. In natural situations, where no such control can be exercised, the extension described in this section will be less useful. Some of the basic ideas involved in what has been referred to as two-way analysis of variance will be useful in helping you understand certain material presented in Chaps. 19 and 20, however.

If it is possible to introduce another nominal-scale variable in such a manner that all combinations of subcategories of the two nominal scales have the same number of cases, the extension of analysis of variance is a straightforward one. Suppose the categories of the second nominal scale are represented by rows. We now obtain a number of subcells, each with an equal number of cases. In order for this condition to be met, we must of course restrict ourselves to column categories of the

Table 16.4. Data for Two-way Analysis of Variance

Per cent Negro	City type			Total
	Industrial	Trade	Governmental	
Low (<10%)	4.3 5.9 2.8 7.7 $\Sigma X = 20.7$ $\bar{X} = 5.18$	5.1 3.6 1.8 3.3 $\Sigma X = 13.8$ $\bar{X} = 3.45$	3.1 3.8 1.6 1.9 $\Sigma X = 10.4$ $\bar{X} = 2.60$	$\sum_j X_{1j} = 44.9$ $\bar{X}_{1\cdot} = 3.74$
High (≥10%)	12.3 9.1 16.3 10.2 $\Sigma X = 47.9$ $\bar{X} = 11.98$	6.2 4.1 9.5 11.2 $\Sigma X = 31.0$ $\bar{X} = 7.75$	6.2 11.4 7.1 12.5 $\Sigma X = 37.2$ $\bar{X} = 9.30$	$\sum_j X_{2j} = 116.1$ $\bar{X}_{2\cdot} = 9.68$
Total	$\sum_i X_{i1} = 68.6$ $\bar{X}_{\cdot 1} = 8.58$	$\sum_i X_{i2} = 44.8$ $\bar{X}_{\cdot 2} = 5.60$	$\sum_i X_{i3} = 47.6$ $\bar{X}_{\cdot 3} = 5.95$	$\sum_i \sum_j X_{ij} = 161.0$ $\bar{X}_{\cdot\cdot} = 6.71$

same size. To the numerical data given in Table 16.1, let us add the variable per cent Negro, dichotomized into "high" and "low" categories. Although it would almost never work out so well in real life, let us suppose that there are the same number of cities in each of the six cells. If this were not the case an approximate method would have to be used (see below). The numerical data are now given in Table 16.4, with subcategory sums and means indicated in each box.

If there are the same number of cases in each subcell it is possible to break the within-columns or unexplained sum of squares into several components. We can, of course, do an analysis of variance across the rows, completely ignoring the columns. Between- and within-rows sums of squares would then be obtained in exactly the same manner that between- and within-column figures were computed. It turns out mathematically that if there are the same number of cases in each subcell, the between-rows sum of squares can be considered to come completely from the within-column or unexplained (by columns) sum of squares. Thus the total variation can now be divided into three portions as follows.

$$\text{Total SS} = \text{between-column SS} + \text{between-row SS} + \text{unexplained SS}$$
$$(16.6)$$

We have taken the total variation and explained all we could by means of the first nominal scale (city type). Of that which is left unexplained (the within-column sum of squares), a certain portion can then be explained by the second nominal scale (per cent Negro). The remainder, often called an error term, is the proportion of the total variation left unexplained by both variables. There are now three estimates of the common variance in addition to the estimate based on the total sum of squares, and these can be used to make two separate F tests. The error term can be used in the denominators of both F tests since the estimate based on the unexplained sum of squares will always be unbiased and independent of the other two. The numerators of the F's will be the estimates based on the between-columns and between-rows sums of squares. Each test will be a test for the existence of a relationship between the interval-scale variable and one of the nominal-scale variables, controlling for the other nominal scale.

Although we shall discuss this type of controlling operation in greater detail in Chap. 19, a few words on the subject are necessary at this point since controlling by using two-way analysis of variance involves a somewhat different principle from that discussed in connection with contingency problems. You will recall that up to this point our controlling procedure has involved literally holding the control variable constant by examining what happens within each category of the control variable. For example, we made a series of chi-square tests, one for each of these categories. Here we make a *single F* test instead of many. Also, we do not actually hold the control variable constant. Instead we take its presence into consideration by *adjusting* values of the interval scale according to the category of the control variable.

You will note from Table 16.4, for example, that the mean murder rate for all cities with low percentages of Negroes is 3.74, whereas the mean for those with high percentages is 9.68. Suppose we were to pretend that all cities had the same percentages of Negroes, performing a statistical adjustment of the murder rates by adding a fixed quantity (i.e., 2.97) to all cities in the "low" category and in this case subtracting the same quantity from those in the "high" category so that both categories had the same mean (i.e., the grand mean 6.71). Such a controlling operation involves raising the hypothetical question of what the murder rates would be like *if* all cities actually had the same minority

percentages.   Rather than actually treating the per cent Negro categories
separately, thereby sacrificing cases, we make use of a poor man's substitute by adjusting the murder-rate scores to take this control variable
into consideration.   What we lose in scientific rigor we gain in efficiency
of design since we can then make use of a single test involving the total
number of cases.

In adjusting the murder rates in such a fashion we are actually reducing
the total variation in the scores.   In effect, we are subtracting out that
portion of the variation due to per cent Negro.   Taking the *adjusted
scores*, we could then compare the between- and within-column estimates
in the usual manner.   Fortunately, it is unnecessary actually to obtain
the adjusted scores.   Were we to do so we would find that the results
would be identical with those obtained using two-way analysis of variance.   In other words, the type of analysis we shall describe below is
equivalent to an adjusting operation such as the one we have been discussing.   In effect what we do, first, is let the control variable operate
on the dependent variable, taking out that portion of the total variation
explained by this control variable.   We then take the remainder as a
"new total" variation and determine how much of this remainder can
be explained by the other independent variable.   This "new total" is
equivalent to the total variation in the *adjusted scores*.   In general, we
can control for additional variables in the same manner.   By making
adjustments for each of the control variables, we take out all of the
variation which can be explained by these variables.   We then look at
the remainder to see how much can be explained by the other independent
variable.   We shall make considerable use of this same type of controlling
operation in subsequent chapters.

Interaction.   We are not yet ready for a numerical example since there
is one further complication introduced by the addition of a second
nominal scale.   Whenever there are at least two cases in each subcell,
an additional test should always be made.   This is a test for "interaction," or a possible effect due to the peculiar combinations of the two
nominal-scale variables.   In order to make the two-way analysis-of-
variance test previously described, it is necessary to assume the property
of additivity.   Formally stated, this property requires that mean
population differences between columns be the same for each row and,
conversely, that differences between rows be the same for each column.
Additivity can be illustrated by the following figures representing hypothetical population means:

	A_1	A_2	A_3
B_1	5	10	20
B_2	10	15	25
B_3	25	30	40

Notice that the differences between the first and second columns are 5 for each row; between the second and third, differences are 10 for each row. Also, differences between the first and second rows are all 5, and between the second and third they are 15. Suppose, however, that the mean for the middle cell were 35 instead of 15. Then additivity would not hold, and we would have what is referred to as "interaction." Although A_3 usually produces higher scores than A_2 and B_3 higher than B_2, something peculiar happens when A_2 and B_2 are put together in that a very high mean results. The process is somewhat analogous to what happens when hydrogen and oxygen are combined and water produced. The result is not what would be expected if each element were examined separately.

Let us illustrate the idea with several examples. Suppose that ordinarily industrial cities have higher murder rates than governmental cities and that cities having a large percentage of Negroes have higher murder rates than those with low percentages. Conceivably, we might find industrial cities with a large percentage of Negroes having an unexpectedly low average murder rate. We might then look for some kind of interaction between industry and the presence of this minority which produces a low rate. A second type of example is perhaps more plausible. Suppose a choice between three types of teaching methods is to be made. Four teachers are each asked to use all three methods. Teacher A may be generally more effective than B. Similarly, the first method may generally be superior to the second. But conceivably teacher A may not work well with the first method, producing poorer results than would be expected. In this case there is interaction between teacher and method.

The test for interaction can be made independently of the two tests previously described and involves the same basic procedure. The unexplained sum of squares, or error term, is further broken down by subtracting out that portion which can be accounted for by interaction. The total sum of squares is thus decomposed into

$$\text{Total SS} = \text{between-column SS} + \text{between-row SS}$$
$$+ \text{interaction SS} + \text{error SS} \quad (16.7)$$

This can be accomplished by taking each combination of the categories of A and B and treating it as a category of a combined (single) variable. In other words, we treat the problem as though there were a single nominal scale with categories $A_1B_1, A_2B_1, \ldots, A_kB_l$. Obviously, if there were only one case within each subcell there could be no within-subclass variation. If there is absolutely no interaction we should get exactly the same error term as obtained by adding the separate effects of the rows and columns [as in equation (16.6)]. On the other hand, if there is significant interaction the error term will be smaller using this second approach. For example, you should convince yourself that if cell ij produced effects out of line with the rest, cell ij would be relatively homogeneous as compared with either column j or row i, and the within-subclass sum of squares would be smaller than the residual obtained by subtracting the sum of the between-column and between-row sums of squares from the total sum of squares.

The difference between the amount of variation explained using these subcells and the amount explained assuming additivity can then be attributed to interaction. Thus we have

$$\text{Total SS} = \text{between-subclass SS} + \text{within-subclass SS}$$

where the between-subclass sum of squares has been broken into three components:

$$\text{Between-subclass SS} = \text{between-column SS} + \text{between-row SS}$$
$$+ \text{ interaction SS}$$

Returning once more to the numerical problem involving city types, per cent Negro, and murder rates, we can begin by listing the required assumptions.

1. *Assumptions.*

> *Level of Measurement:* Two nominal scales, one interval scale
> *Model:* Independent random samples
>> All subcell, row, and column populations normal
>> Subcell population variances equal
> *Hypotheses:* 1. Population column means equal
>> 2. Population row means equal
>> 3. Additivity in population (no interaction)

There are now three separate hypotheses which can be tested independently. The test for interaction should be made first, with subsequent tests depending on the outcome of this test. If hypothesis (3) is not rejected, the usual procedure is to assume additivity in the model, throwing the sums of squares due to interaction (in the sample) back into the error term and using this larger error term to test hypotheses (1) and (2). If the hypothesis of no interaction is rejected, the procedure to be used in the other two tests will depend upon the nature of the data (see below). Notice that we now must assume normality and equality of variances for each of the *subcells* in order to test for interaction.

Cases in the different subcells must be selected independently and cannot be matched.

2. *Level of Significance.* .05 level

3. *Sampling Distribution.* F

4. *Computation of Test Statistics.* We have already obtained the total and between-column sums of squares. The between-row sum of squares is computed exactly the same way as the between-column sum of squares. Thus

$$\text{Between-row SS} = \frac{44.9^2}{12} + \frac{116.1^2}{12} - 1{,}080.042$$
$$= 1{,}291.268 - 1{,}080.042 = 211.226$$

In order to obtain the interaction sum of squares, we make use of the sums of each subclass. The between-subclass sum of squares is

$$\text{Between-subclass SS} = \frac{20.7^2}{4} + \frac{47.9^2}{4} + \cdots + \frac{37.2^2}{4} - 1{,}080.042$$
$$= 1{,}341.585 - 1{,}080.042 = 261.543$$

We obtain the error term used in testing for interaction by subtracting the between-subclass sum of squares from the total. Thus

$$\text{Error SS} = 373.538 - 261.543 = 111.995$$

The amount actually due to interaction is the between-subclass sum of squares less the sum of the amounts due to the rows and columns separately. Therefore,

$$\text{Interaction SS} = 261.543 - (42.303 + 211.226) = 8.014$$

The results can be summarized as in Table 16.5.

Table 16.5. Computations for Two-way Analysis of Variance, with Test for Interaction

	Sums of squares	Degrees of freedom	Estimate of variance	F
Total	373.538	$N - 1 = 23$		
Between subclass	261.543	$kl - 1 = 5$		
Between columns	42.303	$k - 1 = 2$	21.152	
Between rows	211.226	$l - 1 = 1$	211.226	
Interaction	8.014	$(k - 1)(l - 1) = 2$	4.007	0.644
Error (within subclass)	111.995	$N - kl = 18$	6.222	

The degrees of freedom are determined by the usual procedures. With l rows and k columns there will be $l - 1$ degrees of freedom associated with the between-row sum of squares. To obtain the degrees of freedom for the interaction term, we take the number of subcells less one $(kl - 1)$ and subtract from this quantity the degrees of freedom associated with the between-row $(l - 1)$ and between-column $(k - 1)$ sums of squares. A simpler rule of thumb is to take the *product* of the degrees of freedom associated with the between-columns and between-rows sums of squares. Thus, if we multiply the between-columns and between-rows degrees of freedom we get $(k - 1)(l - 1) = 2$ degrees of freedom. This is the same result as we would obtain by taking the between-subclass degrees of freedom $(= 5)$ and subtracting from this the sum of the degrees of freedom for the between-rows-and-columns sums of squares $(= 1 + 2)$. This can be expressed algebraically with the following identity.

$$(kl - 1) - (k - 1 + l - 1) = (k - 1)(l - 1)$$

The remaining degrees of freedom, which should equal the total number of cases less 1 degree of freedom for each subclass, can then be associated with the error term.

5. *Decision.* The test for interaction produces an F which is less than unity. We therefore have no reason to reject the null hypothesis of no interaction. This means that the small additional amount explained by interaction within these *samples* can easily be attributed to sampling fluctuations. In this case, we would probably be willing to accept the assumption of additivity even though we are on the wrong end of the test and should therefore be primarily concerned with the risk of a type II error. Incidentally, had tables been available we might have

Table 16.6. Computations for Two-way Analysis of Variance with Interaction Thrown into Error Term

	Sums of squares	Degrees of freedom	Estimate of variance	F	Significance level
Total	373.538	23			
Between columns	42.303	2	21.152	3.525	$p < .05$
Between rows	211.226	1	211.226	35.204	$p < .001$
Error	120.009	20	6.000		

used a level of significance such as .3 if we had really been interested in keeping the additivity assumption. Having decided that there is no interaction, we can now throw the sum of squares due to (sample) interaction back into the error term, using this larger error term as the basis for the error estimate of variance. Doing this, we get Table 16.6 in which the error term of 120.009 is the sum of the interaction and error terms in Table 16.5.

From the table we see that for an F with 2 and 20 degrees of freedom we need an F of 3.49 or larger to attain significance at the .05 level. We also see that an F with 1 and 20 degrees of freedom of 35.204 is highly significant since an F of only 14.82 would be required for significance at the .001 level. Thus there is little doubt that a relationship exists between per cent Negro and murder rates. Notice that when we control for per cent Negro by letting this variable explain all that it can of the variation in murder rates and then letting city type explain what it can of the remainder, we now get a significant relationship between city type and murder rates. It will be recalled that the relationship without a control for per cent Negro was not significant.

It should be noted that if interaction is not significant we practically always gain more than we lose by throwing the interaction back into the error term, using this combined error term in the denominator of F. Although the error sum of squares is thereby slightly increased, there will also be more degrees of freedom associated with the larger error term. Since the interaction term will be relatively small, the net effect will usually be to obtain a smaller denominator for F. Also, of course, there will be a larger number of degrees of freedom associated with F, and therefore a smaller value of F will be required for significance.

We must now ask what we would have done had interaction been significant. The answer to this question is not at all simple, but we can at least give a few suggestions. The reader who is interested in a more complete treatment should consult a text such as McNemar [6] or Anderson and Bancroft [1]. If interaction is significant, it will usually be possible to locate by inspection the subcells contributing most to the interaction term. Separate analysis-of-variance tests might be made omitting these subcells, or a series of difference-of-means tests may be used to evaluate the significance of the contribution to interaction coming from each subcell. It may well turn out to be the case that the discovery of interaction and the necessity of accounting theoretically for its existence are the most important outcomes of the entire study. Therefore, there is no substitute for the careful isolation of those subcells which are out of line with the rest.

In addition to focusing attention on interaction itself, there may also be an interest in whether or not one or the other of the nominal-scale variables is related to the interval scale. What tests of these relationships can be made? The question boils down to this: "Which estimate of the variance should be used in the denominator of F, the error estimate or the estimate based on the interaction term?" The answer to this question seems to depend on the nature of the two nominal-scale variables, and in particular on whether or not the categories used represent all categories in the population or merely a sample of categories. It is frequently the case in sociological problems, in which we do not usually assign individuals randomly to categories, that these categories represent all of the possible categories in the classification scheme. Thus, if we divide all cities into three types and exclude no cities in so doing, or if we simply take cities having high and low percentages of Negroes, we expect to include at least some cities from all types. Similarly, if we classify persons as male or female, or Protestant, Catholic, or Jewish, we ordinarily expect to include some representatives from all (or nearly all) categories. On the other hand, our categories might themselves involve a sampling of all types. For example, we might have selected Methodists, Quakers, and Jehovah's Witnesses as three religious groups representing a much larger number. Perhaps each of these denominations is a representative of a certain type of religion. Let us look at each of these situations in turn.

In the first situation our categories represent all or nearly all possible types. There is certainly no sampling error involved in selecting categories as there might be if only three religious denominations were used for comparison. In most of these problems, our interest is likely to be centered on the degree of homogeneity of each type relative to the magnitude of differences between types. The second nominal-scale variable may be considered primarily as a disturbing variable which needs to be controlled. Interaction may be only an interesting by-product of the analysis. In this case, it would make sense to compare the estimate based on the between sum of squares with the estimate based on the unexplained sum of squares. This latter estimate is a within-subclass estimate and involves the variation which still remains unexplained by the joint operation of the major independent variable (say, city type) and the control variable (per cent Negro). We are letting the control variable operate first, and then letting the major independent variable explain what it can of the remainder. A certain additional amount is also explained by the interaction of the two variables. Each of these "explained" sums of squares can be compared with the "unexplained" sum of squares or error term. We would then take this error estimate as our denominator in each of the separate F tests. In testing for the significance of a difference among columns we would therefore take the between-column estimate divided by the error term, and similarly for rows. In our numerical problem, had interaction been significant these F ratios would have been $21.152/6.222$ and $211.226/6.222$ respectively.

Other considerations arise when the categories of either (or both) nominal-scale variable involve only a small sample of possible categories. If interaction turns out to be significant and therefore is larger than the error estimate, there is always the added question of whether or not this would have occurred had the categories been different. Under these circumstances we may be much more interested in the relative size of the between-column (or row) estimate and the interaction estimate than in comparing between estimates with the error term. For example, if we were interested in relating religion to income, controlling for education, and if we found a highly significant interaction between religion and education (say, highly educated Quakers having very low incomes), we might be very hesitant to generalize about a relationship between religion and income unless religious differences were very large as compared with interaction. Otherwise, a different set of religious denominations might produce very different results. As another example, if three teaching methods were tested by different teachers and if interaction were significant, then one would want to make sure that the average differences among methods were large as compared with interaction. If not, he might emphasize one method only to learn that a large number of teachers (only a few of whom were sampled) could not use this particular method effectively.

In problems in which there has been a sampling of categories, it may thus make more sense to compare between-row and between-column sums of squares with the interaction term. In our problem, had interaction been significant and had there been many more city types, we would have taken $21.152/4.007$ and $211.226/4.007$ as our two F ratios. Although most sociological problems seem to involve the first type of situation in which the error term would be used in the test, you should develop the habit of treating each problem separately and making your decision according to the nature of the data and the kinds of comparisons you are making. Fortunately, or perhaps unfortunately, many sociological problems do not seem to involve highly significant interaction.

Extension to Three or More Nominal Scales. In theory there is nothing that prevents us from extending analysis of variance to additional variables. In practice, however, we are likely to be restricted by the requirement of equal numbers of cases in each subcell unless we are in a position experimentally to control this factor. If we add a third nominal scale we can divide the total sum of squares into between A, between B, between C, interaction, and error terms, and we can make a number of F tests of separate hypotheses. This time, however, there will be more than one kind of interaction. There can be interaction between variables A and B, A and C, B and C, and among all three variables acting together. We first make a test for the second-order interaction ($A \times B \times C$). If this is not significant, we can throw it back into the error term and test for the three first-order interactions. Tests of the significance of A, B, and C can then be made. The extension to four or more nominal scales would be made in a similar way. In the event that the researcher is able to control the number of cases in each category by random assignment, there are numerous other experimental designs available, and a textbook on experimental design should be consulted. Most of these designs have limited applicability to the sociologist because of the fact that contrived experiments are not possible.

* Two-way Analysis of Variance with Unequal Subclasses. When the number of cases in each subclass is unequal, as will usually be the case in sociological research, two-way analysis of variance is no longer straightforward. If the number of cases is sufficiently large, it will of course always be possible to control for a second nominal scale by running separate analyses within each category of the control variable as we did in the case of contingency problems. If the number of cases is relatively small to begin with, certain approximate methods may be used. One of these methods involves the use of logarithms, but in other respects it is straightforward (see [5], pp. 260 to 266).

Another procedure, described in Walker and Lev ([8], pp. 381 to 382), is conceptually much simpler. This latter method involves treating the means of the various subcells as though they were single cases. Sums of squares and estimates of variance can be obtained for the between-rows, between-columns, and interaction terms by essentially assuming that there is only one case (the mean) in each subcell. The error sum of squares is then obtained as in ordinary two-way analysis of variance by subtracting the between-subclass sum of squares from the total sum of squares using the total number of cases rather than the means of each subcell. The error estimate is obtained by dividing by the error degrees of freedom, as before, and then dividing the latter figure by the harmonic mean of the number of cases in each subcell. This latter operation is necessary in order to make the error estimate, based on the total number of cases, comparable to the estimates based only on the subcell means treated as single cases. F tests can then be made in the usual manner.

16.3. Nonparametric Alternatives to Analysis of Variance

In case the assumptions required for analysis of variance are not met, there are nonparametric tests available which can be used as alternatives to one- and two-way analysis of variance. The Friedman two-way analysis of variance with ranks will not be discussed in this text since this particular test is designed for problems in which there is only one observation in each subclass (see [7], pp. 166 to 172). Such problems seldom arise in sociological research unless it is possible to make use of an experimental design in which the number of observations in each subcell can easily be manipulated. We shall therefore confine our attention to one-way analysis of variance.

The test considered in this section was developed by Kruskal and Wallis and is appropriate whenever we have a number of independent random samples and an ordinal-scale level of measurement. Its power efficiency for large samples is approximately 95 per cent. The test is basically a very simple one, involving a comparison of the sums of the rankings for each of the categories of the nominal-scale variable. A statistic H is computed in order to measure the degree to which the

Table 16.7. Data and Computations for Analysis of Variance with Ranks

	Industrial city		Trade city		Political city	
	Rate	Rank	Rate	Rank	Rate	Rank
	4.3	10	5.1	11	12.5	23
	2.8	4	6.2	13.5	3.1	5
	12.3	22	1.8	2	1.6	1
	16.3	24	9.5	18	6.2	13.5
	5.9	12	4.1	9	3.8	8
	7.7	16	3.6	7	7.1	15
	9.1	17	11.2	20	11.4	21
	10.2	19	3.3	6	1.9	3
Sums		$R_1 = 124$		$R_2 = 86.5$		$R_3 = 89.5$

various sums of ranks differ from what would be expected under the null hypothesis. If there are more than five cases in each class, the sampling distribution of H is approximately chi square.[4]

For comparative purposes let us illustrate the use of the Kruskal-Wallis test with the same data. In Table 16.7 the murder rates for the three types of cities have been ranked from high to low (low ranks indicating low murder rates).

1. *Assumptions.*

Level of measurement: Ordinal and nominal scale
Model: Independent random sampling
Hypothesis: Samples drawn from same continuous population

2. *Significance Level and Critical Region.* Let us again use the .05 level.

3. *Sampling Distribution.* The sampling distribution of H will be approximately chi square with $k - 1$ degrees of freedom, where k is the number of categories used.

[4] In the case of three classes and very small N's see [7], pp. 185 to 187.

4. *Computation of Test Statistic.* We compute H by means of the formula

$$H = \frac{\left(\dfrac{12}{N(N+1)} \displaystyle\sum_{i=1}^{k} \dfrac{R_i^2}{N_i}\right) - 3(N+1)}{1 - \Sigma T/(N^3 - N)} \tag{16.8}$$

where N_i and N represent the number of cases in the ith category and in the total sample respectively. The denominator in the above formula represents a correction for ties, where

$$T = t^3 - t$$

t being the number of observations tied for a given rank.

In this particular example there is only one pair of scores which is tied. Hence $T = 2^3 - 2 = 6$. We thus get

$$H = \frac{[12/24(25)](124^2/8 + 86.5^2/8 + 89.5^2/8) - 3(25)}{1 - 6/(24^3 - 24)} = 2.17$$

5. *Decision.* Referring to the chi-square table, we see that for 2 degrees of freedom we need a chi square of 5.991 or larger in order to obtain significance at the .05 level. Since we obtained an H of 2.17, we decide not to reject the null hypothesis at this level of significance. We see, incidentally, that we have reached the same conclusion as before.

16.4. Measures of Association: Intraclass Correlation

Analysis-of-variance tests only enable us to determine whether or not a relationship exists between two variables. As we have already seen, it is fairly easy to obtain statistical significance with even a very slight relationship provided there is a sufficiently large number of cases. Having determined that a relationship exists, subject to the risk of a type I error, of course, we next need to measure the strength or degree of relationship. Some indication of the magnitude of the relationship can be obtained by simply comparing the means of the various categories. If these means are very different, the relationship is likely to be a strong one; if the differences are slight, we may not be able to attach much practical significance to them even though we may have obtained statistical significance. A mere comparison of category means may be misleading, however, unless one also notes the degree of homogeneity within each group. Usually, although perhaps not always, our interest centers on the relative magnitude of differences among means *as compared with* differences within categories. In other words, we wish to obtain a measure of the degree to which categories are homogeneous as compared with the total variability in the interval-scale variable. If the categories are perfectly homogeneous, the association between the two variables will be complete; knowing the category to which an individual belongs enables one to predict his score exactly.

Several closely related and essentially interchangeable measures of association have been developed which make use of the total, between, and within sums of squares or of the estimates of variance based on these sums of squares. The *correlation ratio E²*, perhaps the simplest of these measures, involves our taking the ratio of the explained to the total sum of squares. Thus

$$E^2 = \frac{\text{explained SS}}{\text{total SS}} = \frac{\text{between SS}}{\text{total SS}} \qquad (16.9)$$

As we shall see in the next chapter, the interpretation for the correlation ratio is directly analogous to that for ordinary product-moment correlation, and we shall make use of this measure in testing for the nonlinearity of the relationship between two interval scales.

The correlation ratio is seldom used directly as a measure of association in analysis-of-variance problems, however. You will remember that the sample standard deviation or variance tends to underestimate the population standard deviation or variance, the degree of bias becoming fairly serious for small samples. For this reason we used $N - 1$ rather than N in the denominator in order to obtain an unbiased estimate. Likewise, when the number of cases in each category becomes rather small, the variability within each sample, as measured by the standard deviation, s, will tend to be less than that within the population. In order to correct for a comparable bias in the correlation ratio, we can obtain what is referred to as the *unbiased correlation ratio* by making use of the correct degrees of freedom and working directly with the estimates of variance rather than the sums of squares.

The formula for the unbiased correlation ratio ϵ^2 turns out to be

$$\epsilon^2 = 1 - \frac{V_w}{V_t} \qquad (16.10)$$

where V_w and V_t stand for the within and total *estimates* respectively. Although we have not as yet found it necessary to compute the total estimate, its value can easily be obtained by dividing the total sum of squares by $N - 1$. In the numerical example we have been using, the values of E and ϵ are

$$E^2 = \frac{42.303}{373.538} = .113 \qquad\qquad E = .34$$

$$\epsilon^2 = 1 - \frac{15.773}{373.538/23} = .029 \qquad \epsilon = .17$$

Notice that the value of ϵ is smaller than that of E.

A somewhat more commonly used measure of association is the *intraclass correlation coefficient*. This measure derives its name from the fact that basically it involves a product-moment correlation between all possible pairs of cases *within* categories of the nominal-scale variable.[5] Like the other measures discussed in this section, the intraclass correlation coefficient r_i can also be considered as a measure of the degree of homogeneity of the classes relative to the total variability in the interval scale. Its formula is as follows

$$r_i = \frac{V_b - V_w}{V_b + (\bar{n} - 1)V_w} \tag{16.11}$$

where V_b and V_w are the between and within estimates respectively and $\bar{n}$ represents an average number of cases in each class.

If the number of cases in each class is the same, there will of course be no question as to the value of $\bar{n}$. For unequal classes a simple arithmetic mean may be used to give the value of $\bar{n}$. Haggard [3] recommends a somewhat different kind of average value which should be used whenever the number of cases differs considerably from one category to the next. This formula for computing $\bar{n}$ is

$$\bar{n} = \frac{1}{k - 1}\left(\sum_{i=1}^{k} N_i - \frac{\sum_{i=1}^{k} N_i^2}{\sum_{i=1}^{k} N_i} \right) \tag{16.12}$$

where N_i represents the number of cases in the ith category and k the number of categories. In our numerical example all categories are of the same size and therefore $\bar{n} = 8$.

Thus
$$r_i = \frac{21.152 - 15.773}{21.152 + 7(15.773)} = \frac{5.379}{131.563} = .041$$

Several properties of the intraclass correlation coefficient can be noted. When the categories are all perfectly homogeneous there will be no within-class variation, and the value of r_i will be $+1.0$. At the other extreme, suppose that all of the variation occurred within classes and that the category means were exactly equal. In this case V_b would vanish, and the lower limit would be

$$\frac{-V_w}{(\bar{n} - 1)V_w} = -\frac{1}{\bar{n} - 1}$$

[5] After reading Chap. 17 you may wish to consult [3] to see the precise nature of the relationship between these two measures.

Thus, the lower limit is not -1.0 except in the special case where there is an average of 2 cases within each class. Ordinarily, therefore, the lower limit will be less than unity in absolute value. Actually this seldom bothers us since we rarely find categories which are substantially less homogeneous than would be expected by chance. When the between and within estimates are exactly equal, i.e., when the value of F is exactly unity, r_i will be zero. Thus $r_i = 0$ whenever categories are exactly as homogeneous as would be expected by chance if there were no relationship between the two variables. Ordinarily the values of r_i will be between 0 and 1.0. Unfortunately, there seems to be no simple interpretation for values of r_i between these limits.

*The notion of intraclass correlation can easily be generalized to cover two-way analysis of variance. In those situations in which we would use the error term in the denominator of F, we may obtain a measure of the degree of relationship between the column variable and the interval scale, controlling for the row variable, by taking as V_b the between-column estimate and replacing V_w by the error term. Similarly, we might also take the between-row estimate as V_b, thus obtaining a measure of the degree of association between the interval scale and the row variable after having subtracted out the variation due to the column variable. As we shall see in Chap. 19, this procedure is directly analogous to what we do in obtaining "partial" correlations between two interval scales, controlling for a third interval scale. We can also compute a measure of the degree to which the two nominal scales act together to explain the variation in the interval scale. Such an intraclass "multiple" correlation could be obtained by replacing V_b by the between-*subclass* estimate, using the within-subclass estimate as V_w. After you have studied Chap. 19 and have become more accustomed to partial and multiple correlations, you may wish to review this section.

16.5. Additional Remarks

Analysis of variance is undoubtedly of most value in those scientific disciplines in which experimental designs are possible. For example, if one can assign individuals to categories on a random basis he will gain control over the number of cases in each subcell, thereby permitting the use of highly efficient analysis-of-variance designs. In addition, he will be in a much better position to make causal inferences on the basis of his results. Although the problem of causality will be considered in more detail in Chap. 19, we can at least inject a word of caution at this point. Suppose, for example, that we had found highly significant differences among the three types of cities. We can legitimately infer that the three samples were probably not drawn from identical populations.

This means that we can argue that the three populations actually differ with respect to murder rates. We would certainly not want to infer, however, that industrial characteristics are direct causes of this particular type of criminal behavior. Among other things, the three types of cities may have selected different types of migrants. Had we been able to assign individuals randomly to cities or assign cities to one of the three types on a random basis, afterwards observing the murder rates, we might have been in a much better position to infer a causal relationship. Even so, we would have to make certain assumptions about the effects of other variables which may also be operating. The assignment of individuals to a category on a random basis has the advantage of ruling out the self-selection effect and is therefore our best insurance that "other things" are in fact equal or nearly so. Nevertheless, it will still be true that if we wish to make causal inferences we must go beyond a purely statistical interpretation of the data.

It is sometimes the case that we have collected information on all of the cases that are available. For example, all cities within the United States may have been placed within one of the three categories. We could then take the position that our task is a purely descriptive one, since there may be no existent larger population to which one can generalize. This may very well be the case. On the other hand, one's interest may be primarily in developing a generalization which could apply to other as yet nonexistent cities. One way to conceptualize the problem is to imagine that the particular cities studied constitute a random sample from a hypothetical infinite "universe of possibilities." Such a universe might consist of all cities which might develop "under similar circumstances."

If this way of conceptualizing the problem seems philosophically unsatisfactory, a somewhat simpler approach may be more appealing. We can admit that there is no question of generalizing to a larger population, but we can raise the following question: "What would happen if we had taken the entire population of cities and selected three completely random samples from this population so as to include all of the cities in one or another of the samples?" What is the probability that in so doing we would have obtained differences at least as large as those we have computed using city type as the criterion for classification? Obviously, if we have obtained differences which could very easily have arisen by chance, we cannot have too much faith in our conclusion that the three city types actually differ with respect to murder rates. A skeptic can legitimately claim that had he divided the cities into three classes according to almost any irrelevant criterion, he would probably have obtained differences as large as ours. In short, we are arguing that some sort of significance test will practically always be helpful in evalu-

ting one's findings. Especially in instances where random assignment
as been impossible, one must be very careful not to make causal
iferences.

GLOSSARY

Correlation ratio
Explained and unexplained variation
Homoscedasticity
Interaction
Intraclass correlation

EXERCISES

1. Since the F test can be used to test the null hypothesis that we have two independent estimates of the same variance, we can use this test to test the assumption
that $\sigma_1 = \sigma_2$ in difference-of-means problems. Since it will ordinarily not be possible
to predict which value of s^2 will be the larger, we take the ratio of the larger to the
smaller and then double the probability value given in the F table. With these
facts in mind, take the data of Exercise 1, Chap. 13, and test the hypothesis that
$\sigma_1 = \sigma_2$.
2. Suppose that the data given below represent the incomes of the chairmen of the
boards of various types of community organizations. You have randomly selected
five organizations of each type for both large and small communities and therefore
have obtained equal numbers of cases in each subclass.

    a. Make use of one-way analysis of variance to test for a relationship between
        organization type and income of board chairmen, ignoring the size of the
        community. What are the values of E and ϵ?
  b. Using two-way analysis of variance, what can you say about the relationship
        between organization type and income, controlling for community size?
        How do results compare with those in (*a*)?
    c. Compute the intraclass correlation for both (*a*) and *(b)* above.

Size of community	Organization type		
	Religious	Social welfare	Civic
Large	$ 8,000 6,500 12,300 14,100 11,700	$10,000 5,600 7,300 6,400 5,800	$15,800 13,100 9,600 17,300 11,500
Small	10,000 7,300 8,900 9,300 6,700	4,300 5,400 7,900 6,000 4,100	9,400 5,800 4,700 7,300 8,100

3. Convert the income data for Exercise 2 to ranks and, using the Kruskal-Wall test, test for a relationship between organization type and income:

 a. Ignoring community size
 b. Controlling for community size

*4. Analysis of variance can be performed on grouped as well as ungrouped data. To reduce confusion it will be simplest to make use of equations (16.4) and (16.5) in unmodified form, remembering, however, that in the case of grouped data we treat scores as though they were concentrated at the mid-points of intervals. With these facts in mind, perform a one-way analysis of variance on the data of Exercise 2 Chap. 13. As a check on your computations, how do the values of F and t compare

REFERENCES

1. Anderson, R. L., and T. A. Bancroft: *Statistical Theory in Research*, McGraw-Hi Book Company, Inc., New York, 1952, chaps. 17 and 18.
2. Dixon, W. J., and F. J. Massey: *Introduction to Statistical Analysis*, 2d ed McGraw-Hill Book Company, Inc., New York, 1957, chap. 10.
3. Haggard, E. A.: *Intraclass Correlation and the Analysis of Variance*, The Dryde Press, Inc., New York, 1958, chaps. 1–5.
4. Hagood, M. J., and D. O. Price: *Statistics for Sociologists*, Henry Holt an Company, Inc., New York, chap. 22.
5. Johnson, P. O.: *Statistical Methods in Research*, Prentice-Hall, Inc., Englewoo Cliffs, N.J., 1949, chaps. 10 and 11.
6. McNemar, Q.: *Psychological Statistics*, John Wiley & Sons, Inc., New York 1955, chaps. 15 and 16.
7. Siegel, S.: *Nonparametric Statistics for the Behavioral Sciences*, McGraw-Hi Book Company, Inc., New York, 1956, pp. 166–172, 184–193.
8. Walker, H. M., and J. Lev: *Statistical Inference*, Henry Holt and Company, Inc New York, 1953, chap. 14.

Chapter 17

CORRELATION AND REGRESSION

In the present chapter and in Chap. 18 we shall consider the relationship between two interval scales. An extension to three or more interval-scale variables will be made in Chap. 19 when we discuss multiple and partial correlation. For the time being, our concern is with situations in which we have two interval-scale measures on each individual. For example, we may know both the number of years of education completed and the annual income of adult males in a given community. Or we may be interested in relating the percentage of the labor force engaged in manufacturing to a city's population growth.

In certain problems of this sort we are often not only interested in significance tests and measures of degree of relationship but also may want to describe the *nature* of the relationship between the two variables so that we can predict the value of one variable if we know the other. For example, we may want to predict a person's future income from his education or a city's rate of growth from the percentage of its labor force engaged in manufacturing. When interest is focused primarily on the exploratory task of finding out *which* variables are related to a given variable, we are likely to be mainly interested in measures of degree or strength of relationship such as correlation coefficients. On the other hand, once we have found the significant variables we are more likely to turn our attention to regression analysis in which we attempt to predict the exact value of one variable from the other.

Although you are already familiar with significance tests and measures of association, it will be advisable to begin our discussion by studying the prediction problem. This is because the notion of regression is both logically prior to and theoretically more important than that of correlation. The reason for this will be more apparent as we proceed. After discussing the prediction problem, we shall turn our attention to measuring the strength of relationship. In Chap. 18, which actually represents a continuation of the present chapter, we shall discuss various significance tests as well as rank-order correlation which can be used in relating two ordinal scales.

17.1. Linear Regression and Least Squares

In one sense the ultimate goal of all sciences is that of prediction. This does not imply, of course, that one is only secondarily interested in "understanding" why two or more variables are interrelated as they are. Perhaps it is correct to say that such "understanding" is the ultimate goal and that to the degree that understanding becomes perfected, prediction becomes more and more accurate. Presumably, if understanding were complete, perfect prediction would also be possible. Regardless of the philosophical implications of such a deterministic point of view, it remains that prediction is the goal of every science.

Predictive statements in sociology and other social sciences are often of necessity rather crudely worded. Usually this is because we have not reached the interval-scale level of measurement. Thus we might predict that the higher a person's status in the group, the greater his conformity to group norms. Such a statement need not imply one-way causality; it merely says that status and conformity are positively related. Making an analogy with mathematical terminology which is not strictly correct, we say that status is a *function* of conformity or conformity is a function of status, begging the question of causality. Notice, however, that we have said very little about the *form* of this relationship other than that it is positive. Unless we have an interval-scale level of measurement for both variables it becomes very difficult to say much more.

Suppose, however, that we do have two interval scales. It then becomes possible to describe more exactly how the one variable varies with the other. For example, we might be able to say that for every year of schooling completed the expected income will increase by $1,000. If this were indeed the case we would have a very simple relationship, a linear or straight-line relationship. But most relationships are not nearly this simple although, as we shall see, it is frequently possible to obtain a very good approximation to the true relationship by assuming linearity. The most elegant and simple way to express a relationship between two (or more) variables is by means of a mathematical equation. Thus, you are acquainted with certain laws of physics which state a relationship between pressure, volume, and temperature ($PV/T = k$) or which indicate a relationship between the rate of acceleration of a falling body, the distance it has fallen, and the length of time it has been falling. We can also represent each of these mathematical equations as some sort of a geometrical curve. Fortunately, in sociology we usually deal with very simple equations and the simplest possible curves (straight lines).

When we add more variables, we cannot so easily represent equations as geometrical figures since we run out of dimensions, but we need not worry about this for the present.

Suppose there is a dependent variable Y which is to be predicted from an independent variable X. In some problems X will clearly precede Y in time. For example, a person usually completes his education before earning his income. In these instances such a conceptualization makes very good sense, although we want to be careful not to imply a necessary or causal relationship or that X is the only variable influencing the value of Y. In other problems, the dependent and independent variables must be arbitrarily chosen since we may be equally interested in predicting Y from X or X from Y. Let us assume, however, that Y is taken as the dependent variable.

We have seen that if X and Y are independent, we cannot predict Y from X, or more exactly, knowledge of X does not improve our prediction of Y. Presumably, then, when the variables are not independent, knowledge of X does help us predict Y. The stronger the dependence, the more accurate our prediction will be. Later we shall measure the strength of this relationship by means of correlation coefficients. We now focus on *how* we predict Y from X. For example, we may wish to estimate a man's future income, given that he has completed three years of high school. Without this knowledge of education, our best guess (assuming no inflation) would be the mean income of all adult males. Knowing his education, however, ought to enable us to obtain a better prediction.

The Regression Equation. Let us conceptualize the problem in the following way. We imagine that for every fixed value of the independent variable X (education) we have a distribution of Y's (incomes). In other words, for each educational level there will be a certain income distribution in the population. Not all persons who have completed high school will have exactly the same income, but these incomes will be distributed about some mean. There will be similar income distributions for grammar school graduates, college graduates, postgraduates, etc. Each of these separate income distributions (for fixed X's) will have a mean, and we can plot the position of these means in the familiar rectangular coordinates. We refer to the resulting *path of these means* of the Y's for fixed X's as a *regression equation of Y on X*. Such a regression equation can be illustrated in Fig. 17.1.

These regression equations are the "laws" of a science. In some instances there is very little dispersion about the regression equation. In these instances very accurate predictions can be made, and deviations from the law are often thought of in terms of measurement error or as being due to minor uncontrolled forces. The "law" can then be stated as though a perfect relationship between Y and X existed. In the ideal, all points would be thought of as falling exactly on the curve, and the relationship would be abstracted as a perfect mathematical function in which there is a unique Y for each X. In the social sciences we cannot be nearly this pretentious. We expect considerable variability about the regression equation and prefer to think in terms of means and variances of a Y distribution for each X. Nevertheless, in principle the procedure is the same in all sciences, although the "laws" of social science are nowhere near as precise as those of physics. When we come

Fig. 17.1. General form of regression of Y on X or the path of the means of Y values for fixed values of X.

to measure the degree of association we shall see that unless the association is very high by present social science standards, we probably have no right to speak of "laws" at all.

In Fig. 17.1 we have indicated the general nature of regression equations as involving the paths of the means of Y values for given values of X. We shall now have to make some simplifying assumptions in order to make the problem manageable statistically. Although the idea of regression is perfectly general, most statistical work has been carried out on only the simplest of models. In particular, we shall for the present assume (1) that the form of the regression equation is linear, (2) that the distributions of the Y values for each X are normal, and (3) that the variances of the Y distributions are the same for each value of X. We can look at each of these assumptions in turn, giving most of our attention to the first.

If the regression of Y on X is linear, or a straight-line relationship, we

can write an equation as follows

$$Y = \overset{\rho \circ \rho}{\alpha} + \beta X \qquad (17.1)$$

where both α and β are constants. Greek letters have been used since for the present we are dealing with the total population. In such an equation both α and β have definite geometrical interpretations. If we set X equal to zero, we see that $Y = \alpha$. Therefore, α represents the point where the regression line crosses the Y axis (i.e., where $X = 0$).

The slope of the regression line is given by β since this constant indicates the magnitude of the change in Y for a given change in X. The fact

Fig. 17.2. The linear regression equation, showing geometrical interpretations for α and β.

that the relationship is linear means that any given change in X, say 5 units, always produces the same change in Y (i.e., 5β units) regardless of the position on the X axis. (See Fig. 17.2.) You should convince yourself that if $\beta = 1$ and if the units of X and Y are indicated by equal distances along the respective axes, the regression line will be at a 45-degree angle with the X axis. A β larger than unity indicates a steeper slope. The steeper the slope, the larger the change in Y for a given change in X. Similarly, if β is less than unity but greater than zero it will take a larger change in X to produce a given change in Y. In the limiting case where the line is horizontal, β becomes zero and changes in X produce no change in Y. In other words, if $\beta = 0$ there is no linear relationship between X and Y. Knowledge of X will not help one predict Y if a linear model is assumed.[1] If β is negative we know that

[1] As we shall see later, independence assures us that β will be zero, but it does not follow that if β is zero we necessarily have independence.

there is a negative relationship between the two variables: as X increases, Y decreases.

A straight line can always be completely determined if we know either two points on the line or a single point and the slope. Therefore, there is a unique line with the equation $Y = \alpha + \beta X$ provided, of course, that α and β are assumed to be fixed (but general) quantities. If the α and β are given, the line can be drawn by simply taking two points on the line. We know that when $X = 0$, $Y = \alpha$. Therefore the point $(0,\alpha)$ lies on the line. Also, when $Y = 0$ we have $0 = \alpha + \beta X$ or $X = -\alpha/\beta$. This

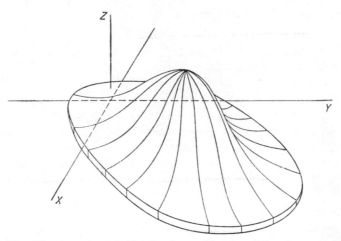

Fig. 17.3. The bivariate normal distribution. (*By permission from A. M. Mood, Introduction to the Theory of Statistics, McGraw-Hill Book Company, Inc., New York, 1950, fig. 41, p. 165.*)

point $(-\alpha/\beta,0)$ is, of course, the point where the line crosses the X axis. If it is inconvenient to use these two points, any other points can be determined by the same procedure.[2]

It was indicated above that we shall assume that the Y's are distributed normally about each value of X. It will also be convenient to assume that for each fixed value of Y the X's are also distributed normally. We say that the joint distribution of X and Y is a *bivariate normal* distribution, meaning that there are two variables, each of which is distributed about the other normally. Such a bivariate normal distribution has a definite mathematical equation and can be represented as a three-dimensional surface as in Fig. 17.3. The height of the surface at any given point (X,Y) is proportional to the number of cases at that point. Thus it takes a three-dimensional diagram to represent the joint distribution between X and Y just as we required two dimensions

[2] For a numerical example see page 284.

to represent the frequency distribution of X alone. The exact shape of this figure, which looks very much like a fireman's hat, will depend on how closely the variables are related. If both variables have been expressed in terms of standard-deviation units, then the more highly related the two variables, the narrower the hat. In the extreme case in which Y can be exactly predicted from X, and therefore all points are exactly on the regression equation, the standard deviations of Y's for each X would be zero and there would be no thickness to the hat at all. On the other hand, if there were no relationship between X and Y, the base of the hat would be circular. Any plane perpendicular to the XY plane will cut the surface in a normal curve. A plane parallel to the XY plane will cut it in an ellipse (or circle if X and Y are independent).

The bivariate normal distribution has the property that the regression of Y on X is linear. Therefore if we have a bivariate normal distribution, we know that if we trace the means of Y's for each X the result will be a straight line. It does not follow, however, that if the regression is linear, the joint distribution is necessarily bivariate normal. Bivariate normality will have to be assumed when we come to tests of significance, and since the sociologist is usually interested in making such tests he will probably need to make this assumption. If one is merely interested in point estimates rather than confidence intervals or significance tests, he can estimate the population parameters of the regression equation without having to assume bivariate normality.

We shall also need to assume that the standard deviations of the Y's for each X are the same regardless of the value of X. This assumption will be discussed in connection with the topic of correlation since correlation is essentially a measure of spread about the regression line. For the present it is sufficient to point out that if the joint distribution is bivariate normal, the standard deviations of the Y's for each X will in fact all be identical. This property of equal variances is referred to as *homoscedasticity* and is analogous to the assumption made in analysis of variance that $\sigma_1 = \sigma_2 = \cdots = \sigma_k$.

Linear Least Squares. The regression model we have been discussing is conceptually rather simple, but unfortunately it is not directly useful in its theoretical form. Seldom do we have enough cases to examine the distribution of Y's for successive fixed values of X. More commonly, we find that there are relatively few cases in which the X's are identical or nearly so. If we plot the distribution of cases on the X and Y axes in the conventional manner, we usually find a scattering of dots such as indicated in Fig. 17.4. When we plot the distribution of points in this manner we obtain what is referred to as a *scattergram* or scatter diagram. You should develop the habit of always drawing a scattergram before proceeding with further analysis. Mere inspection of the scattergram may indicate that there is no point in going any further. For example, if dots appear to be randomly distributed on the diagram there is clearly no relationship, or a very weak one, between the two variables.

Having plotted the scores on a scattergram, you may want to approximate these points by some sort of a best-fitting curve. One way of doing this is to draw a curve (in this case a straight line) by inspection. There are other more precise methods of doing this, however. One of these is the method of least squares which will be discussed in the present

$$Y = a + bX$$

Fig. 17.4. Scattergram and least-squares line.

section. Our goal is now somewhat different from that of regression analysis in which we traced the path of the mean of the Y's. Here we want to approximate a number of dots by a best-fitting curve of some type.

In order to use least-squares theory, we must postulate the form of the curve to be used in fitting the data. In the case of regression analysis the form of the curve would actually be determined by the path of the means, assuming that data for the entire population were available. Again we shall take the simplest possible curve, the straight line, as our least-squares curve. This means that we shall fit the data with a best-fitting straight line according to the least-squares criterion, getting an equation of the form

$$Y = a + bX \tag{17.2}$$

It will then turn out that the a and b obtained by this method are the most efficient unbiased estimates of the population parameters α and β if the regression equation actually is a straight line.

The least-squares criterion involves our finding the unique straight line which has the property that the sum of the squares of the deviations of the actual Y values from this line is a minimum. Thus if we draw vertical lines from each of the points to the least-squares line, and if we square these distances and add, the resulting sum will be less than a comparable sum of squares from any other possible straight line. (See Fig. 17.5.) Notice that it is the vertical distances rather than the perpendicular or horizontal distances which are being considered here. It would be possible to minimize the sum of the squares of perpendicular

Fig. 17.5. Least-squares equation minimizing sum of squares of vertical distances and estimating the regression of Y on X.

distances (referred to as orthogonal least squares), but the resulting equations are not nearly as convenient. If the horizontal distances were used, the resulting least-squares line could be used to estimate the regression of X on Y. You should convince yourself that minimizing the sum of squares of vertical distances does not necessarily minimize the sum of squares of horizontal distances. Thus we can obtain two distinct least-squares lines. Only if all points lie exactly on a single line will these lines coincide. It also turns out that by minimizing the sum of squares of vertical distances we are in effect finding the straight line having the property that the sum of the positive and negative vertical distances will be zero *and* the standard deviation of the points from the line will be a minimum. The notion of the standard deviation of the Y's from the line will be discussed below in more detail.

In order to obtain the least-squares line, then, we need to compute the a and b which determine the line with the desired property. This type of problem can easily be solved by means of calculus and leads to the following computing formulas for a and b.

$$a = \frac{\sum_{i=1}^{N} Y_i - b \sum_{i=1}^{N} X_i}{N} = \bar{Y} - b\bar{X} \qquad (17.3)$$

and

$$b = \frac{\sum_{i=1}^{N} (X_i - \bar{X})(Y_i - \bar{Y})}{\sum_{i=1}^{N} (X_i - \bar{X})^2} = \frac{\sum_{i=1}^{N} x_i y_i}{\sum_{i=1}^{N} x_i^2} \qquad (17.4)$$

where $x_i = X_i - \bar{X}$ and $y_i = Y_i - \bar{Y}$. Notice that in these equations a and b are the unknowns, the other quantities being determined directly from the data. Once b has been obtained, a can readily be computed from the first of the two formulas. We can thus focus our attention on the computation of b.

The numerator of b involves the expression $\sum_{i=1}^{N} (X_i - \bar{X})(Y_i - \bar{Y})$ which is referred to as the *covariation* of X and Y. This quantity is directly analogous to the sums of squares for either X or Y except that instead of squaring $(X - \bar{X})$ or $(Y - \bar{Y})$ we take the product of these two terms. We thus get a measure of how X and Y vary together, hence the name *covariation*. If we divide this expression by N we obtain, by analogy, what is called the *covariance*. It will be seen immediately that b can be set equal to the ratio of the covariance to the variance in X.

Taking a more detailed look at the covariation of X and Y we see that, unlike a sum of squares, the covariation can take on both positive and negative values. If X and Y are positively related, then large values of X will ordinarily be associated with large values of Y. Thus if $X > \bar{X}$, it will usually be true that $Y > \bar{Y}$. Also, for a positive relationship, if $X < \bar{X}$ we shall ordinarily have $Y < \bar{Y}$. Therefore the product of $(X - \bar{X})$ and $(Y - \bar{Y})$ will usually be positive, and the sum of these products will also be positive. Similarly, if X and Y are negatively related we would expect that if $X > \bar{X}$ then Y will be less than $\bar{Y}$, and the resulting sum of the products will be negative. If there is no relationship, then about half of the products will be positive and half negative since X and Y will vary independently. In this case b will be zero or close to zero. Therefore the higher the degree of the relationship, regardless of direction, the larger the numerical value of the covariation. As we shall see shortly, the covariation also appears in the numerator of the correlation coefficient, our measure of degree of association. In the case of b, we take the covariation and divide this by the sum of squares in X in order to obtain our estimate of the slope of the regression equation.

It is more convenient to use a computing formula for the covariation which is directly analogous to the computing formula for the sum of squares and which can be derived in a similar manner. We can write the computing formula for b as follows:

$$b = \frac{N\Sigma XY - (\Sigma X)(\Sigma Y)}{N\Sigma X^2 - (\Sigma X)^2} \qquad (17.5)$$

In equation (17.5) both numerator and denominator have been multiplied by N in order to reduce rounding errors due to division and in order to facilitate machine computation.[3]

Problem. Suppose we have the data given in Table 17.1, with X representing the percentage of Negroes in large Midwestern cities and Y indicating the difference between white and Negro median incomes as a measure of economic discrimination.

Table 17.1. Data for Correlation Problem

Per cent Negro X	Discrimination Y	Per cent Negro X	Discrimination Y
2.13	$809	4.62	$859
2.52	763	5.19	228
11.80	612	6.43	897
2.55	492	6.70	867
2.87	679	1.53	513
4.23	635	1.87	335
		10.38	868

SOURCE: U.S. Census, 1950.

From the raw data we can compute five sums which, together with N, are all that we need in order to handle regression and correlation problems. All but one of these sums will be used in computing a and b. Computations can be summarized as follows:

$$N = 13 \qquad \Sigma Y = 8{,}557$$
$$\Sigma X = 62.88 \qquad \Sigma Y^2 = 6{,}192{,}505$$
$$\Sigma X^2 = 432.2768 \qquad \Sigma XY = 43{,}943.32$$

The only new quantity here is ΣXY. Placing these values in the formulas

[3] In this and succeeding formulas the subscripts have been dropped since we are always summing over the total number of cases N.

for a and b we now get

$$b = \frac{N\Sigma XY - (\Sigma X)(\Sigma Y)}{N\Sigma X^2 - (\Sigma X)^2}$$

$$= \frac{13(43,943.32) - (62.88)(8,557)}{13(432.2768) - (62.88)^2} = \frac{33,199.0}{1,665.7} = 19.931$$

and

$$a = \frac{\Sigma Y - b\Sigma X}{N}$$

$$= \frac{8,557 - (19.931)(62.88)}{13} = 561.83$$

The resulting linear equation is therefore

$$Y_p = a + bX = 561.83 + 19.931X$$

where we have used Y_p to indicate that the Y value has been predicted from a least-squares equation. As previously mentioned, the a and b obtained by this method are the most efficient unbiased estimates of α and β, the actual regression coefficients. The least-squares line therefore will be the best estimate of the true regression if the regression equation actually is linear. The least-squares equation also has the property of passing through the point $(\bar{X}, \bar{Y})$ representing the means of both X and Y. This can be seen from equation (17.3). Since

$$a = \bar{Y} - b\bar{X}$$

we have
$$\bar{Y} = a + b\bar{X}$$

indicating that these values of X and Y satisfy the equation. Therefore the point $(\bar{X}, \bar{Y})$ lies exactly on the line.

In the above problem if we know the X value (per cent Negro) for any given Midwestern city, our best guess as to the Y value would be that value of Y on the least-squares equation corresponding to the given X. Since discrimination scores indicate differences (in dollars) between the median incomes of whites and Negroes, we see that an increase of 1 per cent Negro corresponds to a difference of \$19.93 in the median incomes of whites and Negroes. A scattergram and the least-squares equation have been drawn in Fig. 17.6. To illustrate the use of such a prediction equation, if we knew that there were 8 per cent Negroes in a given city, the estimated median income differential would be

$$Y_p = a + b(8) = 561.83 + (19.931)(8) = \$721.28$$

We can see from the figure that approximately the same result would have been obtained graphically. Incidentally, by setting $X = 8$ and

solving for Y we have located a second point on the line which can then
be used for the purpose of drawing in the line on the scatter diagram.

Fig. 17.6. Scattergram and least-squares line for data of Table 17.1.

17.2. Correlation

Not only do we want to know the *form* or nature of the relationship
between X and Y so that one variable can be predicted from the other,
but also it is necessary to know the *degree* or strength of the relationship.
Obviously, if the relationship is very weak there is no point in trying to
predict Y from X. Sociologists are often primarily interested in discovering *which* of a very large number of variables are most closely
related to a given dependent variable. In exploratory studies of this
sort, regression analysis is of secondary importance. As a science
matures and as important variables become identified, attention can
then be focused on methods of exact prediction. Some statisticians are
of the opinion that entirely too much attention has been given to correlation and too little to regression analysis. Whether or not this is true
depends, of course, on the state of knowledge in the science concerned.
We can admit that the ultimate goal of any science is precise prediction.
On the other hand, in many of our problems the use of regression equations as predictors would be highly pretentious. As we shall see, correlations of a very high order are necessary for even moderately accurate
prediction.

The correlation coefficient r to be discussed in this section was introduced by Karl Pearson and is often referred to as product-moment correlation in order to distinguish it from other measures of association. This coefficient measures the amount of spread about the *linear* least-squares equation. There is a comparable population coefficient rho (ρ) which measures the goodness of fit to the true regression equation. We obtain an estimate r of this parameter by measuring deviations from the line computed by least squares.

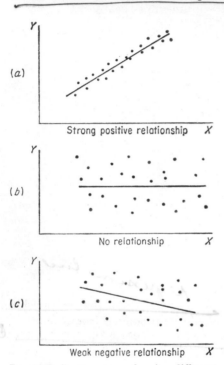

(a) Strong positive relationship X

(b) No relationship X

(c) Weak negative relationship X

Fig. 17.7. Scattergrams showing different strengths and directions of relationships between X and Y.

Since the regression equation represents the path of the means of Y's for given X's, it would also be possible to measure spread about this line by taking a standard deviation from the line.[4] Researchers in most applied fields have become accustomed to the correlation coefficient, however, and although some mathematical statisticians seem to prefer the second kind of measure, the correlation coefficient is probably here to stay. It has the advantage of being easily interpreted, and its range is from -1.0 to 1.0, a fact which is appealing to most practitioners. As we shall see, the relationship between the correlation coefficient and the standard deviation about the least-squares line is a very simple one, and this fact can be used to provide an interpretation for r.

It has been mentioned that r has an upper limit of 1.0. If all points are exactly on the straight line, r will be either 1.0 or -1.0 depending on whether the relationship is positive or negative. If the dots are randomly scattered r will be zero. The better the fit, the larger the magnitude of r. This is indicated in Fig. 17.7.

Notice that r is a measure of *linear* relationship, being a measure of the goodness of fit of the least-squares straight line. You should not be

---

[4] The exact nature of such a measure will be discussed below. For the present we can simply point out that it represents an extension of the notion of a standard deviation, where the mean of the Y's is no longer taken as fixed but is considered to be a function of X.

mislead into thinking that if $r = 0$ (or if $\rho = 0$) there is no relationship whatsoever. If there is no relationship, it follows that r will be approximately zero and there will be a random scatter of points. There may, however, be a perfect curvilinear relationship and yet r can be zero, indicating that there is no *straight line* which can fit the data. In Fig. 17.8 this is actually the case. Therefore, if a researcher finds a correlation of zero he should be careful not to infer that the two variables are unrelated. Usually, inspection of the scattergram will indicate whether there

Fig. 17.8. Scattergram for perfect nonlinear relationship for which $r = 0$.

is in fact no relationship or whether the relationship is sufficiently nonlinear to produce a zero correlation. In most sociological problems relationships can be approximated reasonably well with straight lines. This does not mean that one should not be alert for possible exceptions, however.

We have not as yet defined the correlation coefficient, but we can easily do so in terms of the formula

$$r = \frac{\Sigma(X - \bar{X})(Y - \bar{Y})}{\sqrt{[\Sigma(X - \bar{X})^2][\Sigma(Y - \bar{Y})^2]}} = \frac{\Sigma xy}{\sqrt{(\Sigma x^2)(\Sigma y^2)}} \qquad (17.6)$$

In words, the correlation coefficient is the ratio of the covariation to the square root of the product of the variation in X and the variation in Y. Dividing numerator and denominator by N, writing this quantity as N^2 within the radical, we see that r can also be defined as the ratio of the covariance to the product of the standard deviations of X and Y. The covariance is a measure of the joint variation in X and Y, but its magnitude depends on the total amount of variability in both variables.

Since the numerical value of the covariance can be considerably greater than unity, it is inconvenient to use it directly as a measure of association. Instead, we standardize by dividing by the product of the two standard deviations, thereby obtaining a measure which varies between -1.0 and 1.0.

We have already seen that the covariance will be zero whenever X and Y are unrelated. It can also easily be shown that the upper limit of r is unity. Let us take the case where b is positive and where all points lie exactly on the line. Then for every Y we can write $Y = a + bX$. Since $(\bar{X}, \bar{Y})$ also lies on the line we have $\bar{Y} = a + b\bar{X}$. Therefore for all points on the line

$$Y - \bar{Y} = (a + bX) - (a + b\bar{X}) = b(X - \bar{X})$$

Hence
$$\Sigma(X - \bar{X})(Y - \bar{Y}) = b\Sigma(X - \bar{X})^2$$

and
$$\Sigma(Y - \bar{Y})^2 = b^2\Sigma(X - \bar{X})^2$$

Inspection of the numerator and denominator of r now indicates that under these conditions $r = 1.0$. Similarly, it can be shown that if all points lie exactly on a line with negative slope, the resulting r will be -1.0.

The relationship between the correlation coefficient and the slopes of the two least-squares equations should also be noted. If we let b_{yx} be the slope of the least-squares equation estimating the regression of Y on X, and if we let b_{xy} indicate the slope of the estimate of the regression of X on Y, we have by symmetry that

$$b_{xy} = \frac{\Sigma(X - \bar{X})(Y - \bar{Y})}{\Sigma(Y - \bar{Y})^2}$$

where
$$X = a_{xy} + b_{xy}Y$$

Thus, r has the same numerator as both b's. If the b's are zero it follows that r must also be zero and vice versa.

For given sums of squares in X and Y, the value of b_{yx} (or b_{xy}) will be proportional to r. This might seem to lead to the conclusion that the strength of relationship is proportional to the slope of the least-squares line. This will be true only if the denominator remains fixed, however. Thus b is a function not only of the strength of the relationship but also of the standard deviations.[5] If there is considerable variability in X relative to Y, the value of b will be relatively small, indicating that it takes a large change in X to produce a moderate change in Y. As will be discussed below, the numerical values of the b's therefore depend on the size of the units of measurement.

[5] Except in cases where confusion might arise, we shall continue to make use of b without the subscripts to represent b_{yx}.

The value of r has been standardized so that it is independent of the relative sizes of the standard deviations in X and Y. It would indeed be unfortunate if this were not the case, since we would hardly want a measure which varied according to whether we selected dollars or pennies as our monetary unit. It will be noted from the formulas for r and the b's that r^2 can be expressed in terms of the b's. Thus

$$r^2 = b_{yx} b_{xy} = \frac{[\Sigma xy]^2}{\Sigma x^2 \Sigma y^2} \qquad (17.7)$$

You should verify that when r is 1.0 (or -1.0), $b_{yx} = 1/b_{xy}$ and that this means that the two least-squares equations coincide. Generally, as r approaches zero, the angle between the two lines becomes larger and larger until when $r = 0$ the lines have become perpendicular.

Finally, we can introduce a computing formula for r which involves the five sums previously obtained in connection with the computations of a and b. The formula is

$$r = \frac{N\Sigma XY - (\Sigma X)(\Sigma Y)}{\sqrt{[N\Sigma X^2 - (\Sigma X)^2][N\Sigma Y^2 - (\Sigma Y)^2]}} \qquad (17.8)$$

The numerator has, of course, already been computed, and so has part of the denominator. Thus the correlation between per cent Negro and the index of discrimination is

$$r = \frac{13(43{,}943.32) - (62.88)(8{,}557)}{\sqrt{[13(432.2768) - (62.88)^2][13(6{,}192{,}505) - (8{,}557)^2]}}$$

$$= \frac{33{,}199}{110{,}120} = .301$$

It should be noted that one can add or subtract values from either X or Y without affecting the value of the correlation coefficient. Likewise, a change of scale can be made for either variable by multiplying or dividing by any constant. This says in effect that the correlation between income and education is the same regardless of whether income is measured in dollars or pennies. But although the correlation coefficient is invariant under transformations of this sort, the least-squares equation is not. Adding or subtracting values will affect the numerical value of a. A change of scale will affect the slope of the line. For example, if every X is divided by 10 while Y is kept fixed, the resulting b will be multiplied by 10. You should verify that these properties hold by examining the formulas for r, a, and b. These facts may be used in order to simplify computations. For example, if X involves either a very large number or a very small decimal, a change of scale may reduce the risk of computing errors. Or if the X variable consists of values such as 1,207, 1,409, 1,949, and 1,568, it would probably be advisable to subtract 1,000 from each score. Certain computing routines require that all values be positive. In computing r, therefore, it may be necessary to add to each value a number which is slightly larger than the largest negative score.

Another fact about the correlation coefficient should be noted at this time. Since this measure involves both variances and covariances, it is highly affected by a few extreme values of either variable. Furthermore,

Fig. 17.9. Scattergrams showing possible effects of extreme X values.

the magnitude of r depends on the degree of general variability in the independent variable. Figure 17.9 illustrates these points. In Fig. 17.9a, the effect of one or two extreme values is to produce a moderately high correlation where none exists among the remaining cases. In Fig. 17.9b, we have a moderately high linear relationship except for the fact that extreme cases are out of line with the rest. In this latter instance we probably have an example of a nonlinear relationship. A scattergram will always be helpful in indicating the nature of the situation in any given problem. Let us now discuss what can be done if either of these situations should occur.

Figure 17.9a illustrates the point made above that the magnitude of the correlation coefficient depends on the range of variability in both varia-bles. Had there been a larger number of extreme cases, the resulting distribution might have been as in Fig. 17.10. In this instance the over-all correlation may be high, but within any limited range of X's the correlation may be close to zero. In effect, this indicates that there is insufficient variability in X within this limited range to counteract the effects of numerous uncontrolled variables. In reality, X is almost being held constant. Therefore, if a scattergram turns out to be similar to the one in Fig. 17.9a, one should always attempt to extend the range of variability in X by finding more extreme cases.

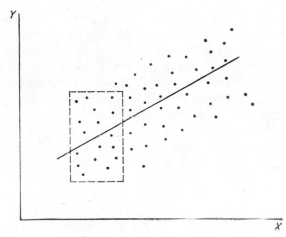

Fig. 17.10. Scattergram showing no relationship within a limited range of variation in X but a positive relationship over the total range.

If extending the range of variability is not feasible empirically or if the researcher's interest is focused primarily on less extreme cases, it may be more sensible to exclude the extreme cases from the analysis altogether. For example, suppose X is size of city and New York City appears in the sample. Unless there are a large number of cities of comparable size, and there aren't, it may become necessary to confine one's attention to cities of less than 500,000. In some instances it would seem advisable to compute r both with and without the extreme cases. Obviously, the decision made will depend upon the nature of the problem and the research interests of the social scientist. You should be alerted to the fact that one or two extreme scores can have a very pronounced effect on the magnitude of r, and you should always take this into consideration in some manner. The range of variability should therefore be reported with correlation coefficients. This is another illustration of the important point that a single summarizing measure, no matter how superior it may be to other measures, can often be misleading.

If the data turn out to be as in Fig. 17.9b, we would obviously suspect nonlinearity. Again, if possible, additional extreme cases should be obtained. If there are only one or two extremes it may be advisable to exclude these from the analysis. Situations of this sort illustrate the fact that within a limited range of variation a relationship may be approximately linear, but when extended the linear model may be inappropriate. You should therefore be careful not to generalize beyond the limits of the data. A cautious statement such as, "Within the limits of _____ and _____ the relationship appears to be approximately linear" would be most appropriate.

Computations from Grouped Data. If the number of cases is large or if modern desk calculators are unavailable, the computation of correlation coefficients may become extremely tedious. In such instances it may be more convenient to make use of grouped data in spite of the fact that certain slight inaccuracies will be introduced. In principle, these computations for grouped data are straightforward extensions of the procedures used in obtaining the mean and standard deviation. We now have two variables which must be cross classified as in Table 17.2. We shall guess a mean for each variable, taking step deviations from each guessed mean, and make use of correction factors in each case. In addition, we shall need a cross-product term equivalent to Σxy. Since deviations for both X and Y will be taken from the respective *guessed* means, we shall need to make use of a correction factor to be subtracted from the estimated cross-product term. We can then modify the computing formulas for r and b so as to take into consideration the fact that we have used guessed means rather than correct means.

You will recall that one of the computing formulas for s using grouped data was (dropping the subscripts)

$$s = \frac{i}{N} \sqrt{N\Sigma fd'^2 - (\Sigma fd')^2}$$

Since we now have two variables X and Y, we shall make use of subscripts in order to distinguish frequencies and step deviations for X (i.e., f_x and d'_x) from those for Y (i.e., f_y and d'_y). In computing the cross-product term we also need to obtain the frequencies f_{xy} in each subcell. These latter frequencies will ordinarily be smaller than either f_x or f_y. Thus, although there are 24 cases in the category 40.0 to 49.9 for the X variable and 30 cases in the 15.0 to 19.9 category of Y, there are only 6 cases in the subcell corresponding to both of these categories. You should convince yourself that the computing formula for r (equation 17.8) can be modified as follows

$$r = \frac{N\Sigma f_{xy}d'_x d'_y - (\Sigma f_x d'_x)(\Sigma f_y d'_y)}{\sqrt{[N\Sigma f_x d'^2_x - (\Sigma f_x d'_x)^2][N\Sigma f_y d'^2_y - (\Sigma f_y d'_y)^2]}} \qquad (17.9)$$

Similarly, the formula for b becomes

$$b = \frac{N\Sigma f_{xy}d'_x d'_y - (\Sigma f_x d'_x)(\Sigma f_y d'_y)}{N\Sigma f_x d'^2_x - (\Sigma f_x d'_x)^2} \frac{i_y}{i_x} \qquad (17.10)$$

where i_y and i_x represent the interval widths for Y and X respectively. The value of a can now be computed from the equation

$$a = \frac{\Sigma Y - b\Sigma X}{N} = \bar{Y} - b\bar{X}$$

where $\bar{X}$ and $\bar{Y}$ can be obtained using the usual formula for grouped data.

Let us now compute the values of these coefficients for data on 150 Southern counties given in Table 17.2. We shall take as the dependent

Table 17.2. Data Cross Classified for Obtaining Correlations from Grouped Data

Per cent rural-farm, X	Percentage of females in the labor force, Y							Totals
	10.0–14.9	15.0–19.9	20.0–24.9	25.0–29.9	30.0–34.9	35.0–39.9	40.0–44.9	
0.0– 9.9	0	0	0	1	8	4	0	13
10.0–19.9	1	2	0	2	4	1	3	13
20.0–29.9	2	5	1	2	3	3	0	16
30.0–39.9	2	0	5	5	7	3	0	22
40.0–49.9	4	6	6	7	1	0	0	24
50.0–59.9	3	10	9	6	2	0	0	30
60.0–69.9	2	4	3	7	4	0	0	20
70.0–79.9	2	3	4	1	0	0	0	10
80.0–89.9	1	0	1	0	0	0	0	2
Totals	17	30	29	31	29	11	3	150

SOURCE: U.S. Census, 1950.

variable Y the percentage of females in the labor force, the independent variable being the percentage of the population classed as rural-farm. It will be convenient to make use of a computing form such as that given in Table 17.3. In this table the class limits and mid-points are given across the top (for Y) and down the left-hand margin (for X). Focus your attention on the boxed-in area of the table. Notice that there are three numbers in each subcell. In each subcell the top number represents the number of cases in the subcell as given in Table 17.2. The remaining numbers in the subcell are used in computing the cross-product term. The middle figure in each subcell represents the product of the step deviations $d'_x d'_y$. Thus in the bottom left-hand subcell (corresponding to the categories 80.0 to 89.9 and 10.0 to 14.9) the entry -12 is the product of 4 and -3. In other words, the category 80.0 to 89.9 is four step deviations *above* the hypothesized mean of X, and the category 10.0 to

Table 17.3. Computations for Correlations from Grouped Data*

Class limits	Y	10.0–14.9	15.0–19.9	20.0–24.9	25.0–29.9	30.0–34.9	35.0–39.9	40.0–44.9	f_x	d'_x	$f_x d'_x$	$f_x(d'_x)^2$
X	Mid-points	12.45	17.45	22.45	27.45	32.45	37.45	42.45				
0.0–9.9	4.95				1 0 0	8 −4 −32	4 −8 −32		13	−4	−52	208
10.0–19.9	14.95	1 +9 9	2 +6 12		2 0 0	4 −3 −12	1 −6 −6	3 −9 −27	13	−3	−39	117
20.0–29.9	24.95	2 +6 12	5 +4 20	1 +2 2	2 0 0	3 −2 −6	3 −4 −12		16	−2	−32	64
30.0–39.9	34.95	2 +3 6		5 +1 5	5 0 0	7 −1 −7	3 −2 −6		22	−1	−22	22
40.0–49.9	44.95	4 0 0	6 0 0	6 0 0	7 0 0	1 0 0			24	0	0	0
50.0–59.9	54.95	3 −3 −9	10 −2 −20	9 −1 −9	6 0 0	2 +1 2			30	1	30	30
60.0–69.9	64.95	2 −6 −12	4 −4 −16	3 −2 −6	7 0 0	4 +2 8			20	2	40	80
70.0–79.9	74.95	2 −9 −18	3 −6 −18	4 −3 −12	1 0 0				10	3	30	90
80.0–89.9	84.95	1 −12 −12		1 −4 −4					2	4	8	32
f_y		17	30	29	31	29	11	3	N = 150		−37	643
d'_y		−3	−2	−1	0	1	2	3				
$f_y d'_y$		−51	−60	−29	0	29	22	9	−80		$\Sigma f_{xy} d'_x d'_y$ = −200	
$f_y(d'_y)^2$		153	120	29	0	29	44	27	402			

* This computing form has been taken, with slight adaptations, from [1], table 19.4, p. 476, with the kind permission of the publisher.

14.9 is three step deviations *below* the hypothesized mean of Y. Finally, the bottom number in each subcell represents the product of the first two numbers and therefore can be represented symbolically as $f_{xy}d'_x d'_y$. The sum of these bottom figures over the entire number of subcells therefore gives us the cross-product term uncorrected for errors introduced by using guessed means. This sum, which will be used in the first term of the numerator of r, is numerically equal to -200 and has been placed in the lower right-hand corner of the table.

The remaining quantities needed in the computation of r and b can be obtained in the familiar manner. The last four columns in the table are used to obtain f_x, d'_x, $f_x d'_x$, and $f_x(d'_x)^2$, the sums of the latter two quantities being directly used in the formula for r. Notice that in computing the numerical values for these last four columns we are completely ignoring the Y values. Thus, if we ignore the boxed-in area, we have exactly the same kind of table as was used in computing the mean and standard deviation from grouped data. Similarly, the bottom four rows can be used to obtain comparable sums for the Y variable. All of the quantities needed in the formulas for r and b can now be placed in the bottom right-hand cells of the larger table.

We now obtain the values of r and b as follows:

$$r = \frac{150(-200) - (-37)(-80)}{\sqrt{[150(643) - (-37)^2][150(402) - (-80)^2]}} = \frac{-32,960}{71,590} = -.460$$

$$b = \frac{150(-200) - (-37)(-80)}{150(643) - (-37)^2} \frac{5.0}{10.0} = \frac{-32,960}{95,081} \frac{1}{2} = -.1733$$

Since the values of $\bar{X}$ and $\bar{Y}$ are 42.48 and 24.78 respectively, we get

$$a = \bar{Y} - b\bar{X} = 24.78 - (-.1733)(42.48) = 32.14$$

and the least-squares equation can be written as

$$Y_p = 32.14 - .1733X$$

little

Interpretations for the Correlation Coefficient. In order to obtain an interpretation for r which will be meaningful when r is neither 0 nor 1.0, let us return to the notion of variability about the regression equation. We have defined the variance about the mean of Y as

$$\sigma_y^2 = \frac{\Sigma(Y - \mu_y)^2}{M}$$

where M represents the size of the population (as contrasted with the sample size N) and where we use the subscripts to emphasize the fact that there are now two variables which must be distinguished. Thus the ordinary concept of variance involves deviations from a *fixed* measure of central tendency, the over-all mean. But we can also obtain the mean of Y's for a fixed X, and we are assuming that these values vary with X so as to produce a linear regression. We thus can generalize the concept of a mean, obtaining a kind of conditional mean of Y for a given X which we may symbolize as $\mu_{y|x}$.

If we generalize the concept of variance in a similar manner we can obtain as a measure of spread about the regression equation

$$\sigma_{y|x}^2 = \frac{\Sigma(Y - \mu_{y|x})^2}{M} \qquad (17.11)$$

where the symbol $\sigma_{y|x}^2$ is used to emphasize the fact that the magnitude of variability about the regression equation, as well as the mean of Y, depends upon the value of X. In other words, for each X there is both a mean of the Y's and a variance about this mean. The amount of spread about the line need not always be the same for each X although we are going to *assume* the property of homoscedasticity or equal variances. We now have two measures of variability for Y. The first measures the spread about that value of Y, the grand mean μ_y, which would be the best single predicted value of Y if X were not known. In other words, if one were asked to predict Y with no knowledge of X his best guess would be μ_y (or $\bar{Y}$ if only sample data were available). Knowing X, however, he would predict the corresponding value of Y which lay on the regression equation. Unless there were no relationship between X and Y, knowledge of X should help him predict the value of Y. If the relationship were perfect he could predict Y exactly since all points would be exactly on the line. Ordinarily, he will not be able to do this well, but since we are assuming a normal distribution of Y's and a fixed standard deviation $\sigma_{y|x}$, we can make probability statements about the risks and magnitude of his error. More important for our purposes, we can compare the two standard deviations (or variances) and obtain a measure of how much the prediction has been improved by knowing X. In so doing, we can make use of processes familiar from analysis of variance.

In analysis of variance we took the total variation or sum of squares and divided this quantity into explained and unexplained portions. We shall now use exactly the same procedure, obtaining almost as a by-product the values of $\sigma_{y|x}^2$ and r^2. We can then give a meaningful interpretation for the correlation coefficient. First, we express the deviations of each Y from $\bar{Y}$ as the sum of two quantities $(Y - Y_p) + (Y_p - \bar{Y})$. (See Fig. 17.11.) The first of these quantities represents the deviation of the Y value from the least-squares line and indicates the amount of error made when Y_p is used to predict Y. The second expression indicates the deviation of the least-squares line (at a given X) from $\bar{Y}$. For most cases, this quantity will represent the amount by which the error is reduced when Y_p is known. If we now square both sides of the equation and then sum over all cases, we obtain

$$\Sigma(Y - \bar{Y})^2 = \Sigma(Y - Y_p)^2 + 2\Sigma(Y - Y_p)(Y_p - \bar{Y}) + \Sigma(Y_p - \bar{Y})^2$$

Fortunately, the middle term again drops out, and we are left with

$$\Sigma(Y - \bar{Y})^2 = \Sigma(Y - Y_p)^2 + \Sigma(Y_p - \bar{Y})^2 \qquad (17.12)$$
$$\text{Total SS} = \text{unexplained SS} + \text{explained SS}$$

The first quantity on the right-hand side of the equation represents the sum of the squares of the deviations of the actual Y values from the

Fig. 17.11. Geometric representation showing deviations from mean $\bar{Y}$ as a sum of deviations from least-squares line and deviations of least-squares line from $\bar{Y}$.

least-squares line. This quantity is unexplained since it indicates the amount of error in prediction. The remaining quantity indicates what we have gained in using Y_p in preference to $\bar{Y}$ and can be referred to as the explained sum of squares. By "explained," of course, we do not imply a causal explanation but merely an association between the two variables. Let us now look more closely at each of these quantities.

If we take the unexplained sum of squares and divide by the total number of cases, we obtain the sample variance $s_{y|x}^2$ about the least-squares line. Thus

$$s_{y|x}^2 = \frac{\Sigma(Y - Y_p)^2}{N} \qquad (17.13)$$

If we wish to obtain an unbiased estimate of the population variance $\sigma_{y|x}^2$ about the true regression, we must divide not by N but by the appropriate degrees of freedom. In this case we have lost 2 degrees of freedom in calculating a and b as estimates of α and β. Therefore, if we wish to estimate $\sigma_{y|x}^2$ we would use

$$\hat{\sigma}_{y|x}^2 = \frac{\Sigma(Y - Y_p)^2}{N - 2} \qquad (17.14)$$

Thus the unexplained sum of squares can readily be converted into an estimate of the variance about the regression equation. You should convince yourself that what we have done is directly parallel to our earlier treatment of analysis of variance. The variability about the least-squares equation has replaced the notion of variability *within* categories of X.

Turning now to the explained sum of squares $\Sigma(Y_p - \bar{Y})^2$, we can easily show that this quantity is equivalent to $r^2[\Sigma(Y - \bar{Y})^2]$ or $r^2\Sigma y^2$. Since $Y_p = a + bX$ and $\bar{Y} = a + b\bar{X}$, we have

$$(Y_p - \bar{Y}) = b(X - \bar{X})$$

Therefore

$$\Sigma(Y_p - \bar{Y})^2 = b^2\Sigma(X - \bar{X})^2 = b^2\Sigma x^2$$
$$= \frac{(\Sigma xy)^2}{(\Sigma x^2)^2}(\Sigma x^2) = \frac{(\Sigma xy)^2}{\Sigma x^2}$$
$$= \frac{(\Sigma xy)^2}{\Sigma x^2 \Sigma y^2}(\Sigma y^2) = r^2\Sigma y^2$$
$$= r^2\Sigma(Y - \bar{Y})^2$$

We have thus shown that

$$r^2 = \frac{\Sigma(Y_p - \bar{Y})^2}{\Sigma(Y - \bar{Y})^2} = \frac{\text{explained SS}}{\text{total SS}}$$

By a similar argument we could show that r^2 represents the ratio of explained variation in X to total variation in X. The square of the correlation coefficient can therefore be interpreted as the proportion of the total variation in the one variable explained by the other. The quantity $\sqrt{1 - r^2}$, sometimes referred to as the *coefficient of alienation*, represents the square root of the proportion of the total sum of squares that is unexplained by the independent variable.

It should be noted that there is no direct and simple interpretation for r itself. In fact it is possible to be mislead by values of r since these values will be numerically larger than those of r^2 (unless r is 0 or ± 1.0). Thus it might appear that an r of .5 is half as good as a perfect correlation whereas we see that in this case we are explaining only 25 per cent of the variation. A correlation of .7 indicates that slightly less than half of the variation is being explained. We see also that correlations of .3 or less mean that only a very small fraction of the variation is being explained. Table 17.4 indicates the relationships among the various quantities.

Since $1 - r^2$ represents the proportion of unexplained variation, we have

$$(1 - r^2)[\Sigma(Y - \bar{Y})^2] = \Sigma(Y - Y_p)^2$$

Therefore
$$(1 - r^2)\frac{\Sigma(Y - \bar{Y})^2}{N} = \frac{\Sigma(Y - Y_p)^2}{N}$$

or
$$(1 - r^2)s_y^2 = s_{y|x}^2$$

Hence
$$s_{y|x} = \sqrt{1 - r^2}\, s_y$$

This result gives us an indication of how much we can reduce the standard deviation by knowing X. (See the last column of Table 17.4.) When r is zero the two standard deviations are equal. This fact is obvious, of course, when we realize that the least-squares line would in this case be a

Table 17.4. Numerical Relationships between r, r^2, $1 - r^2$, and $\sqrt{1 - r^2}$

r	r^2	$1 - r^2$	$\sqrt{1 - r^2}$
.90	.81	.19	.44
.80	.64	.36	.60
.70	.49	.51	.71
.60	.36	.64	.80
.50	.25	.75	.87
.40	.16	.84	.92
.30	.09	.91	.95
.20	.04	.96	.98
.10	.01	.99	.995

horizontal line having the equation $Y = \bar{Y}$. When r^2 is unity, $s_{y|x}$ will of course be zero since all points will be exactly on the line.

From Table 17.4 we see that the magnitude of r has to be large before we get a substantial reduction in standard deviations. For an r of .80 the standard deviation about the least-squares line is .60 of the ordinary standard deviation, but for an r of .40 we see that we have not gained a great deal in estimating Y from X. It is for this reason that prediction equations are not as practical as they might appear to be. Unless the correlation is reasonably high (say, .7 or above), it may be rather misleading to make use of prediction equations. When we note that most correlations in the social sciences are considerably less than .7 we realize that exact prediction becomes out of the question. In most problems in social science, attention is rightly focused more on locating the important variables. In exploratory work of this sort, correlational analysis becomes more important than regression analysis.

GLOSSARY

Bivariate normal distribution
Coefficient of alienation
Coefficient of correlation
Covariance
Least-squares equation
Regression of Y on X

EXERCISES

1. The following data for 29 non-Southern cities of 100,000 or more are taken from R. C. Angell's study of moral integration of American cities. The moral-integration index was derived by combining crime-rate indices with those for welfare effort. Heterogeneity was measured in terms of the relative numbers of nonwhites and foreign-born whites in the population. A mobility index measuring the relative numbers of persons moving in and out of the city was also computed as a second independent variable.

City	Integration index	Heterogeneity index	Mobility index
Rochester	19.0	20.6	15.0
Syracuse	17.0	15.6	20.2
Worchester	16.4	22.1	13.6
Erie	16.2	14.0	14.8
Milwaukee	15.8	17.4	17.6
Bridgeport	15.3	27.9	17.5
Buffalo	15.2	22.3	14.7
Dayton	14.3	23.7	23.8
Reading	14.2	10.6	19.4
Des Moines	14.1	12.7	31.9
Cleveland	14.0	39.7	18.6
Denver	13.9	13.0	34.5
Peoria	13.8	10.7	35.1
Wichita	13.6	11.9	42.7
Trenton	13.0	32.5	15.8
Grand Rapids	12.8	15.7	24.2
Toledo	12.7	19.2	21.6
San Diego	12.5	15.9	49.8
Baltimore	12.0	45.8	12.1
South Bend	11.8	17.9	27.4
Akron	11.3	20.4	22.1
Detroit	11.1	38.3	19.5
Tacoma	10.9	17.8	31.2
Flint	9.8	19.3	32.2
Spokane	9.6	12.3	38.9
Seattle	9.0	23.9	34.2
Indianapolis	8.8	29.2	23.1
Columbus	8.0	27.4	25.0
Portland (Ore.)	7.2	16.4	35.8

SOURCE: R. C. Angell, "The Moral Integration of American Cities," *American Journal of Sociology*, vol. 57, part 2, p. 17, July 1951, with the kind permission of the author and publisher. (Copyright 1951 by the University of Chicago.)

    a. Draw a scattergram, relating moral integration to heterogeneity.

    b. Compute r, a, and b for these same variables and draw in the least-squares line on your scattergram, taking moral integration as Y.

    c. How large is the standard deviation about the least-squares line as compared with the standard deviation about $\bar{Y}$?

2. You will need to obtain the correlations between moral integration and mobility and between heterogeneity and mobility in order to handle exercises in Chap. 19. Compute both of these r's.

3. Group the moral-integration and heterogeneity indices into intervals and compute r, a, and b using formulas for grouped data. Compare results with those for ungrouped data.

REFERENCES

1. Croxton, F. E., and D. J. Cowden: *Applied General Statistics*, Prentice-Hall, Inc., Englewood Cliffs, N.J., 1955, chaps. 19 and 20.

2. Hagood, M. J., and D. O. Price: *Statistics for Sociologists*, Henry Holt and Company, Inc., New York, 1952, chap. 23.

3. McNemar, Q.: *Psychological Statistics*, John Wiley & Sons, Inc., New York, 1955, chaps. 8, 9, and 10.

4. Wallis, W. A., and H. V. Roberts: *Statistics: A New Approach*, Free Press, Glencoe, Ill., 1956, chap. 17.

Chapter 18

CORRELATION AND REGRESSION (CONTINUED)

In the present chapter we shall continue the discussion of correlation and regression. First, various tests of significance will be considered. We shall then turn to nonlinear relationships, a subject which will also be discussed briefly in Chap. 19. Finally, the topic of rank-order correlation will be treated.

18.1. Significance Tests and Confidence Intervals

Significance Test for r and b. Since r and the least-squares coefficients a and b are descriptive only of the sample data, our interest usually centers on the comparable population parameters ρ, α, and β. In particular, we may wish to test the null hypothesis that there is no (linear) relationship in the population, or we may want to obtain confidence intervals for ρ or the regression coefficients. We shall first consider a test of the null hypothesis that there is no linear relationship in the population. As we shall see, if we can assume a bivariate normal distribution we can use analysis of variance to test the hypothesis that $\rho = \beta = 0$.

Let us make use of the fact that since r and b (and therefore ρ and β) have the same numerators, a test of the hypothesis $\rho = 0$ is also a test of the hypothesis $\beta = 0$ and vice versa. In other words, if there is no linear association in the population, the slope of the regression equation will be zero and the line will therefore be horizontal. Remembering that a regression equation represents the path of the means of the Y's for fixed values of X, we see immediately that whenever $\beta = 0$ the means of the Y's must be the same for every value of X (see Fig. 18.1). This assumes, of course, that the regression equation is actually linear in form. In particular, if we were to divide the X axis into a number of categories we would find the population category means to be exactly equal. Thus we can translate the hypothesis that $\rho = 0$ into the statement that the means for Y will be equal for each of the X categories. If we imagine an infinite population, as will be necessary in order to meet the assumption of normality, we can imagine the X axis being divided into an indefinitely large number of categories each having identical means in Y. Thus our null hypothesis becomes $\mu_{y1} = \mu_{y2} = \mu_{y3} = \cdots$, where we have used the double subscript to emphasize that it is the means of the Y's with which we are concerned and that we have an indefinitely large number of X categories.

Fig. 18.1. Geometric representation of the fact that the hypothesis that $\beta = 0$ is equivalent to the hypothesis $\mu_1 = \mu_2 = \cdots = \mu_k$.

The above line of reasoning obviously suggests an extension of the analysis-of-variance test covering an indefinitely large number of categories of the nominal-scale variable (now X). Let us recall the assumptions required in analysis of variance. In addition to the null hypothesis and the assumption that cases have been selected randomly and independently from each of the categories, we must also assume normal populations and equal variances within each category. Provided we can also assume random sampling, we see that all of these assumptions can be met if we assume the joint distribution of X and Y to be bivariate normal. You will recall that this latter assumption simultaneously assures us of a linear regression equation, normality of the Y's for each fixed value of X, and equal variances for all values of X. In effect, therefore, the assumptions of random sampling and bivariate normality enable us to make use of analysis of variance to test the hypothesis that $\rho = \beta = 0$.

Previously we found it necessary to obtain the total and between sums of squares and then to subtract in order to get the within sum of squares. In testing the hypothesis that $\rho = 0$, the process is substantially simplified, however. We have already seen that the *proportion* of the total sum of squares of Y explained by X is given by r^2. Likewise, the proportion left unexplained by X will be $1 - r^2$. Since the total sum of squares can be symbolized by Σy^2, the explained and unexplained sums of square therefore become $r^2 \Sigma y^2$ and $(1 - r^2) \Sigma y^2$ respectively.

The degrees of freedom associated with the total sum of squares is o course $N - 1$. In computing the unexplained sum of squares we take the sum of the squared deviations about the least-squares line rather than about the grand mean of the Y's. But in order to obtain the least squares line we have had to make use of two coefficients a and b. We have therefore lost 2 degrees of freedom, one more than was lost in taking deviations about the single value $\bar{Y}$. We thus can associate $N - 2$

Table 18.1. Analysis of Variance Test of the Hypothesis that $\rho = 0$

	Sums of squares	Degrees of freedom	Estimates of variance	F
Total	Σy^2	$N - 1$		
Explained	$r^2 \Sigma y^2$	1	$\dfrac{r^2 \Sigma y^2}{1}$	$\dfrac{r^2(N - 2)}{(1 - r^2)}$
Unexplained	$(1 - r^2) \Sigma y^2$	$N - 2$	$\dfrac{(1 - r^2) \Sigma y^2}{N - 2}$	

degrees of freedom with the unexplained sum of squares, and by subtraction we see that there is 1 degree of freedom to be associated with the explained sum of squares.

The results can now be summarized as in Table 18.1. The advantage of inserting symbols rather than numbers into the table is that we see immediately that the quantity Σy^2 disappears when we take the ratio of the explained to unexplained estimates. In other words, the total sum of squares cancels out and we can write a formula for F in terms of the *proportions* of explained and unexplained sums of squares. The formula for F then involves only the quantities r^2 and $1 - r^2$ along with the degrees of freedom of $N - 2$ and 1. Therefore we may use the formula

$$F_{1,N-2} = \frac{r^2}{1 - r^2}(N - 2) \tag{18.1}$$

without actually bothering to construct an analysis-of-variance table as was necessary in the previous chapter.

We can illustrate the use of this analysis-of-variance test for the significance of r with the data of Table 17.1. We obtained a correlation of $r = .301$ between per cent Negro and our index of discrimination. In testing for the significance of r we are asking the very important question, "How likely is it that we would obtain an r of .301 or larger (in absolute value) if there were actually no linear association in the population?" In order to make the F test, we simply compute r^2 and $1 - r^2$ and make use of equation (18.1). Thus, since r was based on 13 cases,

$$F_{1,11} = \frac{(.301)^2}{[1 - (.301)^2]} \, 11 = \frac{.0906}{.9094} \, 11 = 1.10$$

Referring to the F table, we see that for 1 and 11 degrees of freedom we would need an F of 4.84 or larger in order to reject at the .05 level. We therefore decide not to reject the null hypothesis that $\rho = 0$. Apparently, we could have gotten an r of .301 or larger fairly frequently by chance even if there were absolutely no association in the population.

Again, it is necessary to emphasize the distinction between a test of significance and a measure of the degree of relationship. Had we obtained an r of .301 with a sample size of 50 we would have gotten

$$F_{1,48} = \frac{.0906}{.9094} \, 48 = 4.78$$

a value which is significant at the .05 level. In both cases we have explained approximately 9 per cent of the total sample variation, but in the latter case we have more faith that there is a relationship, however slight, in the population.

Confidence Intervals. Whenever a bivariate normal population can be assumed or approximated, it is possible to construct confidence intervals for ρ, β, and the regression line. The standard error of r is given by the formula

$$\sigma_r = \frac{1 - \rho^2}{\sqrt{N - 1}}$$

Unfortunately, the sampling distribution of r will not in general be symmetrical except in the special case where $\rho = 0$. In fact, the sampling distribution becomes more and more skewed as the absolute value of ρ approaches unity. In addition, we note that in order to make use of the above formula for the standard error of r it would be necessary to know or estimate the value of ρ. Both of these complications make it difficult to obtain confidence intervals for ρ in the straightforward manner.

In computing a confidence interval about r, we shall first convert r to a new statistic Z which has a sampling distribution which is approximately normal. We then place a confidence interval about Z in the usual way. Finally, after noting the upper and lower confidence limits for Z, we reconvert these particular Z values back into r's, thereby obtaining the confidence limits for r.

We transform r into Z by means of the formula

$$Z = 1.151 \log \frac{1 + r}{1 - r}$$

where Z can take on values from zero to infinity. It should be called to your attention that the Z value computed from the above formula has absolutely no connection with the Z values we have been using with the standard normal curve. Values of Z can be directly obtained from Table K, Appendix 2, rather than making use of logarithms. The first two digits of r are located by going down the left-hand margin, the third being given across the top. The corresponding Z values are given in the body of the table. For example, a Z of 0.3228 corresponds to an r of .312; a z of 1.3892 corresponds to an r of .883. In using Table K we ignore the sign of r, affixing to Z the proper sign after its numerical value has been located. Notice that the numerical values of Z are only slightly larger than r whenever $r \leq .40$ but that as r increases Z begins to take on values greater than unity.

We may now make use of the Z transformation in a confidence-interval problem. The sampling distribution of Z is approximately normal even for relatively small N's and moderate departures from normality. Its standard error is given by

$$\sigma_Z = \frac{1}{\sqrt{N - 3}} \tag{18.2}$$

Not only does this make it possible to use the normal table, but we have eliminated the necessity of estimating ρ since the standard error of Z depends only on N. Taking as our numerical example the correlation of .301 between per cent Negro and discrimination, we find that the corresponding Z value is 0.3106. Since there were only 13 cases,

$$\sigma_Z = \frac{1}{\sqrt{13 - 3}} = \frac{1}{\sqrt{10}} = 0.3162$$

Suppose we wish to obtain a 95 per cent confidence interval for ρ. We first compute such an interval in terms of Z values. Thus we would take

$$Z \pm 1.96\sigma_Z = 0.3106 \pm 1.96(0.3162)$$
$$= 0.3106 \pm 0.6198$$

Therefore the confidence interval about Z runs from $-.3092$ to $+.9304$. Notice that in obtaining the lower limit we had to subtract a number which was numerically larger than 0.3106. This yields a negative result which, in turn, means that the value of r corresponding to this lower limit must also be taken as negative. Looking up the values of r corresponding to the two confidence limits for Z we get values of $-.300$ and $.731$ for the lower and upper limits respectively.

Notice that the interval is not quite symmetrical about the obtained r of $.301$. In this case the upper limit is somewhat closer to r than is the lower limit. Had we found an r of $.80$, the resulting interval would have been even more highly skewed in the same direction. This can be seen to make sense intuitively when we realize that whenever we begin to approach the upper limit of unity we also place a restriction on the upper limit of the confidence interval. Thus it would be impossible to obtain a confidence interval of $.86 \pm .16$. If r happens to be negative, the direction of skewness will of course be opposite to that obtained above. Only when $r = 0$ will the interval be exactly symmetrical about r.

We can interpret this confidence interval in the usual manner. Our procedure is such that in the long run we can expect to obtain intervals which will include the (fixed) value of ρ 95 per cent of the time. We may also use such confidence intervals as implicit tests of hypotheses. In the above problem we have already noted that the lower limit of the interval is negative. Since zero is included in the interval we know immediately that we would not reject the null hypothesis that $\rho = 0$. If we ever wanted to test any other specific hypothesized value of ρ we could also do so. For example, had we hypothesized that $\rho = .80$ we would have rejected at the .05 level since this value is beyond the upper limit of $.731$.

It would also be desirable to compute confidence intervals about other measures of degree of relationship. Unfortunately, too little is known about the sampling distributions of most measures of association for contingency problems to permit the construction of confidence intervals for these measures. Haggard [2] suggests a method for computing confidence intervals about the intraclass correlation r_i.

*Occasionally one may want to put a confidence interval about b, or he may need to find a band within which the true regression equation can be expected to lie. In both cases we can make use of the t distribution in a fairly straightforward manner. The estimate of the standard error of b is given by

$$\hat{\sigma}_b = \frac{\hat{\sigma}_{y|x}}{\sqrt{\sum_{i=1}^{N} (X_i - \bar{X})^2}} \qquad (18.3)$$

where you will recall that

$$\hat{\sigma}_{y|x} = \sqrt{\sum_{i=1}^{N} \frac{(Y_i - Y_\rho)^2}{N - 2}}$$

For computational purposes it can be shown algebraically that

$$\hat{\sigma}_{y|x} = \sqrt{\frac{\sum_{i=1}^{N} (Y_i - \bar{Y})^2 - b \sum_{i=1}^{N} (X_i - \bar{X})(Y_i - \bar{Y})}{N - 2}} \tag{18.4}$$

We can now make use of numerical computations already obtained for the discrimination data of Table 17.1, getting

$$\hat{\sigma}_{y|x} = \sqrt{\frac{560,024 - 19.931(2,553.77)}{11}} = \sqrt{46,284} = 215.1$$

and

$$\hat{\sigma}_b = \frac{215.1}{\sqrt{128.131}} = \frac{215.1}{11.32} = 19.00$$

If we wish to compute the 99 per cent confidence interval we go directly to the t table using $N - 2$ or 11 degrees of freedom. We thus get

$$b \pm (3.106)(19.00) = 19.931 \pm 59.014$$

*In estimating the regression equation we have seen that our best single ("point") estimate is the least-squares line. Since the quantity we are now estimating is no longer a single value but rather an entire line, our "interval estimate" will no longer be an interval but instead will consist of a band on either side of the least-squares line. At first thought, one might expect such a band to consist of two lines running parallel to the least-squares line. But such a band would imply that we knew the correct slope and that the only source of error came in estimating α. We must remember that there are now two quantities being estimated (α and β) and therefore two sources of error. You should convince yourself that since the slope may also have been estimated incorrectly, the further one goes in either direction from the point $(\bar{X}, \bar{Y})$, the greater the possible inaccuracy. The confidence band takes the general form shown in Fig. 18.2.

*In order to draw such a confidence band, it will be necessary to compute the standard error of Y_p for various values of X. The estimated standard error is given by the formula

$$\hat{\sigma}_{y_p} = \hat{\sigma}_{y|x} \sqrt{\frac{1}{N} + \frac{(X - \bar{X})^2}{\sum_{i=1}^{N} (X_i - \bar{X})^2}} \tag{18.5}$$

where the particular value of X to be used in $(X - \bar{X})^2$ may be set at any desired location on the X axis. Notice, incidentally, that the further X is from $\bar{X}$, the larger the numerical value of the standard error. Suppose we wish to obtain the estimated standard error when $X = 10.0$. Since $\bar{X} = 4.837$ we get

$$\hat{\sigma}_{y_p} = 215.1 \sqrt{\frac{1}{13} + \frac{(10.0 - 4.837)^2}{128.131}} = 215.1 \sqrt{.28496} = 114.86$$

*Again using the t table and a 99 per cent interval about Y_p computed for this fixed value of X, we would get

$$Y_p \pm (3.106)(114.86) = Y_p \pm 356.8$$

Once we have obtained similar intervals about Y_p for other particular values of X we can plot the entire band. Needless to say, the procedure involved would become quite tedious if the entire band were

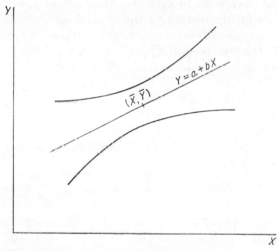

Fig. 18.2. Confidence band about least-squares line.

desired. Therefore unless the correlation between the two variables is quite high and unless one's interest centers primarily on obtaining accurate predictions from the least-squares equation, he would seldom find it advisable to compute such a confidence band.

Testing the Difference between Two Correlations. It is frequently the case that one has obtained several correlations and wishes to establish that one is significantly higher than another. As long as he is content to describe relationships within his particular sample, he may simply compare the relative sizes of the two r's and note the magnitude of the difference. If he wishes to generalize to some larger population, however, the question will arise as to whether or not the obtained difference is likely to be due to chance. Suppose, for example, that he has obtained one r of .50 and another of .30.   He may wish to test the null hypothesis that the two population correlations are identical, i.e., $\rho_1 = \rho_2$.

Two different situations in which such tests might be made come to mind.   First, one may have *two independent samples* and may wish to compare the degrees of relationships between X and Y within each of these samples.   For example, the relationship between per cent Negro and discrimination may not be the same in the South as it is in the North. One might set up the research hypothesis that ρ_{xy} is higher in the South than in the North, testing the null hypothesis that the two correlations are equal.   A second type of situation, likely to be confused with the first, may occur when one has a *single sample*.   There may be a single dependent variable (say, discrimination) and two independent variables (say, per cent Negro and percentage of the labor force engaged in manufacturing).   One may wish to establish that one of these independent variables is more highly related to the dependent variable than is the other.   Referring to the second independent variable as Z, he would then be interested in testing the null hypothesis that $\rho_{xy} = \rho_{zy}$.   Let us first see how the former type of situation can be handled, then turn to the single-sample test.

If the two correlations are based on independent samples, we can transform each of the r's into Z's and then make use of a formula for the standard error of the difference between two Z's, which is analogous to that for the standard error of a difference between means, and which is as follows

$$\sigma_{Z_1 - Z_2} = \sqrt{\frac{1}{N_1 - 3} + \frac{1}{N_2 - 3}} \qquad (18.6)$$

We can then either put a confidence interval about $(Z_1 - Z_2)$ or look up the value of

$$Z = \frac{(Z_1 - Z_2) - 0}{\sigma_{Z_1 - Z_2}}$$

in the normal table.   Zero appears in the above formula because of the fact that our null hypothesis takes the form $\rho_1 = \rho_2$.

Suppose that for 17 Southern cities the correlation between per cent Negro and discrimination turns out to be .567 as compared with the result of .301 for Northern cities.

Thus $r_1 = .301 \qquad r_2 = .567$
                             $Z_1 = 0.3106 \qquad Z_2 = 0.6431$

and $\sigma_{Z_1 - Z_2} = \sqrt{\tfrac{1}{10} + \tfrac{1}{14}} = \sqrt{.1000 + .0714} = .414$

Therefore $Z = \dfrac{.3106 - .6431}{.414} = \dfrac{-.3325}{.414} = -.803$

and we see that this difference in r's is not significant at the .05 level. Thus even though the correlation is higher for Southern cities, such a difference could have occurred fairly frequently by chance.

In the second type of situation mentioned above, we do not have two independent samples and cannot use the same formula for the standard error of $Z_1 - Z_2$. A method of handling this latter type of problem is available, provided we are interested in generalizing only to a subpopulation of all possible samples for which X and Z (the two independent variables) have the same sets of values as those in the particular sample we have obtained. For most practical purposes, this restriction can be safely ignored unless there is reason to suspect that the range of variation is much greater in the population than in the sample studied—in which case one should be very much on guard against generalizing anyway.

If we are testing the null hypothesis that $\rho_{xy} = \rho_{zy}$ we form t as follows

$$t = (r_{xy} - r_{zy}) \sqrt{\frac{(N - 3)(1 + r_{xz})}{2(1 - r_{xy}{}^2 - r_{xz}{}^2 - r_{zy}{}^2 + 2r_{xy}r_{xz}r_{zy})}} \qquad (18.7)$$

We can then look up the value of t in the table, using $N - 3$ degrees of freedom. In our numerical example, suppose the correlation for Northern cities between X and Z turns out to be .172 and that between Y and Z is .749. We would then get

$$t = (.301 - .749) \sqrt{\frac{10(1 + .172)}{2[1 - .301^2 - .172^2 - .749^2 + 2(.301)(.172)(.749)]}}$$
$$= -1.72$$

Since we have 10 degrees of freedom we see that we cannot reject the null hypothesis of no difference between the population correlations of each of the independent variables with discrimination.

You may have noted that in discussing measures of association for contingency problems and also in treating intraclass correlation, no mention was made of comparable tests for the significance of a difference between two such measures. As was the case with confidence intervals, not enough is known about the sampling distributions of contingency measures to make such comparative tests. In the case of intraclass correlation, a comparable test can be made for independent samples (see [2]).

18.2. Nonlinear Correlation and Regression

Up to this point we have assumed that the regression equation was linear in form. In many practical sociological problems the linear model, although perhaps not exact, yields a close enough approximation to the true form of the equation that we need not concern ourselves with alternative more complicated models. This will especially be true for exploratory studies in which the degree of fit is not too exact. There are instances, however, when inspection of the scattergram may clearly indicate a nonlinear relationship or when one's theory has predicted such a relationship. Whenever such a nonlinear relationship does exist, the product-moment coefficient will obviously underestimate the true degree of relationship since this coefficient measures only the goodness of fit of the best single straight line. You have already seen that in the case of a U-shaped curve it is possible to have a strong relationship with an r of approximately zero, and you have been cautioned that it is therefore incorrect to conclude that two variables are independent merely because r is zero. If the scattergram indicates a more or less random distribution of dots we may then conclude that no relationship exists, but we must also be on the lookout for nonlinear relationships. This is of course all the more reason why one should form the habit of always drawing scattergrams before proceeding with his analysis.

The general topic of nonlinear correlation and regression is far too complex to be covered adequately in this text. The reason for the complexity of nonlinear analysis is that once we get beyond the equation of the straight line, there are numerous types of equations representing the different possible forms that nonlinear relationships can take. Only the simplest of these equations can be treated in a year's course in statistics. Fortunately, these relatively simple equations will usually be adequate for the kinds of nonlinear relationships arising from sociological research. One general type of nonlinear function can be represented in terms of polynomials of the nth degree which have equations of the form

$$Y = a + bX + cX^2 + dX^3 + \cdots + kX^n$$

Our discussion of nonlinear relationships of this general type will be postponed until the next chapter when we take up multiple-regression problems. Once these latter regression problems are understood, we shall have a relatively simple method for handling those types of nonlinear relationships which can adequately be described by means of polynomials.

Certain other relatively simple types of nonlinear relationships can often be handled by a transformation of variables which permits the use of the familiar linear model. The process can be illustrated in the case of logarithmic functions represented by equations of the type

$$Y = a + b \log X$$

and which have the general form illustrated in Fig. 18.3. In an equation of this type, Y is actually a linear function not of X itself but of log X. This suggests that if we transform each of the X scores into a new variable $Z = \log X$ we can write Y as a linear function of Z. Thus

$$Y = a + b \log X = a + bZ$$

We can now compute the correlation between Y and Z (i.e., Y and log X) in the usual manner. If we plot the distribution of scores on the Y and Z axes, the result should be approximately linear in form. If we wish, we can compare the degree of relationship between Y and Z with that between Y and X and test for the significance of the difference between

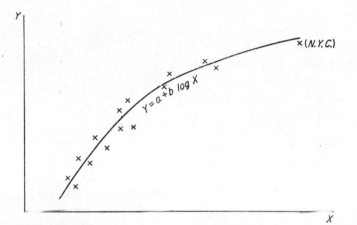

Fig. 18.3. Logarithmic least-squares equation of the form $Y = a + b \log X$.

them in the manner to be described below. If r_{yz} is significantly larger than r_{xy}, the logarithmic model gives a better fit than the linear model between X and Y.

Logarithmic models of the above sort often arise in instances where the independent variable X takes on a wide range of values but where once a certain value has been reached, further increases produce less and less effect on the dependent variable. City size is a variable which often has this kind of effect. Cities over 500,000 may all have very much the same scores on Y. But if New York is included in the sample, the value of X for this city will be so much greater than that of the remainder that the net effect will be to bend the relationship in much the same manner as shown in Fig. 18.3. In such a case, it may be preferable to relate Y to log X since taking the logarithm of city size will have the effect of bunching together the extremely large scores and lessening the "bending effect" of these large cities.

In a number of instances the researcher may have no real interest in finding the exact form of the prediction equation which best fits his data.

He may simply wish to show that the relationship is nonlinear in form or to obtain a measure for the degree of relationship regardless of its form. When a simple transformation such as the log transformation can be made, it will undoubtedly be to one's advantage to make use of such a procedure. Even so, he may still wish to test whether or not the measure he has obtained is a good approximation of the result he would have gotten had the best possible fit been found. In order to handle problems of this sort we can make use of the basic principles of analysis of variance and

Fig. 18.4. Comparison of deviations about least-squares line with deviations about category means.

some of the measures of degree of association developed in the previous chapter.

You will recall that in obtaining the within sum of squares for one-way analysis of variance we took the sum of the squared deviations from each of the category means. Now let us suppose that X were subdivided into a number of categories and that the sum of squares in Y were analyzed in the usual manner. We know for any given category of X that the sum of squares about the category mean will produce a smaller numerical result than the sum of squares about any other number. In particular, it follows that the within sum of squares will be smaller than the sum of squared deviations about those points on the least-squares line falling at the mid-points of the intervals (see Fig. 18.4).

If the regression equation happens to be linear in form, we can expect that the $\bar{Y}_{\cdot j}$ will all fall approximately on the least-squares line so that it will make little difference whether deviations are taken about the category means or the least-squares line. On the other hand, if the relationship is actually nonlinear, then for at least some of the categories the sum of squares about the category mean will be quite a bit smaller than that about the least-squares line. In other words, the within or unexplained sum of squares will be minimized by using the category means, and therefore the between or explained sum of squares will be maximized. Thus the proportion of variation explained by the categories, as measured by the correlation ratio E^2, will be larger than the proportion explained by the least-squares line unless the true relationship is actually linear in form.

We can take advantage of this fact in making a test for nonlinearity. If we form the quantity $E^2 - r^2$ we get the proportion of variation explained assuming any form of relationship which is not explained by a linear relationship. It is clear that in obtaining E^2 we are permitting the relationship to take any possible form since we have simply taken deviations about category means, regardless of where these category means happen to lie. We are essentially asking ourselves how much we can improve our ability to predict values of Y if we do not restrict ourselves to the linear model. If the improvement is greater than we would expect by chance under the assumption that the regression equation is actually linear, then we may conclude that the relationship is nonlinear.

The analysis-of-variance test we shall use to test for nonlinearity takes a form that will soon become familiar. We first find the amount of variation that can be explained using the linear model. Algebraically, this quantity can be represented as $r^2 \Sigma y^2$. Of the variation left unexplained by the linear model, $(1 - r^2)\Sigma y^2$, we then find out how much can be accounted for by the general model. Since $E^2 \Sigma y^2$ gives us the sum of squares that can be explained by X when there is no restriction placed on the form of the relationship, the quantity $(E^2 - r^2)\Sigma y^2$ represents the explained increment due to nonlinearity. Assuming no rounding errors this quantity should always be positive. Since the quantity $(1 - E^2)\Sigma y^2$ gives us the sum of squares which is unexplained by even the best-fitting model, we can make an F test as indicated in Table 18.2. As usual, the denominator of F is the error term, and since we are testing for departures from linearity, we take as the numerator the estimate of variance based on $(E^2 - r^2)\Sigma y^2$ or the amount explained by the best general model which has not already been explained by the linear model. The degrees of freedom associated with the numerator can be obtained by subtraction.

Again we note that the total sum of squares cancels, leaving us with the following formula for F:

$$F_{k-2, N-k} = \frac{(E^2 - r^2)(N - k)}{(1 - E^2)(k - 2)} \qquad (18.8)$$

where k represents the number of categories into which X has been divided.

Table 18.2. Analysis-of-variance Test for Nonlinearity

	Sums of squares	Degrees of freedom	Estimates of variance	F
Total	Σy^2	$N - 1$		
Explained by linear model	$r^2 \Sigma y^2$	1		
Additional explained by nonlinear model	$(E^2 - r^2)\Sigma y^2$	$k - 2$	$\dfrac{(E^2 - r^2)\Sigma y^2}{k - 2}$	$\dfrac{(E^2 - r^2)(N - k)}{(1 - E^2)(k - 2)}$
Unexplained	$(1 - E^2)\Sigma y^2$	$N - k$	$\dfrac{(1 - E^2)\Sigma y^2}{N - k}$	

Let us illustrate the test for nonlinearity with the data which were grouped in Table 17.2. As can easily be verified, the total and between sums of squares in Y are as follows:

$$\text{Total SS} = 101{,}115.38 - 92{,}132.04 = 8{,}983.34$$
$$\text{Between SS} = 94{,}792.59 - 92{,}132.04 = 2{,}660.55$$

where we have treated all Y scores as though they were at the mid-points of their respective intervals and where we have made use of procedures for grouped data (see Sec. 6.4). Therefore,

$$E^2 = \frac{\text{between SS}}{\text{total SS}} = \frac{2{,}660.55}{8{,}983.34} = .2962$$

Since we previously found an r of $-.460$ assuming a linear relationship, we get

$$F_{7,141} = \frac{.2962 - (-.460)^2}{1 - .2962} \frac{150 - 9}{9 - 2} = \frac{.0846}{.7038} \frac{141}{7} = \frac{11.929}{4.927} = 2.42$$

and we see that at the .05 level we may reject the null hypothesis of a linear relationship between the percentage of persons classified as rural-farm and the percentage of females in the labor force.

If a relationship turns out to be nonlinear in form, it is quite possible that r will not be statistically significant whereas E will be. The significance of E can of course be tested by a straightforward analysis of variance by taking the ratio of the explained and unexplained estimates of variance. There are thus three distinct tests that can be made: (1) the significance of r, (2) the significance of departures from linearity ($E^2 - r^2$), and (3) the significance of E.

If a nonlinear relationship is found and an estimate of the degree of relationship in the population desired, it is preferable to use the unbiased correlation ratio ϵ discussed in Chapter 16 and given by the formula

$$\epsilon^2 = 1 - \frac{V_w}{V_t}$$

since the numerical value of E is a function of the number of categories used and will generally slightly overestimate the relationship in the population. If E has already been computed, the value of ϵ can be computed from the formula

$$\epsilon^2 = \frac{E^2(N-1) - (k-1)}{N-k} \tag{18.9}$$

18.3. Ordinal Scales: Rank-order Correlation

We have now taken up measures of association which can be used to relate two nominal scales (ϕ^2, τ_b, etc.), a nominal and an interval scale (intraclass correlation), and two interval scales (r). The two measures to be discussed in this section, Spearman's r_s and Kendall's tau, can be used to correlate two ordinal scales. As long as both variables can be ranked, either of these latter measures can be used to give correlations which are somewhat analogous to product-moment correlations. Both measures can be used if ties occur, although Kendall's tau seems to be more satisfactory whenever the number of ties is quite large. Since Spearman's measure seems to be somewhat less useful than tau, although easier to compute, we shall discuss this former measure rather briefly.

Spearman's r_s. The principle behind Spearman's measure is very simple. We compare the rankings on the two sets of scores by taking the differences of ranks, squaring these differences and then adding, and finally manipulating the measure so that its value will be $+1.0$ whenever the rankings are in perfect agreement, -1.0 if they are in perfect disagreement, and zero if there is no relationship whatsoever. If we symbolize the difference between any pair of ranks as D_i, we then find the value of $\sum_{i=1}^{N} D_i{}^2$ and compute r_s by means of the formula

$$r_s = 1 - \frac{6 \sum_{i=1}^{N} D_i{}^2}{N(N^2 - 1)} \tag{18.10}$$

Let us illustrate with some data collected by the author. Members of a work-camp group were ranked from high to low with respect to both popularity, as measured by friendship choices, and participation in group discussions. For both variables a rank of one indicates a high score. Tied ranks are computed by giving each tied score the arithmetic mean of the scores that would have been received had there been no ties. The values of D_i are then computed as indicated in Table 18.3. If the number of ties is relatively small, as is presently true, we need make no

Table 18.3. Computation of Spearman's Coefficient of Rank-order Correlation

Person	Popularity rank	Participation rank	D_i	$D_i{}^2$
Ann	1	5.5	4.5	20.25
Bill	2.5	5.5	3.0	9.00
Jim	2.5	1	−1.5	2.25
Hans	4	2	−2.0	4.00
Marcia	5	3	−2.0	4.00
Joan	6	9.5	3.5	12.25
Ruth	7	5.5	−1.5	2.25
Doris	8	13.5	5.5	30.25
Barbara	9	9.5	0.5	0.25
Cynthia	10	16	6.0	36.00
Ellie	11.5	5.5	−6.0	36.00
Flo	11.5	11.5	0.0	0.00
Nancy	13.5	8	−5.5	30.25
Mart	13.5	15	1.5	2.25
Stan	15	11.5	−3.5	12.25
Sarah	16	13.5	−2.5	6.25
Total			0.0	207.50

modifications in the formula for r_s. If there is a substantial number of ties a correction factor can be computed (see [6], pp. 206 to 210). We get

$$r_s = 1 - \frac{6(207.50)}{16(255)} = 1 - .305 = .695$$

Notice that if the rankings agree perfectly, $\sum_{i=1}^{N} D_i{}^2$ will be zero and the value of r_s will be unity. Although direct inspection of the formula does not immediately give us the values of r_s for independence and perfect negative association, it turns out that for perfect negative association the value of the second term will be -2.0 and therefore r_s will be -1.0. For no association, the second factor will be exactly unity.

If $N \geq 10$ the sampling distribution of r_s is approximately normal with standard deviation $1/\sqrt{N-1}$. In the above example the standard error will therefore be $1/\sqrt{15}$. As a test of the null hypothesis of no relationship in the population we can compute Z as follows

$$Z = \frac{r_s - 0}{1/\sqrt{N - 1}} = .695 \sqrt{15} = 2.69$$

Making use of the normal table we see that the relationship is significant at the .01 level.

Kendall's Tau. In computing Spearman's r_s we made use of the squares of the differences in ranks. Kendall's tau, which also varies between -1.0 and 1.0, is based upon a somewhat different operation. We first compute a statistic S by looking at all possible pairs of cases and noting whether or not the ranks are in the same order. For example, suppose we have the following sets of ranks:

	a	b	c	d
A	1	2	3	4
B	2	3	1	4

Since the scores of set A have been given in ascending order we may compute S by examining each of the B rankings in turn. Focusing on the first value in the B row (individual a), we see that the B score is in the proper order for the pairs (a,b) and (a,d). In other words, individual a has received a lower rank than b and d on both variables A and B. On the other hand, the B score is out of order (with respect to the A score) for pair (a,c) since a has a lower rank than c for A but the opposite is true for B.

Let us make use of $+1$ every time a given pair is ordered the same way for both A and B and -1 whenever they are ordered oppositely. The value of S is obtained by summing these $+1$'s and -1's for all possible pairs. The contribution of pairs (a,b), (a,c), and (a,d) is therefore $+1 - 1 + 1 = (2 - 1) = 1$. In order to pick up the remaining pairs we move across the table. We see that the contribution of pairs (b,c) and (b,d) is $-1 + 1$ or 0. Finally, the contribution of pair (c,d) is $+1$. Notice that in effect we can obtain the total value of S by first arranging A in the proper order and then examining successive rankings in the B row, each time counting the number of ranks falling to the right which are in the proper order and subtracting out those which are in the opposite order. Thus in this simple example we get

$$S = (2 - 1) + (1 - 1) + (1 - 0) = 2$$

If we now divide S by the maximum possible value that it could have, i.e., $(N - 1) + (N - 2) + \cdots + 2 + 1 = N(N - 1)/2$, we obtain a coefficient which can vary from -1 to $+1$. Thus

$$\tau = \frac{S}{\tfrac{1}{2}N(N - 1)} \tag{18.11}$$

Clearly, if there is perfect disagreement between the two ranking systems (i.e., if B were ranked 4, 3, 2, 1), the value of S would be $-\tfrac{1}{2}N(N - 1)$ and τ would be -1.0. Also, if the two variables are completely unrelated, the positive and negative contributions to S will exactly cancel and τ will be zero.

In order to illustrate the case of tied rankings let us again make use of the work-camp example. Let us arrange the individuals in horizontal arrays and substitute letters for names. Our rankings thus become

	a	b	c	d	e	f	g	h	i	j	k	l	m	n	o	p
A	1	2.5	2.5	4	5	6	7	8	9	10	11.5	11.5	13.5	13.5	15	16
B	5.5	5.5	1	2	3	9.5	5.5	13.5	9.5	16	5.5	11.5	8	15	11.5	13.5

We must now follow the rule that whenever any pair involves a tie in either the A or B score, its contribution to S will be zero. Looking first at all pairs that can be made with a, we see that pairs (a,b), (a,g), and (a,k) will contribute nothing to S since the B scores for all these individuals are tied at 5.5. Therefore, the contribution from all the remaining a pairs will be

$$(a,c)\ (a,d)\ (a,e)\ (a,f)\ (a,h)\ (a,i)\ (a,j)\ (a,l)\ (a,m)\ (a,n)\ (a,o)(a,p)$$
$$-1\quad -1\quad -1\quad +1\quad +1\quad +1\quad +1\quad +1\quad +1\quad +1\quad +1\quad +1$$
$$= 9 - 3 = 6$$

We next compare the b ranks with each of the ranks to the right of b. Notice, however, that b and c are tied with respect to A. Since b and c could therefore just as well have been given in the reverse order, we must eliminate the pair (b,c). Likewise, the pairs (b,g) and (b,k) are tied on B and will also make no contribution to S. Thus for b pairs we get a sum of $9 - 2$ or 7. Continuing across we get

$$S = (9 - 3) + (9 - 2) + (13 - 0) + (12 - 0) + (11 - 0) + (6 - 3)$$
$$+ (8 - 0) + (2 - 5) + (5 - 2) + (0 - 6) + (4 - 0) + (2 - 1)$$
$$+ (2 - 0) + (0 - 2) + (1 - 0) = 60$$

We must now make an adjustment in the denominator of tau in order to correct for ties. Such an adjustment has an effect of increasing the numerical value of tau, although the increase will be slight unless the number of ties is quite large. The formula for tau can be generalized as follows

$$\tau = \frac{S}{\sqrt{\frac{1}{2}N(N-1) - T}\sqrt{\frac{1}{2}N(N-1) - U}} \qquad (18.12)$$

where $T = \frac{1}{2}\Sigma t_i(t_i - 1)$, t_i being the number of ties in each set of ties in A, and $U = \frac{1}{2}\Sigma u_i(u_i - 1)$, u_i being the number of ties in each set of ties in B. In the above example, we have three ties of two each in variable A (popularity). Thus

$$T = \frac{1}{2}[2(1) + 2(1) + 2(1)] = 3$$

Similarly, there are three ties of two each and one score with four ties in variable B (participation). Therefore

$$U = \frac{1}{2}[2(1) + 2(1) + 2(1) + 4(3)] = 9$$

Hence

$$\tau = \frac{60}{\sqrt{[8(15) - 3][8(15) - 9]}} = \frac{60}{\sqrt{(117)(111)}} = \frac{60}{114.0} = .526$$

Notice that the numerical value of tau is somewhat less than that of r_s. This will usually, although not always, be the case. In comparing the two measures, we see that r_s gives relatively more weight to extreme differences in ranks, since all differences are squared. Tau, on the other hand, gives equal weight to all pairs of scores as we can note from the formula. Neither measure can be interpreted in terms of the percentage of variation explained since the notion of variation, as we have been using the term, is meaningless with ordinal scales. About the only interpretations we can give to numerical scores between -1.0 and $+1.0$ are in terms of the formulas themselves. Thus tau is a measure of the degree to which pairs in the proper order exceed in number those in the reverse order.

Computation of Tau for Large Numbers of Ties. One advantage of tau over r_s is that the former measure can readily be used when there are very large numbers of ties. Although the computing routine described above would become extremely tedious in such instances, we may greatly simplify the procedure whenever both variables have been grouped into several rather crude categories. For example, persons may have been placed into one of five social classes, with all those in the same class being considered as tied with respect to status. If the second variable has been categorized in a similar manner, we can use a modified formula for tau and thereby make use of the information that the data have actually been ranked rather than simply categorized.

We can compute S by a procedure to be described below. Using the formulas given above, we would find that the upper limit of tau would be unity only when the number of rows and columns were equal. In order to correct for the possibility that $r \neq c$ we form the ratio

$$\tau_c = \frac{S}{\frac{1}{2}N^2[(m-1)/m]} \qquad (18.13)$$

where
$$m = \text{Min } (r,c)$$

Here we follow Kendall in using the symbol τ_c in order to distinguish equation (18.13) from the previous two formulas. Let us now see how τ_c is computed.

Table 18.4. Data Cross Classified for Computing Kendall's Tau from Grouped Data

Strength of desire to join organizations (A)	Concern with proper behavior (B)				Total
	High	Moderately high	Moderately low	Low	
High	18	19	12	8	57
Moderately high	16	16	12	10	54
Moderately low	11	14	18	16	59
Low	5	5	15	22	47
Total	50	54	57	56	217

The data given in Table 18.4 represent rankings given to 217 students of introductory sociology at the University of Michigan. Variable B involves the student's general concern that he engage in the "proper" or "correct" forms of behavior in conventional settings. Variable A involves his desire to join organizations merely to improve his social status. Since the measurement of both variables was somewhat crude, it was decided to divide each variable into four categories: high, moderately high, moderately low, and low. Thus, although each variable involves an ordinal scale with large numbers of ties, the results can be summarized in the form of a contingency table.

In computing S we first note that scores on A have again been ranked from high to low except that we now have 57 individuals "tied" for high, 54 for moderately high, 59 for moderately low, and 47 for low. Looking first at those with high scores on A, we see that 18 are also high on B, 19 moderately high, and so forth. In obtaining the contributions to S we note that since all of the individuals in the high category of A are tied, none of these pairs will contribute to S. Likewise, none of the pairs in the same column will contribute to S because of the fact that they are all tied with respect to B. If we look at any given cell, all the scores which are below it and to the right will contribute positively to S, whereas those below it and to the left will yield negative scores. For example, each of the 18 individuals in the top left-hand cell will produce positive scores with any of the

$$16 + 14 + 5 + 12 + 18 + 15 + 10 + 16 + 22$$

scores which are beneath and to the right of this cell. In total, then, the contribution from this cell to S will be

$$18(16 + 14 + 5 + 12 + 18 + 15 + 10 + 16 + 22) = 18(128)$$

Next, we focus on the 16 cases immediately below the top left-hand corner. Each of these individuals also has high B scores. In order to count the number of pairs with positive contributions to S we again add the quantities appearing below and to the right. Multiplying by the number of cases in this cell we get

$$16(14 + 5 + 18 + 15 + 16 + 22) = 16(90)$$

When we move over into the second and subsequent columns we begin to find negative contributions since columns to the left will have higher B scores. Thus for the first cell in the second column we get as the contribution to S

$$19(12 + 18 + 15 + 10 + 16 + 22 - 16 - 11 - 5) = 19(61)$$

By continuing down and across the table in a similar manner we can obtain S rather simply, as follows:

$$\begin{aligned}
S = \ &18(128) + 16(90) + 11(42) + 19(61) + 16(55) \\
&+ 14(32) + 12(-19) + 12(3) + 18(12) \\
&+ 8(-112) + 10(-68) + 16(-25) = 4{,}741
\end{aligned}$$

Thus
$$\tau_c = \frac{4{,}741}{\frac{1}{2}(217)^2[(4-1)/4]} = .268$$

Notice that the numerical value of tau is relatively small in spite of what on inspection appears to be a moderately strong relationship. Since it can be shown that tau can reach unity only when all cells are empty except those in the diagonal, we can seldom expect to get a value of tau approaching unity. Among other things, the numerical upper limit of tau depends upon the marginal totals in much the same manner as does that of ϕ^2. In fact, it can be shown that in the special case of the 2×2 table, the value of tau as computed from the original formula with a correction for ties [equation (18.12)] will be exactly equal to ϕ. Had ϕ or some other measure based on chi square been used in the general case, however, we would not have been able to make use of the information that the categories of A and B are ordered.

Tests of Significance for Tau.   Kendall [4] has shown that for sample sizes of 10 or more the sampling distribution of S under the null hypothesis will be approximately normal with mean of zero and variance given by

$$\sigma_s{}^2 = \tfrac{1}{18}N(N-1)(2N+5) \tag{18.14}$$

Strictly speaking, the above formula holds only when there are no ties but can safely be used when the number of ties is relatively small.   If there is a very large number of ties a rather lengthy correction factor must be used (see [4], p. 55).

To test for the significance of tau for the work-camp data, we first compute $\sigma_s{}^2$ as follows

$$\sigma_s{}^2 = \tfrac{1}{18}(16)(15)(37) = 493.3$$

Taking the square root we get

$$\sigma_s = 22.21$$

which can be used in the denominator of Z in testing the null hypothesis that A and B are unrelated.   Thus

$$Z = \frac{S - 0}{\sigma_s} = \frac{60.0}{22.21} = 2.70$$

and we see that a value of tau of .526 is significant at the .01 level.

In concluding this section it should be noted that Kendall's tau can be used in connection with partial correlation to be discussed in the next chapter.   There are also certain other measures that can be used with ranked data in other types of problems.   For example, if a number of judges have each ranked individuals with respect to a certain criterion, a measure referred to as the coefficient of concordance W can be used to measure the degree to which the judges are in agreement on their rankings. For these and other uses of rank-correlation methods, you should refer to Kendall [4] or Siegel [6].

EXERCISES

1. In Exercises 1 and 2, Chap. 17, you computed three correlation coefficients.

    a. For each of these coefficients, make use of analysis of variance to test the null hypothesis that $\rho = 0$.
    b. Place 99.9 per cent confidence intervals about all three r's.
    c. Test the relationship between moral integration and heterogeneity for nonlinearity.
    d. Convert these same data to ranks and obtain both Kendall's tau and Spearman's r_s for all three correlations.
    e. Test each of these rank-order coefficients for significance.

2. In Exercise 3, Chap. 17, you grouped both the moral integration and hetero-geneity indices. Compute Kendall's tau for these grouped data and compare the result with that obtained above in Exercise 1*d*.

REFERENCES

1. Croxton, F. E., and D. J. Cowden: *Applied General Statistics*, Prentice-Hall, Inc., Englewood Cliffs, N.J., 1955, chaps. 19 and 20.

2. Haggard, E. A.: *Intraclass Correlation and the Analysis of Variance*, The Dryden Press, Inc., New York, 1958, pp. 22–26.

3. Hagood, M. J., and D. O. Price: *Statistics for Sociologists*, Henry Holt and Company, Inc., New York, 1952, chap. 23.

4. Kendall, M. G.: *Rank Correlation Methods*, Hafner Publishing Company, New York, 1955, chaps. 1, 3, and 4.

5. McNemar, Q.: *Psychological Statistics*, John Wiley & Sons, Inc., New York, 1955, chaps. 8, 9, and 10.

6. Siegel, S.: *Nonparametric Statistics for the Behavioral Sciences*, McGraw-Hill Book Company, Inc., New York, 1956, chap. 9.

7. Wallis, W. A., and H. V. Roberts: *Statistics: A New Approach*, Free Press, Glencoe, Ill., 1956, chap. 17.

Chapter 19

MULTIPLE AND PARTIAL CORRELATION

In the last two chapters we have been concerned with the relationship between two interval scales, between a dependent variable and a single independent variable. Correlation and regression analysis can readily be extended to include any number of interval scales, one of which can be taken as dependent and the remainder independent. The problem can be conceptualized as a prediction problem in which we attempt to predict a dependent variable Y from the variables $X_1, X_2, \ldots, X_k$. We shall again have to make use of a very simple model which will be directly analogous to linear regression except for the fact that there will be more than two dimensions.

The notion of correlation will be generalized in two ways. We shall use the term *partial correlation* to refer to the correlation between any two variables when the effects of the other variables have been controlled. *Multiple correlation*, on the other hand, will be used to indicate how much of the total variation in the dependent variable can be explained by all of the independent variables acting together. You will find that, for the most part, the materials discussed in the present chapter involve straightforward extensions of arguments previously presented. Once we have extended the notions of correlation and regression we shall be in a position in the next chapter to take up analysis of covariance which involves a combination of correlational techniques with analysis of variance.

19.1. Multiple Regression and Least Squares

In multiple regression we attempt to predict a single dependent variable from any number of independent variables. If there are a large number of interval-scale variables which are to be interrelated, it will of course be possible to predict any particular variable from any combination of the others. It will usually be clear from context which variables are to be taken as independent and which dependent. For example, one may want to predict performance in college from a series of aptitude scores and performance in high school. Or it may be possible to predict the rate of growth of cities knowing such factors as present size, percentages of the labor force in various types of occupations, or the size and distance of the nearest large city.

In multiple regression analysis we define the regression equation as the path of the mean of the dependent variable Y for all combinations of $X_1, X_2, \ldots, X_k$. In other words, for every combination of fixed X's there will be a distribution of Y's. Each distribution will have a mean $\mu_{Y|X_1, X_2, \ldots, X_k}$ and a standard deviation $\sigma_{Y|X_1, X_2, \ldots, X_k}$, and we shall again assume that these distributions are all normal and that the standard deviations are equal (homoscedasticity). The path of the means will no longer be a curve in two-dimensional space. Instead it will be a kind of hypersurface in $(k + 1)$-dimensional space. Obviously, we shall no longer be able to represent such a path except in the case where there are only two independent variables X_1 and X_2.

In the previous chapter we assumed a linear regression equation of the form $Y = \alpha + \beta X$. We shall again have to assume a simple form for the regression equation. Let us assume that the path of the means of Y takes the form

$$Y = \alpha + \beta_1 X_1 + \beta_2 X_2 + \cdots + \beta_k X_k \qquad (19.1)$$

where $\alpha, \beta_1, \beta_2, \ldots,$ and β_k are constants. This is the simplest possible type of multiple regression equation and is directly analogous to linear regression in the two-variable case. In fact, if all β's except one are zero, the problem reduces to the two-dimensional case.

If we can assume a "multivariate normal" population in which each variable is distributed normally about all of the others, then we can meet all three of our required assumptions. In other words, a multivariate normal distribution assures us that regression equations will be of the above form, that the distributions of Y's for fixed X's will all be normal, and that the variances are also equal. This is an obvious generalization of the properties of the bivariate normal. Needless to say, the multivariate normal distribution cannot be pictured geometrically (though it has a definite algebraic equation) since we have already used three dimensions in depicting the bivariate case.

In order to give you a better intuitive grasp of the nature of the extensions involved, it will be helpful to examine the case where there are only two independent variables (see Fig. 19.1). The regression equation $Y = \alpha + \beta_1 X_1 + \beta_2 X_2$ can in this instance be represented by a *plane* in three-dimensional space. If we let $X_1 = X_2 = 0$, we get $Y = \alpha$, indicating that the regression plane crosses the Y axis at a height α. In order to get an interpretation for the β's, we take the intersections of the regression plane with planes perpendicular to the X_1 and X_2 axes.   For example, if we take a plane perpendicular to the X_2 axis, we are in effect holding X_2 constant since all points on this plane will have the same X_2 value.   This plane intersects the regression plane in a straight line, and the slope of this line will be β_1.   In other words, if we hold X_2 at a fixed value, β_1 represents the slope of the regression *line* of Y on X_1.   Similarly, holding X_1 constant gives us a plane which intersects the regression plane in a line with slope β_2.

Fig. 19.1. Geometrical interpretation of multiple regression of Y on X_1 and X_2.

It should be noted that the β's used in multiple regression will not ordinarily be the same as those obtained in the two-variable case. Referring to the two-variable case as "total" regression, we see that the β used in total regression is obtained by *ignoring* other independent variables, not by holding them constant.   The β's obtained in multiple regression equations are referred to as *partial* coefficients, since they involve slopes that would be obtained by holding out or holding constant each of the remaining independent variables considered in the regression equation.

The concept of least squares can be extended in a similar manner. Since it is practically always necessary to estimate a regression equation by fitting an equation to empirical data, we shall again require that the estimating equation have a particular form and use the least-squares criterion to obtain the "best" fit.   We shall use a least-squares equation of the form

$$Y_p = a + b_1X_1 + b_2X_2 + \cdots + b_kX_k \tag{19.2}$$

and it will again turn out that, provided the true regression equation is actually of this same form, the least-squares equation represents the best estimate of the regression equation.   In other words if we use a to estimate α and b_i to estimate β_i, these estimates will be unbiased and also of maximum efficiency. Our attention can then be focused on least-squares analysis as a practical method for estimating a theoretical equation which applies to the population. If there are only two independent variables, we shall be fitting a series of points in three-dimensional space with a best-fitting plane. In a $(k + 1)$-dimensional space we shall be fitting points with a k-dimensional hyperplane, if such a figure can be imagined.

Taking the three-dimensional case, we shall minimize the quantity $\Sigma(Y - Y_p)^2$ which represents the sum of the squared deviations from the least-squares plane in the vertical Y dimension (see Fig. 19.2). The result will be a unique best-fitting plane determined by specific values of $a, b_1,$ and b_2. As we shall see, a multiple correlation coefficient can then be used to measure the goodness of fit of the points to the least-squares plane. It would, of course, also be possible to measure goodness of fit by means of a standard deviation about the plane, and we could compare this standard deviation with the standard deviation about the fixed $\bar{Y}$ (now represented as a *plane* perpendicular to the Y axis). Algebrai-

Fig. 19.2. Least-squares plane minimizing sum of squared deviations in vertical Y dimension.

cally, the more general case is a straightforward extension of the three-variable one. The quantity $\Sigma(Y - Y_p)^2$ is minimized, and there will be $(k + 1)$ coefficients to compute, i.e., $a, b_1, b_2, \ldots, b_k$. The actual computation of these coefficients will be discussed later after we have taken up partial correlation.

19.2. Partial Correlation

We can make use of this multiple regression model to obtain measures of the degree of relationship between a dependent variable Y and any of the independent variables, controlling for one or more other independent variables. The term *partial correlation* is used to refer to this type of controlling procedure which, as we shall see, is basically very different from that used in connection with contingency tables but similar to that involved in two-way analysis of variance. In contingency problems we controlled by literally holding constant one or more control variables.

This was accomplished by investigating the relationship between two variables within categories of the control variable(s). A serious disadvantage of this method of controlling, it will be recalled, was in the fact that a very large number of cases was required if more than one simultaneous control was used.

Fig. 19.3. Least-squares lines indicating residuals between (a) Y and X_2 and (b) X_1 and X_2.

In partial correlation, the control variables are not actually held constant in this manner. Instead, we control by *adjusting* values of the dependent and independent variables in order to take into consideration the scores of the control variables. In a sense, then, we pretend that the control variables are actually held constant. In so doing, we sacrifice scientific rigor but gain in efficiency of design in that fewer cases will be required. In order to understand the nature of partial correlation and the adjusting procedure, we shall for the present confine our attention to the simplest problems involving only three variables and shall assume linear regression models between all three combinations of variables taken two at a time.

Let us assume we wish to measure the degree of relationship between a dependent variable Y and an independent variable X_1, controlling for a second independent variable X_2. To make use of a concrete example, we may be interested in predicting the rate of economic discrimination against Negroes, as measured by income differentials between whites and Negroes, and degree of urbanization, as indicated by the percentage of a county which is defined as urban. It is certainly expected that the percentage of Negroes in the county will also affect the rate of discrimination, and it is therefore decided to use per cent Negro as a control variable.

Suppose that the least-squares lines between discrimination Y and per cent Negro X_2 and between per cent urban X_1 and per cent Negro are as indicated in Fig. 19.3. The relationship between discrimination and per cent Negro is positive, indicating that high rates of discrimination are associated with high minority percentages. On the other hand, the relationship between the urbanization index and per cent Negro is negative. On the basis of this information alone, we would predict a negative relationship between discrimination rates and urbanization.

In other words, urban areas might have low rates simply because of the fact that, on the average, they have relatively fewer Negroes. Suppose, however, that we could in some manner "force" all counties to have the same minority percentages. We could then cancel out the disturbing effect of this third variable. In reality, of course, we cannot actually make all minority percentages equal, but we can at least make adjustments for the fact that they differ. Since we know (or can estimate) the relationship between the control variable and each of the other two variables, we can predict how both variables would behave with changes in the control variable. In fact, the least-squares equations represented in Fig. 19.3 are our prediction equations and can be used in the adjusting process.

In relating discrimination Y to per cent Negro X_2, we can think of variation in discrimination rates as being the result of two components: the first component being per cent Negro and the remainder being due to other factors, one of which may be urbanization. As we have already seen, this second component can be represented as *deviations* from the least-squares equation involving Y and X_2. In terms of X_2, these deviations or *residuals* represent error. Even if X_2 were held constant they would still remain. It is these residuals, therefore, in which we are really interested since they represent the amount of variation in discrimination left after per cent Negro has explained all of the variation it could.

Similarly, we shall be interested in the residuals or deviations from the equation used to predict per cent urban from per cent Negro. In other words, we let per cent Negro explain all of the variation it can in both of the other variables. If we now correlate the residuals, we obtain a measure of the relationship between Y and X_1 which is independent of the effects of X_2. *The partial correlation between Y and X_1, controlling for X_2, can be defined as the correlation between the residuals of the regressions of Y on X_2 and X_1 on X_2.* In a sense, then, a partial correlation represents the correlation between "errors" with respect to the control variable.

The reason why it makes sense to control for X_2 by correlating residuals may still be obscure. Perhaps the explanation will be made intuitively more appealing if we look more closely at an hypothetical relationship between these residuals. Suppose, for example, that for county A we find a large negative residual when we correlate Y with X_2. This means that county A has considerably less discrimination than would be expected knowing only its percentage of Negroes. The point representing this particular county would of course be somewhere below the least-squares line. Suppose, also, that the residual for this same county was positive when we correlated X_1 with X_2. In this case we know that the county is more highly urbanized than would be expected knowing only its minority percentage. We therefore have a relatively urbanized county with low discrimination rates, and furthermore we know that these values are high and low respectively as compared with other counties having the same percentage of Negroes. We thus cannot attribute the negative relationship between the residuals to the fact that the per cent Negro figure happens to be either large or small. Similarly, county B may have large positive residuals for Y but negative ones for X_1. This county, therefore, would be one with higher discrimination rates than expected but would also be less urbanized than other counties having the same minority percentage. Clearly, if most counties are similar to either county A or B we shall obtain a negative correlation between the residuals, indicating a negative relationship between discrimination and urbanization, adjusting for per cent Negro.

Partial correlation yields a single measure summarizing the degree of relationship between two variables, controlling for a third. As we shall see when we discuss computational procedures, the argument can readily be extended to additional control variables. We can visualize several multiple regression equations, one involving Y and all the control variables and the other relating X_1 to these same control variables. Residuals can be obtained from each of these multiple regression equations and then correlated. We shall thus be adjusting for all of the control variables simultaneously. The important point, here, is that we obtain only one partial correlation, whereas in controlling with contingency tables we obtained a separate measure for each of the categories of the control variables.

In Chap. 15 we saw that the degree of relationship between two variables may vary from one category of the control variable to the next. Thus, had per cent Negro been categorized, it is entirely possible that we might have found a high negative correlation between discrimination and urbanization for counties with very low minority percentages but even a positive correlation at the opposite end of the per cent Negro continuum. The fact that we have obtained a single summarizing measure in the partial correlation may therefore obscure certain information. The advantages of the one method of controlling are the disadvantages of the other. In partial correlation we are adjusting for the control variable rather than holding it constant; we thus get by with fewer cases, but we obtain a single measure which may obscure some important information.

What, then, is the relationship between the two methods of controlling? It turns out that the partial correlation coefficient can be interpreted as a *weighted average* of the correlation coefficients that would have been obtained had the control variable been divided into very small intervals and separate correlations computed within each of these categories. The exact nature of this weighting procedure is unimportant since in practice we never make use of it. Consequently, it does not make sense to think of partial correlations as relating two variables "holding constant" a third variable, since the strength of their relationship may vary according to the particular value at which the control variable is held constant.

In the case of the multivariate normal distribution we know that all regression equations will have the special form described by equation (19.1). The multivariate normal distribution has another remarkable property as well. The strength of relationship between two variables will be the same regardless of the values of the control variables. In other words, if a large number of categories of a control variable were selected and correlations obtained within each of these categories, all correlations would have the same value. Therefore the partial correlation would have the same value as each of these within-category correlations. In this special case it would thus make some sense to think in terms of holding the third variable constant. Since the multivariate normal distribution can at best be only approximated with real data, however, it is safer to think of a partial correlation as a weighted average or as involving an adjustment for the control variable.

Computation of Partial Correlation Coefficients. The computation of partial correlations is extremely simple unless it is desired to control for three or more variables simultaneously. Before presenting the formula for partial correlation we must introduce a change of notation. Unfortunately, what is a convenient notation for one purpose may not be so for another, nor is conventional usage completely consistent. We have been letting the dependent variable be represented by Y and the independent variables by $X_1, X_2, \ldots, X_k$. In recognition of the fact that sometimes the choice of dependent variable is more or less arbitrary and that we may therefore want to compute partial correlations between various combinations of variables, it will be convenient simply to renumber the variables from 1 to $k + 1$ and to represent the correlation between variables 1 and 2 controlling for 3 by $r_{12 \cdot 3}$. Similarly, the correlation between variables 2 and 3 controlling for 1 would be $r_{23 \cdot 1}$.

This notation can readily be extended to any number of control variables by adding further numbers to the right of the center dot. Thus, the relation between variables 5 and 7, controlling for variables 1, 2, 3, 4, and 6, would be given by $r_{57 \cdot 12346}$. The order of the two variables to the left of the dot is irrelevant as is that to the right. To distinguish between partials with differing numbers of control variables, we refer to the number of controls as the *order* of the correlation. Thus, a first-order partial will have one control, a second-order two controls, and so on. In keeping with this terminology, a correlation with no controls is often referred to as a zero-order correlation. As indicated above, the term *total correlation* is also used to indicate a correlation between two variables with no controls.

We can now give the formula for the general first-order partial $r_{ij\cdot k}$:

$$r_{ij\cdot k} = \frac{r_{ij} - (r_{ik})(r_{jk})}{\sqrt{1 - r_{ik}^2}\,\sqrt{1 - r_{jk}^2}} \tag{19.3}$$

Notice that the first correlation in the numerator is the total correlation between the two variables to be related (i and j). The control variable appears in the second expression of the numerator, where it is related to each of the other variables, and in both terms of the denominator. Any particular partial correlation can be obtained from this general formula by substituting the proper numbers for i, j, and k. Thus

$$r_{13\cdot 2} = \frac{r_{13} - (r_{12})(r_{23})}{\sqrt{1 - r_{12}^2}\,\sqrt{1 - r_{23}^2}}$$

In a study of 150 Southern counties [2], the correlation between income discrimination and per cent Negro was .536; that between income discrimination and per cent urban was .139; and the correlation between per cent Negro and per cent urban was −.248. Calling the discrimination index variable 1, per cent Negro variable 2, and per cent urban variable 3, we can obtain the partial between discrimination and per cent urban, controlling for per cent Negro. We have

$$r_{13\cdot 2} = \frac{.139 - (.536)(-.248)}{\sqrt{1 - (.536)^2}\,\sqrt{1 - (-.248)^2}} = \frac{.2719}{.8178} = .332$$

The result can be interpreted as the correlation between discrimination and per cent urban after per cent Negro has been allowed to explain all it can of both variables.

Although it will not be immediately apparent that the above formula can be derived from the definition of a partial correlation in terms of a correlation of residuals, the computing formula at least makes sense. In the numerator we are essentially subtracting a correction factor from the total correlation. The denominator consists of two correction factors, neither of which can be greater than unity, which take into consideration the fact that the control variable explains a certain proportion of the variation in the other variables. If we square the partial correlation coefficient, the resulting number will represent the proportion of variation in variable 1 (discrimination) which is left unexplained by 2 (per cent Negro) but which can be explained by 3 (per cent urban).

Let us examine equation (19.3) more carefully to note how the partial correlation behaves in relation to the three total correlations. For the sake of simplicity, let us first assume that r_{ij} is positive. If r_{ik} and r_{jk} both have the same signs (either positive or negative), their product will be positive, and either the numerator will be a smaller positive number than r_{ij} or it may even be zero or negative. On the other hand, the denominator will always be less than unity unless $r_{ik} = r_{jk} = 0$. The resulting fraction may therefore be almost any number between -1.0 and $+1.0$, depending on the magnitudes of the three total correlations. We shall see later just what we can and cannot say about the behavior of the partial under these circumstances.

Now suppose the correlations with the control variable are of opposite signs. We then obtain a negative product to be subtracted from a positive number, and the result will be a larger positive number. This means that if we start with two variables which are positively related and if we can find a control variable which is negatively related to one of them but positively related to the other, the resulting partial will be larger than the zero-order correlation. If the correlation of the control variable with either of the other variables happens to be zero, the correction factor in the numerator will be zero. But if the control variable is correlated either positively or negatively with the remaining variable, the denominator will be less than unity, and the partial correlation will again be larger than the total correlation.

If we had started with a negative total correlation, a control variable related to each of the other two in the same direction (either positive or negative) would produce a larger negative correlation. If it were related oppositely to the other two, however, the result would be analogous to the one first described (where the total correlation was positive and the correction factor also positive). Why? Again, if the control variable were not related to one of the other variables, the result would be a partial correlation with a larger absolute value than the total correlation. If the control variable were unrelated to *both* other variables, the partial correlation would of course exactly equal the total correlation. After we have discussed the relationship between partial correlation and causal interpretations, we shall be able to give an intuitive justification for the behavior of partial correlations under these various conditions.

The formulas for second- and higher-order partials are directly analogous to that for the first-order partial. We simply add successive control variables, each time starting with the partial of order one less than that desired. Thus the formulas for $r_{ij \cdot kl}$ and $r_{ij \cdot klm}$ will be

$$r_{ij \cdot kl} = \frac{r_{ij \cdot k} - (r_{il \cdot k})(r_{jl \cdot k})}{\sqrt{1 - r_{il \cdot k}^2} \; \sqrt{1 - r_{jl \cdot k}^2}} \tag{19.4}$$

and
$$r_{ij \cdot klm} = \frac{r_{ij \cdot kl} - (r_{im \cdot kl})(r_{jm \cdot kl})}{\sqrt{1 - r_{im \cdot kl}^2} \; \sqrt{1 - r_{jm \cdot kl}^2}} \tag{19.5}$$

Notice in equation (19.4) that we assume we have already controlled for variable k. Therefore, k appears to the right of each dot in all three first-order partials. Similarly, in equation (19.5) we have previously controlled for both k and l, and therefore both of these quantities appear in each of the second-order partials.

Fourth- and fifth-order partials could be obtained in a similar manner, and it will be instructive to try to write out formulas for these higher-order partials. The form for computing higher-order partials is thus identical to that used for the first-order case. But the work involved rapidly becomes tedious. For example, in order to obtain a third-order partial by this method, one must first have obtained three second-order partials, each of which in turn must be obtained by computing first-order partials from the zero-order correlations. If you were to try to express the formula for third-order partials directly in terms of the zero-order correlations, you would begin to see how much work would actually be involved.

Fortunately, it is seldom necessary in sociological research to go much beyond second- or third-order partials. Usually, the addition of controls beyond a second or third control produces very few new insights. If it is necessary to make use of higher-order partials, or of multiple regression equations involving four or more variables, there are computing routines which can do the job much more simply. You may wish to refer to either the abbreviated Doolittle method or Dwyer's square-root method in order to handle such problems (see [3], [6], and [7]). Of these two methods, the latter is perhaps more satisfactory in that it enables one to obtain directly the successive partials $r_{12 \cdot 3}$, $r_{12 \cdot 34}$, $r_{12 \cdot 345}$, etc.

Partial Rank-order Correlation. The theory with respect to partial rank-order correlations is less well developed. Kendall's tau can be extended in the case of first-order partials although the interpretation for the partial tau is not as intuitively appealing as in the case of product-moment correlation. If there are no ties, it turns out that the formula for partial tau's is identical to that we have been using. Thus

$$\tau_{ij \cdot k} = \frac{\tau_{ij} - (\tau_{ik})(\tau_{jk})}{\sqrt{1 - \tau_{ik}^2} \sqrt{1 - \tau_{jk}^2}} \qquad (19.6)$$

Strictly speaking, the partial is undefined if there are ties, but if rank-order correlations are being used in an exploratory fashion to give a rough indication of the comparable product-moment partials, it will probably make sense to go ahead unless the number of ties is considerable. Unfortunately, the sampling distribution of the partial tau is unknown so that it is not possible to test the partial for significance.[1]

---

[1] See [8]. A formula for a multiple rank-order correlation analogous to equation (19.15) has also been suggested.

9.3. Partial Correlation and Causal Interpretations

It has been pointed out that correlation analysis cannot be directly used to establish causality because of the fact that correlations merely measure covariation or the degree to which several variables vary together. One of the basic aims of any science, however, is to establish causal relations. Regardless of one's philosophical reservations concerning the notions of cause and effect, it is extremely difficult to think theoretically in any other terms. In Chap. 2 it was pointed out that there is a very real gap between the theoretical language used for thinking and the operational language used for testing hypotheses. The thorny problem of causality is just another indication of the existence of this gap. We often think in terms of causal relationships involving *necessary* temporal sequences. Thus, if A is a cause of B then A must necessarily be followed by B, and if A is absent B must also be absent. This conceptualization of causality is of course greatly oversimplified. For one thing, other variables have not been considered, and it makes sense to think of cause and effect only when certain assumptions can be made about these other factors. Also, both A and B may vary in degree rather than merely being present or absent.

Empirically, we can of course never prove that the connection between two variables is necessary. We can ascertain, however, the degree to which they vary together, and it is also sometimes possible to note the time sequence involved. From these two pieces of information we may make causal inferences if we wish. If our theory is able to show a logical connection between the two variables or to predict that A will be followed by B, we need not be too unhappy about making the intellectual leap to a causal interpretation. On the other hand, if we can find no theoretical reason for directly connecting the two events, we are ordinarily more hesitant. We are more likely to think of the relationship as "spurious," for example. Unfortunately, there is nothing in correlational analysis which can help us make this decision *unless* we are willing to make certain assumptions about these particular variables and about others that might also be operating. Let us see what these assumptions will have to be.

Suppose we are investigating the relationship between the per capita consumption of ice cream and rates of juvenile delinquency. We are likely to find a negative relationship. One possible causal interpretation would be that ice cream is so good for children that it prevents delinquency. Another would be that high rates of delinquency cause children to lose their appetites for sweets. We would of course immediately reject both these interpretations as absurd—although many similarly absurd ones have at one time or another been taken seriously. It would probably be argued that the relationship found was "spurious" in that a third variable, let us say income, was causing both variables to vary in such a manner that a negative correlation was obtained.

One test for spuriousness, and a valid one if used properly, is to control for income level. If the partial correlation between ice cream consumption and delinquency is reduced to zero, or approximately zero, we may conclude that there is no causal relationship between the two variables. Or can we? Let us take another very similar example. Suppose we find a negative relationship between income level and delinquency and decide to control for the percentage of broken homes in the area. Again we may find that the partial is reduced to zero. Is this relationship therefore also spurious? This time we're not so sure, although there may be absolutely nothing about the magnitude of the correlations or the behavior of the partials which is in any way different from the first case. In order to come to grips with the basic problem we are facing here, let us go back and look at it somewhat more systematically.

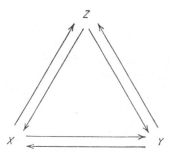

Fig. 19.4. The six possible causal arrows among X, Y, and Z.

Confining our attention for the moment to the three-variable case, we note that there are six possible causal connections between the three variables. Calling the variables X, Y, and Z and indicating the direction of causality by means of an arrowhead, we can diagram these possible connections as in Fig. 19.4. In any given problem, of course, some of these arrows will have to be erased. Let us do away with the possibility of two-way causation by arguing that if discrete events are selected, the time sequence must be in one direction or the other but not both simultaneously. For example, rather than claim that unemployment causes a recession and vice versa, let us say that Jones's unemployment causes him to spend less money, which in turn puts Smith out of work, etc. We are then left with only certain possible causal relationships which have been indicated in Fig. 19.5. In order to reduce the number of figures shown in Fig. 19.5, it was arbitrarily decided to select Y as the dependent variable or the one which must occur last in any time sequence. Therefore, no arrows have been drawn from Y to either X or Z. Of all these possible relationships, the first three are uninteresting and call for no further comment. Also, in order to simplify matters, let us confine our attention to those figures in which only two causal arrows have been drawn (d, e, f, g, and h).

Can we distinguish among these various models by looking at the relative magnitudes of the correlation coefficients? The answer is in the affirmative if we are willing to make two kinds of assumptions. Simon [9] has shown mathematically what these assumptions must be. *First*, we must be able to eliminate certain of the models by postulating that at least some of the possible causal relationships do *not* hold. This we have already done to some extent in that all double arrows were ruled out, and also Y was taken to be the dependent variable, i.e., was assumed to cause neither X nor Z. Still further assumptions will have to be made, but we shall postpone their consideration until later.

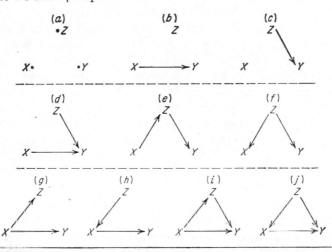

Fig. 19.5. Possible causal relationships among X, Y, and Z taking Y as the dependent variable and ruling out two-way causation.

The *second* type of general assumption we have to make concerns other variables that might be operating. We shall assume, following Simon, that all other variables influencing X are uncorrelated with all other variables affecting Y and Z, and so forth. In other words, we can admit the existence of other uncontrolled variables, but we have to assume that they have essentially a random effect on X, Y, and Z. Notice that this really involves a weaker set of assumptions than is usually implied in the model of the ideal experiment in which it is assumed that all "relevant" variables have been controlled. We recognize the disturbing influence of other variables in that we do not expect correlations to be perfect. On the other hand, we must assume that they operate in such a manner as not to disturb the *pattern* of relationships among X, Y, and Z. This condition can be approximated empirically if there are a large number of other variables operating, no one of which has a very great effect on more than one of the variables under consideration.

If an outside variable with a disturbing effect does exist, it should be brought into the model as a fourth variable. Simon argues that this is essentially what we always must do and that our failure to be satisfied with a causal explanation in the two-variable case is the reason why we introduce the notion of a spurious relationship. For example, if we were satisfied that there were no such variable operating to disturb the relationship between ice cream consumption and delinquency, and if we could rule out the possibility that delinquency caused ice cream sales to go down, then we would be satisfied with the explanation that the causal arrow went in the opposite direction. We introduce the income factor precisely because we expect this latter variable to affect the relationship between the first two. Similarly, we could add a fourth or fifth variable to the system, but at some point we must be willing to stop. At this point, if we are to make any causal inferences at all, we must assume the system to be "closed" in the sense we have been describing.

Notice that we are in the familiar position of having to make certain assumptions which cannot be verified empirically by the statistical analysis. It will therefore not be possible to establish the correctness of any particular causal model, but we can proceed by elimination. For example, one of the models indicated in Fig. 19.5 may appear to work. But the correct model might actually involve four or more variables and the picture might look quite different indeed. Having made these assumptions, however, we can make use of the mathematical analysis formalized by Simon to lead to certain predicted relationships that ought to hold among the correlations if the particular model is actually correct. As we shall see, exactly the same empirical relationships among correlations are predicted by several of the above models, making it necessary to choose between them on other grounds. It is here that we must make use of the first kind of assumption discussed above, namely, that certain causal relationships do *not* hold. Let us first examine the mathematical predictions concerning the interrelations among correlation coefficients, however.

If we look at Fig. 19.5g we see that the relationships between X and Y and between X and Z are direct, whereas that between Y and Z is only indirect. The same is also true in Fig. h. In both these cases, common sense would suggest that if all other variables were operating in an essentially random manner we would expect to find that the correlation between Y and Z is smaller in magnitude than either of the other two correlations. Similarly, in Fig. 19.5e and f we would expect the correlation between X and Y to be the smallest of the three, ignoring signs. As the mathematics works out, we can be even more definite than this. It is possible to show for both (g) and (h) where the relationship between Y and Z is indirect that

$$\rho_{YZ} = \rho_{XY}\rho_{XZ}$$

We have used ρ's to indicate the fact that these exact relationships can be expected only in the population and that the values of sample r's will ordinarily deviate from this predicted relationship because of sampling fluctuations. Similarly, it can be shown that for cases (e) and (f) we shall have

$$\rho_{XY} = \rho_{XZ}\rho_{YZ}$$

Since the absolute values of correlation coefficients cannot be greater than unity, it is clear that in the first case the numerical value of ρ_{YZ} must be less than that of either of the other coefficients unless one of these values happens to be unity. In this special case, of course, one of the variables can be predicted exactly from one of the others, and we have essentially a problem in only two variables.

Looking more closely at the first of these equations which applies to Fig. 19.5g and h, we see immediately that were this equation to hold, the partial correlation (in the population) between Y and Z controlling for X would vanish since the numerator in the formula for the partial would then be zero. Thus if either (g) or (h) should hold, the value of $r_{YZ \cdot X}$ should be zero or very close to zero if we allow for sampling errors. Similarly, for both (e) and (f) the partial between X and Y controlling for Z can be expected to be approximately zero. What are the implications of these facts? Confining our attention to a comparison between (e) and (f), since the relationship between (g) and (h) is directly comparable if X and Z are interchanged, we see that in (f) we would interpret the relationship between X and Y as "spurious" since Z is operating to cause variation in both X and Y. This situation is exactly that described in the example of ice cream consumption X and delinquency rates Y. Because we suspect the relationship between these two variables to be due to a third variable, income level Z, we control for Z to see if the correlation between X and Y is reduced to approximately zero. If (f) in fact is the correct model, we have just seen mathematically that this will happen.

We have also seen, however, that the partial would have been zero if Fig. 19.5e were the correct model. In (e) we have Z operating as an "intervening" variable in the sense that X causes Z which in turn causes Y. But does it make any sense to control for Z under these circumstances? Probably not. For if X is actually a cause of Z, how can we imagine ourselves holding Z constant while still varying X? That the partial reduces to zero is an example of the absurdity of attempting to hold Z constant in this situation. The fact that in using partial correlation we are not literally holding Z fixed means only that the real purpose of what we are doing here is likely to be lost. The manipulation of statistical formulas is no substitute for knowing what one is doing. In this instance, knowing what one is doing consists of being in a position to choose between models (e) and (f) by going beyond the statistical information available and making an assumption about the direction of the arrow between X and Z.

So far we have ignored situation (d) in Fig. 19.5 in which arrows go from both X and Z to Y but in which there is no direct relationship between X and Z. What happens in this case if we control for Z? We note first that it makes sense to control for Z here because Z is conceived as a completely independent variable which also affects Y. From the point of view of the relationship between X and Y, it is operating as a disturbing influence. It is an "outside" variable which is producing essentially random variations in Y with respect to variations in X. We would therefore expect that controlling for Z would increase the magnitude of the relationship between X and Y. It can be shown mathematically that if we make the required assumptions about other variables, the correlation in the population between X and Z will be zero. Incidentally, this fact will enable us to distinguish (d) empirically from each of the other situations we have been discussing. This is the situation, then, in which the control variable is unrelated to one of the other variables, and we have already seen that in this case the partial will be larger in absolute value than the total correlation, a fact which is consistent with common sense.

There is another type of control situation which has not been discussed but which can be handled briefly since there are few, if any, instances in which one would be tempted to use a control. Suppose in either of situations (e) or (h) that one were to relate the intervening and dependent variables, controlling for the independent variable. In (h), for example, what would happen if we were to obtain the partial between X and Y controlling for Z? It can be shown algebraically that the resulting partial would be smaller in magnitude than the total correlation. This is consistent with the intuitive notion that in holding constant the independent variable one necessarily reduces the variation in the intervening variable, thereby weakening the relationship with the dependent variable. Again, it would make little sense to carry out such an operation. Our interest would ordinarily center on the question of whether or not a direct link exists between X and Y and not on the problem of antecedent causes of Y.

We have examined only the three-variable case because of the fact that the introduction of additional variables into the model complicates the analysis considerably. And yet the very nature of most sociological problems prevents us from limiting ourselves to the three-variable case. Theoretically, the method of analysis proposed by Simon can be extended to any number of variables.[2] We therefore have a powerful tool with the potential for enabling one to set up fairly complicated alternative causa-

[2] For an illustration of the four-variable case see [1].

tive models involving a large number of variables.   It should be possible to eliminate some of these models by showing mathematically that they imply certain relationships among correlation coefficients which do not hold up empirically.   We could thus make use of correlational analysis to make inferences about causality, subject to the qualification that we would also have to make certain assumptions which were not subject to testing.   Unfortunately, the mathematical operations have apparently not as yet been simplified to the point where the average sociologist could apply them to his particular empirical problem.   Also, as the number of variables in the system is increased beyond four, the number of cases required in order to overcome inaccuracies introduced by sampling error becomes very large.   It is hoped, however, that before very long some of these problems will have been resolved.

19.4. Multiple Least Squares and the Beta Coefficients

We have been using partial correlations to indicate the degree of relationship between a dependent variable and an independent variable, controlling for one or more other independent variables.   If we have a large number of independent variables we can obtain an indication of their relative importance by relating the dependent variable to each independent variable in turn, always controlling for the remaining variables.   In so doing, we must of course be careful not to control for any intervening variables.   Earlier, in our discussion of multiple regression and least squares, we also noted that the b's and β's which appear in our equations linking Y to the independent variables can in a sense be interpreted as partials.   It will be recalled that they represent the slopes of the regression or least-squares equations in the dimension of the appropriate independent variable, i.e., with all other independent variables held constant.   Each coefficient therefore represents the amount of change in Y that can be associated with a given change in one of the X's with the remaining independent variables held fixed.   Noting this similarity to the partial correlation coefficients, it would not be surprising if the formulas used in computing these partial b's turned out to be very similar to those used in obtaining partial r's and if, furthermore, these slopes could be used to give an indication of the relative importance of each of the independent variables in determining variation in Y.

We must again modify our notation in order to distinguish among the large number of possible combinations of slopes.   Referring to our variables simply as 1, 2, 3, and so forth, we use the symbol $b_{12 \cdot 3}$ if we are predicting variable 1 from variables 2 and 3 and if we are referring to the coefficient of the second variable.   The coefficient $b_{12 \cdot 3}$ must be distinguished from $b_{21 \cdot 3}$ which would be used if the second variable were taken as the dependent variable. In both cases, the fact that the number three has been placed to the right of the dot indicates that the third variable has been controlled. Similarly, $b_{12 \cdot 34}$ is used to indicate the coefficient of the second variable in a prediction equation in which the first variable is taken as the dependent variable and which involves two control variables. In this case, the least-squares equation would be given as

$$X_1 = a_{1 \cdot 234} + b_{12 \cdot 34}X_2 + b_{13 \cdot 24}X_3 + b_{14 \cdot 23}X_4$$

where the subscript for a indicates that we are predicting to variable 1 from variables 2, 3, and 4. The reason we have found it convenient to depart from the practice of denoting the dependent variable by Y is to make use of a simpler set of subscripts for keeping track of the various b's.

The computing formulas for $a_{i \cdot jk}$ and $b_{ij \cdot k}$ are as follows

$$a_{i \cdot jk} = \bar{X}_i - b_{ij \cdot k}\,\bar{X}_j - b_{ik \cdot j}\,\bar{X}_k \tag{19.7}$$

and

$$b_{ij \cdot k} = \frac{b_{ij} - (b_{ik})(b_{kj})}{1 - b_{jk}b_{kj}} \tag{19.8}$$

Notice that although the denominator in (19.8) differs in form from that in the formula for $r_{ij \cdot k}$, the numerator is essentially similar in nature. Recalling that

$$r_{jk}{}^2 = b_{jk}b_{kj}$$

we see that even the denominators are not too dissimilar in form. In using this formula to obtain the partial b's, however, you must be careful to distinguish between b_{jk} and b_{kj} since the subscripts can no longer be interchanged.

The extension to higher-order partials is straightforward (see [4]). The equations for $a_{i \cdot jkl}$ and $b_{ij \cdot kl}$ can be written as

$$a_{i \cdot jkl} = \bar{X}_i - b_{ij \cdot kl}\,\bar{X}_j - b_{ik \cdot jl}\,\bar{X}_k - b_{il \cdot jk}\,\bar{X}_l \tag{19.9}$$

and

$$b_{ij \cdot kl} = \frac{b_{ij \cdot k} - (b_{il \cdot k})(b_{lj \cdot k})}{1 - b_{jl \cdot k}(b_{lj \cdot k})} \tag{19.10}$$

Similarly true in computing higher-order partial correlations, as the number of variables becomes large the use of these formulas may involve considerably more work than that required by the abbreviated Doolittle or Dwyer square-root method.

If the partial b's are to be used to compare various independent variables as to their relative abilities to produce changes in the dependent variable, we must correct for the fact that there will undoubtedly be differences in scale involved. One variable may be measured in terms of dollars, another in years. It would therefore be meaningless to compare a unit change in one variable with a unit change in another. If each variable is standardized by dividing by its standard deviation, just as was done in obtaining the standard normal curve, we can obtain adjusted slopes which are comparable from one variable to the next. We thus measure changes in the dependent variable in terms of standard-deviation units for each of the other variables, a fact which assures us of the same variability in each of these variables. These adjusted partial slopes are called *beta weights*.

Unfortunately we are again involved with notational inconsistencies. These beta weights are not the same as the β's in the regression equation which refer to characteristics of the *population* and which have not been adjusted for differences in variability. The beta weights are obtained from *sample* data and are simple functions of the partial b's. The general formulas for $\beta_{ij \cdot k}$ and $\beta_{ij \cdot kl}$ are

$$\beta_{ij \cdot k} = b_{ij \cdot k} \frac{s_j}{s_i} \tag{19.11}$$

and

$$\beta_{ij \cdot kl} = b_{ij \cdot kl} \frac{s_j}{s_i} \tag{19.12}$$

Thus the beta weight can be obtained by multiplying the comparable b by the ratio of the standard deviation of the independent variable (not controlled) to that of the dependent variable.

The comparability of beta weights and partial correlation coefficients can be seen from the formula

$$\beta_{ij \cdot k} = \frac{r_{ij} - r_{ik} r_{jk}}{1 - r_{jk}^2} \tag{19.13}$$

The two measures differ only in their denominators. In fact, we see immediately that

$$r_{ij \cdot k}^2 = (\beta_{ij \cdot k})(\beta_{ji \cdot k})$$

since $\beta_{ji \cdot k}$ differs from $\beta_{ij \cdot k}$ only in that the denominator of r_{jk}^2 will be replaced by r_{ik}^2. Since the beta weights and partial correlations represent somewhat different types of measures of association, they will not give exactly the same results although usually they will rank variables in the same order of importance. The partial correlation is a measure of the *amount of variation explained* by one independent variable after the others have explained all they could. The beta weights, on the other hand, indicate *how much change* in the dependent variable is produced by a standardized change in one of the independent variables when the others are controlled.

The choice of the appropriate measure will depend upon the nature of the analysis and upon which measure one's audience is most likely to understand. Beta weights would seem to be preferable when attention has been focused on the prediction equation itself rather than measures of degree of relationship. The fact that one finds many more references in the sociological literature to partial correlations may in part be a reflection of the fact that unless the degree of relationship is reasonably strong, prediction equations are of relatively little interest. Perhaps as we increase our ability to predict accurately to a dependent variable, beta weights will replace partial correlations as measures of the relative importance of various independent variables.

19.5. Multiple Correlation

Since our primary interest may be in the explanatory power of a number of independent variables taken together, rather than in the relationship between the dependent variable and each of the independent variables taken separately, we may prefer to make use of the *multiple correlation coefficient* which is a measure of the goodness of fit of the least-squares surface to the data. Just as the square of the zero-order correlation coefficient indicated the percentage of the variation explained by the best-fitting straight line, the square of the multiple correlation coefficient can be used to give the percentage of variation explained by the best-fitting equation of the form

$$Y_p = a + b_1 X_1 + b_2 X_2 + \cdots + b_k X_k$$

Another way of conceiving of multiple correlation is that it represents the *zero-order correlation* between the *actual values* obtained for the dependent variable and those *values predicted from the least-squares equation.* If all of the points are exactly on the least-squares surface, the actual and predicted values will coincide and the multiple correlation will be unity. The greater the scatter about the least-squares equation, the lower the correlation between actual and predicted values.

The formula for the multiple correlation can easily be developed using the fact that the square of the multiple will be equal to the percentage of the variation explained by all of the independent variables. Again, it should be emphasized that a linear-type model is being assumed. In writing a formula for the multiple correlation, we first let one of the independent variables do all of the explaining it can. We then permit the second independent variable to go to work on that portion of the variation left unexplained by the first. In order to avoid duplication, however, we must control for this first independent variable. We then permit the third to explain all it can of the remainder, now controlling for both of the first two independent variables. The process can be extended indefinitely. For the present, we confine ourselves to the three-variable case involving only two independent variables. If we take the first variable as the dependent variable and denote the multiple correlation coefficient by $R_{1\cdot 23}$, we may write

$$
R^2_{1\cdot 23} \quad = \quad r^2_{12} \quad + \quad r^2_{13\cdot 2} \quad (1 - r^2_{12})
$$

$$
\begin{pmatrix} \text{Proportion} \\ \text{explained} \\ \text{by 2 and 3} \end{pmatrix} = \begin{pmatrix} \text{proportion} \\ \text{explained} \\ \text{by 2} \end{pmatrix} + \begin{pmatrix} \text{additional} \\ \text{proportion} \\ \text{explained} \\ \text{by 3} \end{pmatrix} \begin{pmatrix} \text{proportion} \\ \text{unexplained} \\ \text{by 2} \end{pmatrix} \quad (19.14)
$$

Notice that multiple correlations have only one figure to the left of the dot, this figure indicating the dependent variable. Numbers to the right indicate those independent variables which are being used to explain the variation in the dependent variable. The general formula (for three variables) can thus be written

$$
\begin{aligned}
R^2_{i\cdot jk} &= r^2_{ij} + r^2_{ik\cdot j}(1 - r^2_{ij}) \\
&= r^2_{ik} + r^2_{ij\cdot k}(1 - r^2_{ik})
\end{aligned} \quad (19.15)
$$

It is irrelevant, of course, which of the two independent variables is used first in the formula, as long as this variable is controlled in subsequent terms in the equation.

We are dealing with the squares of both the total and partial correlations since we are obtaining the percentages of variation explained. Therefore we do not have to worry about the sign of these correlations. In fact, the direction of the multiple has no meaning since it involves correlations with a number of variables, some of these correlations being positive and others possibly negative. By convention we always take the positive square root of R^2 in denoting the multiple correlation coefficient.

If we solve equation (19.14) for the partial $r^2_{13\cdot 2}$ we obtain

$$
r^2_{13\cdot 2} = \frac{R^2_{1\cdot 23} - r^2_{12}}{1 - r^2_{12}} \quad (19.16)
$$

This enables us to see the relationship between multiple and partial correlation coefficients in a somewhat different perspective. In the numerator we have subtracted the proportion of the variation in 1 explained by 2 alone from the proportion explained by both 2 and 3 acting together ($R^2_{1\cdot 23}$). The result is the increment explained by 3 after 2 has been allowed to operate. When this increment is divided by the proportion of variation left unexplained by 2 we obtain the partial between 1 and 3 controlling for 2. This is consistent with our earlier interpretation of the partial correlation coefficient.

Several alternative but equivalent formulas for $R^2_{1\cdot 23}$ can be derived from equation (19.14). Subtracting both sides of this equation from unity we get

$$1 - R_{1\cdot 23}^2 = 1 - r_{12}^2 - r_{13\cdot 2}^2(1 - r_{12}^2)$$
$$= (1 - r_{12}^2)(1 - r_{13\cdot 2}^2) \tag{19.17}$$

This equation indicates that we can write the proportion of variation left unexplained by 2 and 3 together as the product of the proportion unexplained by 2 and that unexplained by 3, controlling for 2.

The formula for the multiple can also be written completely in terms of zero-order correlations. Making use of equation (19.3) for $r_{13\cdot 2}$ in terms of zero-order coefficients and simplifying the resulting algebraic expression, we get

$$R_{1\cdot 23}^2 = \frac{r_{12}^2 + r_{13}^2 - 2r_{12}r_{13}r_{23}}{1 - r_{23}^2}$$

or, in general,

$$R_{i\cdot jk}^2 = \frac{r_{ij}^2 + r_{ik}^2 - 2r_{ij}r_{ik}r_{jk}}{1 - r_{jk}^2} \tag{19.18}$$

In particular, if the correlation between the two independent variables j and k happens to be zero we get

$$R_{i\cdot jk}^2 = r_{ij}^2 + r_{ik}^2$$

Several relationships between the multiple R and the various total correlations can now be noted. Obviously, R cannot be less in magnitude than any of the total correlations since it is impossible to explain *less* variation by adding further variables. Ordinarily, of course, the multiple R will be larger than any of the total r's. Its maximum value relative to the total coefficients usually occurs when the intercorrelations between independent variables are all zero. As we have just seen, the square of the multiple correlation will in this case be equal to the sum of the squares of the other correlations. On the other hand, if the intercorrelations among independent variables are quite high in magnitude the multiple R will ordinarily not be much larger than the largest total correlation with the dependent variable. In other words, if we wish to explain as much variation in the dependent variable as possible, we should look for independent variables which are relatively unrelated to each other but which have at least moderately high correlations with the dependent variable. Put another way, if we have two highly interrelated independent variables, the second will be explaining essentially the same variation as the first since there will be considerable overlap. If they are uncorrelated, they will each explain a different portion of the total variation.

As a numerical example of the computation of the multiple R, let us see how much of the variation in discrimination can be explained by both per cent Negro and per cent urban.   Using equation (19.14) we get

$$R^2_{1\cdot23} = r^2_{12} + r^2_{13\cdot2}(1 - r^2_{12}) = (.536)^2 + (.332)^2[1 - (.536)^2]$$
$$= .2873 + (.1102)(.7127) = .3658$$

Hence $R_{1\cdot23} = .605$

Therefore, per cent urban explains very little variation over and above that explained by per cent Negro.

As a check on our computations, we note that the same result should be obtained if we allow per cent urban to operate first.   We then get

$$r_{12\cdot3} = \frac{r_{12} - r_{13}(r_{23})}{\sqrt{1 - r^2_{13}}\,\sqrt{1 - r^2_{23}}} = \frac{.536 - (.139)(-.248)}{\sqrt{1 - (.139)^2}\,\sqrt{1 - (-.248)^2}} = .595$$

Thus $R^2_{1\cdot23} = r^2_{13} + r^2_{12\cdot3}(1 - r^2_{13})$
$$= (.139)^2 + (.595)^2[1 - (.139)^2] = .3667$$

and hence $R_{1\cdot23} = .605$

The formulas for the multiple correlation coefficient can also readily be extended to any number of independent variables.   In introducing a third independent variable, denoted as variable X_4, we merely add to the formula for $R^2_{1\cdot23}$ a term involving the product of the square of the partial between 1 and 4, controlling for 2 and 3, and the proportion of variation left unexplained by 2 and 3.   Thus

$$R^2_{1\cdot234} = r^2_{12} + r^2_{13\cdot2}(1 - r^2_{12}) + r^2_{14\cdot23}[1 - r^2_{12} - r^2_{13\cdot2}(1 - r^2_{12})]$$
$$= R^2_{1\cdot23} + r^2_{14\cdot23}(1 - R^2_{1\cdot23}) \qquad (19.19)$$

We can therefore keep adding to the proportion of variation explained as long as we control for all variables previously used and provided that we permit the new partial to work only on that portion of the variation left unexplained by those variables which have preceded it.   Note, incidentally, the parallel with what we did in analysis of variance.   As we shall presently see, we can make use of this fact in tests of significance for both multiple and partial correlation.   If we were to add a fifth variable, we would get

$$R^2_{1\cdot2345} = R^2_{1\cdot234} + r^2_{15\cdot234}(1 - R^2_{1\cdot234})$$

We can again solve these equations for the partial coefficients.   For example, from (19.19) we have

$$r^2_{14\cdot23} = \frac{R^2_{1\cdot234} - R^2_{1\cdot23}}{1 - R^2_{1\cdot23}} \qquad (19.20)$$

indicating that the partial between 1 and 4, controlling for 2 and 3, can be interpreted as the ratio of the proportion of additional variation explained by 4 over and above that explained by 2 and 3 to the proportion of variation left unexplained by the latter two variables. We can also extend equation (19.17) to cover more variables. Thus

$$1 - R^2_{1 \cdot 234} = (1 - r^2_{12})(1 - r^2_{13 \cdot 2})(1 - r^2_{14 \cdot 23})$$

and, in general,

$$1 - R^2_{1 \cdot 234 \cdots k} = (1 - r^2_{12})(1 - r^2_{13 \cdot 2}) \cdots (1 - r^2_{1k \cdot 234 \cdots (k-1)}) \quad (19.21)$$

The Multiple-partial Coefficient. Sometimes it is desirable to compute a multiple correlation between a dependent variable and several independent variables, controlling for one or more independent variables. Suppose, for example, that one is trying to predict actual family size from a number of independent variables. Obviously, certain variables such as the duration of marriage and the age of wife at marriage need to be taken into consideration. On the other hand, they are so obvious that throwing them into the general multiple coefficient might obscure the effects of the remaining variables. Interest might therefore be focused on the variation in family size after such theoretically unimportant variables have explained all of the variation they could. Following Croxton and Cowden [5], we indicate the multiple-partial between variable 1 (dependent) and 2 and 3, controlling for 4, by $r_{1(23) \cdot 4}$. The formula in this case becomes

$$r^2_{1(23) \cdot 4} = \frac{R^2_{1 \cdot 234} - r^2_{14}}{1 - r^2_{14}}$$

The above formula for the multiple-partial is a simple extension of the formulas we have been using for multiple and partial correlations. We first let control variable 4 do all of the explaining it can. We then note that $R^2_{1 \cdot 234}$ represents the proportion of variation explained by all of the three independent variables taken together. The difference, then, must be due to variables 2 and 3. The numerator thus represents the proportion of variation explained by 2 and 3 over and above that explained by 4. But since we must work only on that variation left unexplained by the control variable, we divide by the quantity $1 - r^2_{14}$. Making use of the principle that we allow all control variables to operate first, we can write the general formula for the multiple-partial as

$$r^2_{i(jk \cdots n) \cdot tu \cdots w} = \frac{R^2_{i \cdot jk \cdots w} - R^2_{i \cdot tu \cdots w}}{1 - R^2_{i \cdot tu \cdots w}} \quad (19.22)$$

For example,

$$r^2_{3(56) \cdot 124} = \frac{R^2_{3 \cdot 12456} - R^2_{3 \cdot 124}}{1 - R^2_{3 \cdot 124}}$$

The multiple-partial does not seem to have been used very frequently in sociological research, perhaps because of its lack of familiarity to persons in the field. As a measure which enables one to handle both multiple and partial correlation problems simultaneously, its potential utility would seem to be great, however. In the next section we shall consider another kind of use for this measure.

19.6. Multiple Regression and Nonlinearity

All of our work thus far in the chapter has been based on the assumption of linear-type models. In the previous chapter we took up a test for nonlinearity, but we had very little to say about the form of the nonlinear relationship except in the case of logarithmic transformations. In other words, we simply tested for the existence of a *departure* from linearity, but we made no test for the form of the curve. Although the general problem of nonlinearity is beyond the scope of this text, we can examine briefly how the techniques of multiple regression and least squares can be modified slightly so as to enable us to handle certain types of problems involving nonlinearity.

As pointed out in the previous chapter, there are an extremely large number of different forms a nonlinear relationship can take. Let us consider equations of the type

$$Y = a + b_1X + b_2X^2 + b_3X^3 + \cdots + b_kX^k \qquad (19.23)$$

If all of the coefficients b_2, b_3, . . . , b_k are zero, the equation is reduced to the familiar linear form. In other words, a straight line can be considered as a special case of this general type of curve which is referred to as a *polynomial*. Similarly, if all of the coefficients except a, b_1, and b_2 are zero we get a polynomial of the second degree. The degree of the polynomial refers to the highest exponent of X which has a nonzero coefficient.

Polynomials have a very important property which enables us to tell the degree of the equation that is likely to be the most appropriate to one's data. Note that a polynomial of the first degree is a straight line with no bends in it. It turns out that a second-degree equation will have exactly one bend in it and, in fact, describes the particular curve which we call a parabola. A third-degree polynomial will have two bends, a fourth-degree three bends, and so on. If we ignore certain degenerate cases in which the "bends" do not behave properly, we can diagram these second-, third-, and fourth-degree equations as in Fig. 19.6. The direction in which the parabola or higher-degree curves "open up" will depend upon the sign of the coefficients. The important point is that there will always be one less bend than is indicated by the degree of the equation.

We sometimes get empirical curves which look like one or another of these polynomials, although seldom, if ever, do we need to go higher than a third-degree equation. A simple parabola may often give a reasonably good fit to the data, especially when we realize that the curve may be quite flat and that our data need not extend far enough to complete the

$$Y = a + b_1 X + b_2 X^2 \qquad Y = a + b_1 X + b_2 X^2 + b_3 X^3 \qquad Y = a + b_1 X + b_2 X^2 + b_3 X^3 + b_4 X^4$$

Fig. 19.6. Forms of second-, third-, and fourth-degree polynomials.

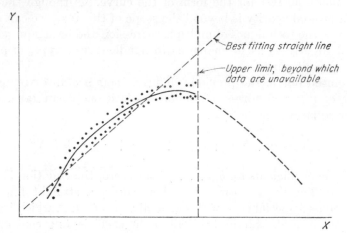

Fig. 19.7. Hypothetical data best fitted by a parabola.

bend. Thus the data might be similar to those indicated in Fig. 19.7. Here, even though there may be no theoretical reason to expect scores to go down again once we have gone a certain distance along the X axis, the parabola may be a reasonable fit *within the limits of variation given in the problem.* It is thus quite possible that a least-squares parabola might fit the data much better than a straight line.

Suppose this turns out to be the case. How can the problem be handled? You have undoubtedly already noticed the similarity between the formula for the general polynomial and the formula for the least-squares equation involving more than one independent variable. The only difference is that in place of X_2 we have written X^2 and so on. Now suppose we were to conceptualize X^2 as a separate and distinct variable from X. As long as we are making use of abstract symbols this is entirely possible, although admittedly this practice would make little sense in terms of a concrete variable. The mathematics of the situation turns out to be identical, however. For example, if we suspect that the relationship between discrimination and per cent Negro can be fitted by a second-degree curve, we take per cent Negro as one independent variable X_1 and (per cent Negro)^2 as the second independent variable X_2. Therefore the second-degree equation

$$Y = a + b_1 X + b_2 X^2$$

which is difficult to handle by least squares is reduced to the familiar equation

$$Y = a + b_1 X_1 + b_2 X_2$$

To obtain a measure of goodness of fit to the parabola, we can now use the multiple correlation between Y and X_1 and X_2. The difference between the square of this multiple correlation and the square of the total r (assuming linearity) will give us a measure of the degree to which we have improved our ability to predict to discrimination by using a second-degree equation rather than a straight line.

In principle, the above procedure can be extended in several ways. Third- and higher-degree equations might be used in order to obtain a somewhat better fit. Also, other variables can be added to the picture. For some of these independent variables a nonlinear model can be assumed, for others a linear one. In predicting discrimination rates from a number of independent variables, we might find that somewhat better prediction equations could be obtained assuming nonlinear models for some of the variables. In particular, perhaps the relationship between discrimination and per cent Negro may be of parabolic form, whereas all the remaining independent variables are linearly related to discrimination. The multiple least-squares equation therefore would take the form

$$Y = a + (b_1 X_1 + b_2 X_2) + b_3 X_3 + \cdots + b_k X_k$$

where the two terms within the parentheses are needed to describe the (nonlinear) relationship between discrimination and per cent Negro. In this case also, the X_2 variable again represents (per cent Negro)^2. Conceivably, some of the other X's in the equation may also be used to indicate nonlinear relationships between discrimination and other variables.

In the above example suppose that we wished to obtain the partial correlation between discrimination and per cent Negro, controlling for the remaining variables. Since X_1 and X_2 have been used to refer to the first and second powers of per cent Negro, it would not make sense to relate Y and X_1, controlling for all of the remaining "variables," including X_2. Rather, we need to obtain the multiple correlation between Y and both X_1 and X_2, controlling for X_3, X_4, . . . , X_k. The multiple-partial coefficient can be used to accomplish this purpose.

There are obviously many more uses and possible extensions of multiple correlation and regression techniques than can be discussed in a general text. A sufficient number of the more elementary basic principles have been given, however, that you should be able to consult intelligently with a statistician if more complicated problems should arise.

19.7. Significance Tests and Confidence Intervals

It will of course be necessary to test both multiple and partial coefficients for significance. The null hypotheses and assumptions will be similar to those made in the case of total correlation. A random sample will as usual be assumed. The assumption of a multivariate normal distribution will assure us that each variable is normally distributed about the others, that variances are equal, and that the regression equation will have the form indicated by equation (19.1). Having made these assumptions, we can make use of analysis-of-variance tests for the significance of various partial and multiple coefficients. We shall first take up tests for the significance of multiple correlations since these are conceptually simpler than tests for partials.

Since the square of the multiple correlation always represents the proportion of the total variation explained by the independent variables acting together, we have in effect divided this total variation into two portions, the explained and unexplained sums of squares. The analysis-of-variance table will therefore always be similar to Table 19.1.

Table 19.1. Analysis-of-variance Test for Significance of Multiple Correlation

	Sums of squares	Degrees of freedom	Estimate of variance	F
Total	Σx_1^2	$N - 1$		
Explained	$R^2\Sigma x_1^2$	k	$\dfrac{R^2\Sigma x_1^2}{k}$	$\dfrac{R^2}{1 - R^2}\dfrac{N - k - 1}{k}$
Unexplained	$(1 - R^2)\Sigma x_1^2$	$N - k - 1$	$\dfrac{(1 - R^2)\Sigma x_1^2}{N - k - 1}$	

In Table 19.1 we have indicated the dependent variable by X_1 and have let k represent the number of independent variables. If R involves, say, a dependent variable and three independent variables, there will be four parameters in the regression equation which must be estimated.

We would therefore lose 4 or $(k + 1)$ degrees of freedom in using the least-squares equation to estimate the dependent variable. Thus the degrees of freedom associated with the error term will in general be $N - (k + 1) = N - k - 1$. The degrees of freedom associated with the explained sum of squares can then be obtained by subtraction. Since the degrees of freedom for the explained and unexplained sums of squares will always turn out to be k and $N - k - 1$, respectively, we may write a general formula for F. Note that as was true with total correlations, the factor representing the total sum of squares cancels. We thus get as a general formula for testing for the significance of a multiple R

$$F_{k,N-k-1} = \frac{R^2}{1 - R^2} \frac{N - k - 1}{k} \qquad (19.24)$$

It is not necessary, therefore, to set up the analysis-of-variance table in conventional form. Testing for the significance of the multiple correlation we obtained in explaining discrimination from per cent Negro and per cent urban (see page 349), we get

$$F_{2,147} = \frac{.3658}{1 - .3658} \frac{150 - 3}{2} = \frac{.3658}{.6342} \frac{147}{2} = 42.39$$

which is significant at the .001 level.

In testing for the significance of partial coefficients we operate on the principle of first letting the control variables do all of the explaining they can. We then take that portion of the total sum of squares which is *unexplained* by the control variable and use this as our new total. This latter quantity is then broken into two components, the explained and the

Table 19.2. Analysis-of-variance Test for Significance of Partial Correlation $r_{13.2}$

	Sums of squares	Degrees of freedom	Estimate of variance	F
Total	Σx_1^2	$N - 1$		
Explained by 2	$r_{12}^2 \Sigma x_1^2$	1		
Unexplained by 2	$(1 - r_{12}^2)\Sigma x_1^2$	$N - 2$		
Explained by 3	$r_{13.2}^2(1 - r_{12}^2)\Sigma x_1^2$	1	$r_{13.2}^2(1 - r_{12}^2)\Sigma x_1^2$	$\dfrac{r_{13.2}^2(N - 3)}{1 - r_{13.2}^2}$
Unexplained by 3	$(1 - r_{13.2}^2)(1 - r_{12}^2)\Sigma x_1^2$	$N - 3$	$\dfrac{(1 - r_{13.2}^2)(1 - r_{12}^2)\Sigma x_1^2}{N - 3}$	

unexplained portions, and an F test made by taking the ratio of the estimates of variance based on these last two components. The process is illustrated in Table 19.2 in which we are testing for the significance of $r_{13.2}$ (i.e., $H_0: \rho_{13.2} = 0$).

Notice that the degrees of freedom decrease by one each time a new variable is added. Again, in the formula for F, the expression simplifies so that it becomes unnecessary to write out the whole table each time we wish to make a test. In the numerical problem we have been using (see page 334), the F value for testing for the significance of the relationship between discrimination and per cent urban, controlling for per cent Negro, becomes

$$
\begin{aligned}
F_{1,N-3} &= \frac{r_{13 \cdot 2}^2}{1 - r_{13 \cdot 2}^2} (N - 3) \\
&= \frac{(.332)^2}{1 - (.332)^2} (147) = 18.21
\end{aligned}
\tag{19.25}
$$

Thus the partial is significant at the .001 level.

In extending this procedure, if we wish to test for the significance of $r_{14 \cdot 23}$ we can take as our new total the unexplained by 2 and 3 combined. This quantity can then be broken into explained and unexplained portions and the F test made as before. Again, all quantities in both numerator and denominator of F will cancel except the factors involving the partials. Since the degrees of freedom associated with the numerator will always be unity and since those for the denominator will be $N - k - 1$, we may write as a general formula for testing the partial $r_{ij \cdot mn \ldots t}$

$$
F_{1,N-k-1} = \frac{r_{ij \cdot mn \ldots t}^2}{1 - r_{ij \cdot mn \ldots t}^2} (N - k - 1)
\tag{19.26}
$$

where the total number of variables is $k + 1$.

Notice that in comparing tests for the significance of multiple and partial correlations, the final error term involving the sum of squares unexplained by all variables should be the same in both tables—provided, of course, that the same dependent and independent variables are used. We have already shown this to be the case since we know that

$$
1 - R_{1 \cdot 23}^2 = (1 - r_{12}^2)(1 - r_{13 \cdot 2}^2)
$$

From Tables 19.1 and 19.2 we see that these expressions are the ones that appear in the bottom rows of the respective tables.

The procedure we have described for testing partial correlations can also be used to test for the significance of the multiple-partial. By now you should be able to verify that in order to test for the significance of $r_{1(23) \cdot 45}$ we would take the sum of squares unexplained by both 4 and 5, then using the square of the multiple-partial to give the proportion of this new sum of squares which is explained by variables 2 and 3.

Confidence intervals can also be computed for both the partial and multiple coefficients by a slight modification of the Z transformation procedure described in the previous chapter. We can again convert either type of coefficient into Z using the table. The only change required is that the standard error of Z be no longer given by

$$\sigma_Z = \frac{1}{\sqrt{N-3}}$$

Instead, we lose one more degree of freedom for each variable added so that the standard error in general becomes

$$\sigma_Z = \frac{1}{\sqrt{N-m-1}} \tag{19.27}$$

where m represents the total number of variables.

We therefore obtain the 95 per cent confidence intervals for $R_{1 \cdot 23}$ and $r_{13 \cdot 2}$ as follows:

$$1.96\sigma_Z = 1.96 \frac{1}{\sqrt{146}} = .1622$$

	Z	$Z_l = Z - 1.96\sigma_Z$	$Z_u = Z + 1.96\sigma_Z$	r_l	r_u
$R_{1 \cdot 23} = .605$	.7010	.5388	.8632	.492	.698
$r_{13 \cdot 2} = .332$	.3451	.1829	.5073	.181	.468

Thus the 95 per cent confidence interval about $R_{1 \cdot 23}$ goes from .492 to .698 whereas that about $r_{13 \cdot 2}$ ranges from .181 to .468.

Before closing the chapter, one further important point should be noted. Each time we add another variable to the least-squares equation we lose only one more degree of freedom. We can therefore add variables with very little loss of efficiency as far as significance tests are concerned. Occasionally, the addition of more variables may lower the significance level because of the fact that they do not help explain enough additional variation to compensate for the loss in degrees of freedom. Nevertheless, we have in multiple and partial correlation a tool which, if properly used, is far more powerful than any of the methods we have previously discussed. If the number of variables used begins to approach the number of cases, however, we can expect to obtain very large multiple correlations simply because we are able to take advantage of chance fluctuations. With 15 cases and 15 variables it will be possible to pass a least-squares surface *exactly* through all of the points even if we assume a linear-type model. The multiple R will therefore automatically be unity. Therefore, like all other statistical techniques, multiple regression and correlational techniques must be used with caution. At this point it should hardly be necessary to point out that except for exploratory purposes, they should not be used unless the required assumptions are met or at least approximated.

GLOSSARY

Beta weights
Multiple correlation
Multiple-partial correlation
Multiple regression equation
Multivariate normal distribution
Partial correlation
Polynomial equation

EXERCISES

1. Using the data of Exercise 1, Chap. 17:

   a. Obtain the partial correlation between moral integration and heterogeneity, controlling for mobility. Also compute the partial between moral integration and mobility, controlling for heterogeneity.
   b. Obtain the multiple least-squares equation, taking moral integration as the dependent variable.
   c. What are the beta weights? How do they compare with the partials obtained in (a)?
   d. Compute the multiple correlation, taking moral integration as the dependent variable. How would you check your computations?
   e. Test for the significance of the partial and multiple correlations computed in parts (a) and (d). Place 99 per cent confidence intervals about each of these correlations.

2. Write out formulas for $r_{37 \cdot 12456}$, $R^2_{4 \cdot 1235}$, and $r^2_{5(23) \cdot 1467}$.

3. Write the formulas for F which would be used in testing for the significance of each of the correlations in Exercise 2 above.

REFERENCES

1. Blalock, H. M.: "Correlational Analysis and Causal Inferences," *American Anthropologist,* vol. 62, pp. 624–631, August, 1960.
2. Blalock, H. M.: "Per Cent Non-white and Discrimination in the South," *American Sociological Review,* vol. 22, pp. 677–682, December, 1957.
3. Bogue, D. J., and D. L. Harris: *Comparative Population and Urban Research via Multiple Regression and Covariance Analysis,* Scripps Foundation, Miami University, Oxford, Ohio, 1954.
4. Cowden, D. J.: "A Procedure for Computing Regression Coefficients," *Journal of the American Statistical Association,* vol. 53, pp. 144–150, March, 1958.
5. Croxton, F. E., and D. J. Cowden: *Applied General Statistics,* Prentice-Hall, Inc., Englewood Cliffs, N.J., 1955, chaps. 21 and 26.
6. Dwyer, P. S.: *Linear Computations,* John Wiley and Sons, Inc., New York, 1951.
7. Hagood, M. J., and D. O. Price: *Statistics for Sociologists,* Henry Holt and Company, Inc., New York, 1952, chap. 25.
8. Kendall, M. G.: *Rank Correlation Methods,* Hafner Publishing Company, New York, 1955, chap. 8.
9. Simon, H. A. "Spurious Correlation: A Causal Interpretation," *Journal of the American Statistical Association,* vol. 49, pp. 467–479, September, 1954.
10. Walker, H. M., and J. Lev: *Statistical Inference,* Henry Holt and Company, Inc., New York, 1953, chap. 13.

Chapter 20

ANALYSIS OF COVARIANCE

We have studied analysis of variance in which a single interval scale can be related to one or more nominal scales.   In the previous chapter we saw how correlation techniques can be used to relate any number of interval scales.   In analysis of covariance we combine the basic ideas of analysis of variance and correlational analysis in order to handle problems involving more than one interval scale in combination with any number of nominal scales.   Thus analysis of covariance is a theoretical extension of these two procedures which ideally enables us to handle problems involving various combinations of interval and nominal scales.

Unfortunately, as we shall presently see, the computations required for analysis of covariance become quite tedious even for the three-variable case.   This fact plus certain limitations imposed by the assumptions required by analysis of covariance severely restricts the utility of analysis of covariance as a general procedure for handling simultaneously large numbers of variables.   Nevertheless, this rather powerful technique seems to be of considerably more potential value to the sociologist than is indicated by its rather infrequent use in the literature.

In this chapter our attention will be confined to the three-variable case in which we have one nominal and two interval scales.   The basic problem which will concern us is that of relating two of these variables, controlling for the third.   Although such controlling could be accomplished by taking categories of the control variable and running separate analyses within each of these classes, it is possible to achieve far greater efficiency through the use of analysis-of-covariance techniques.   In other words, the controlling can be accomplished without having to make use of an extremely large number of cases.   As before, we sacrifice rigidity for efficiency in that we cannot literally hold the control variable constant. Instead, we make use of weighted averages and adjustment procedures as we did in the case of partial correlation.   In using analysis of covariance we can, however, obtain considerably more information than was possible in partial correlation.

There are two types of situations with which we shall be concerned: (1) those in which we wish to relate the two interval scales, controlling for the nominal scale, and (2) those in which one of the interval scales is related to the nominal scale, the control variable being the other interval scale. Although interest will seldom be in both types of problems for any given set of data, it will be necessary to carry out most of the analysis required for the first type of problem even when interest is primarily focused on the second. For this reason, we shall proceed first with the type of problem in which the nominal-scale variable is used as the control.

20.1. Relating Two Interval Scales, Controlling for Nominal Scale

The basic methods of correlation and regression can be used to relate two or more interval scales within categories of the control variable. Having investigated each of the relationships within the separate categories it may then be possible to pool results, obtaining average within-class correlation and least-squares coefficients, provided that it can be assumed that the relationships are the same from one category to the next. If results can be pooled, a single over-all measure can be obtained which may serve as an effective summarizing measure and which will be more reliable as an estimate than any of the measures for the separate categories. The average within-class correlation coefficient so obtained can be interpreted as being directly analogous to a partial correlation coefficient since it can be used to represent the relationship between the two interval-scale variables after the control variable has been allowed to operate.

There are two significance tests we must make in this type of problem. The first is a test to see whether pooling the results for the various classes is legitimate. Here, we are essentially testing for interaction to see whether or not we can assume the same nature of relationship (as measured by the b's) in all the classes. If we cannot, then pooling will make little sense and we must make separate analyses for each of the categories of the control variable. If pooling results does seem justified, we then go ahead and obtain an average within-class correlation, and the second test we make will be to see whether or not this coefficient is significantly different from zero.

As usual, we have to make certain assumptions about the method of sampling and the populations from which the data have been drawn, and as we might expect, these assumptions will be essentially those required by analysis of variance and correlational analysis. In broad outline, this is what we do in this first type of analysis of covariance problem. Let us now look more closely at the details of the procedures.

In order to obtain a clearer picture of what may happen when we make use of analysis of covariance to control for a nominal-scale variable, let us consider two extreme types of situations. In Fig. 20.1 we have a situation in which there is a slight over-all or total negative correlation (indicated by the solid line) between the dependent variable Y and an independent variable X. If we look separately at each of the categories (A_1, A_2, and A_3) of the control variable A, we see that within each class there is a rather strong *positive* relationship between X and Y. In this instance, the means in X within the various categories are sufficiently different that they may obscure the basic relationship between X and Y.

Fig. 20.1. Hypothetical data indicating a weak total correlation between X and Y but stronger correlations within categories of A.

If we were to superimpose the means of the three categories upon each other we would be in effect moving the within-class equations so that they fell on top of each other, thereby obtaining a much stronger relationship between X and Y. In essence, this is what we do when we obtain an average within-class correlation coefficient. One way to visualize the process is to think in terms of our having adjusted for differences among the A categories by taking out that source of variation due to the control variable. Having adjusted for A by superimposing the means for X and Y, we can now compare the relationships between X and Y within categories by investigating the differences among within-class slopes (as indicated by the dashed lines). Superimposing the means will of course affect the a's in each of the least-squares equations but will leave these slopes and the within-class r's unchanged.

Figure 20.2 represents a contrasting situation in which there are extremely weak relationships within categories of A but where the over-all relationship between X and Y is quite strong. Again, the control variable is affecting the relationship between X and Y, but this time if we were to superimpose means we would find essentially no relationship between the two interval scales.   Perhaps there is no causal relationship between X and Y at all, and the over-all relationship is due to the fact that A is causing changes in both X and Y.   In this instance, then, we would consider the relationship between X and Y to be spurious.

In both of these general types of situations, then, it may make very good sense to control for A.   In the first case, the partial or within-class correlation will be larger in magnitude than the total; in the second it will be smaller.   A carefully constructed scattergram, using different

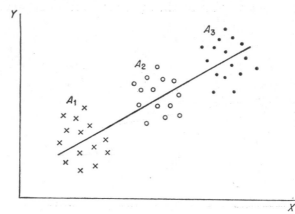

Fig. 20.2. Hypothetical data indicating a strong total correlation between X and Y but weaker correlations within categories of A.

colored dots to represent the various categories of the control variable, will usually indicate whether or not it will be worth the trouble to carry out an analysis of covariance on the data at hand.   If the results are similar to those indicated in either Fig. 20.1 or 20.2 it will probably prove worthwhile to proceed with the analysis.   On the other hand, if the different colored dots are more or less randomly distributed on the scattergram so that the category means are not very different, it cannot be expected that analysis of covariance will produce very interesting results.

In superimposing the means of one category upon those of another we in effect control for the magnitude of these means.   Actually, then, we are measuring variations and covariations about the individual category means rather than the grand means.   You will remember that this is exactly what was done in analysis of variance when we divided the total sum of squares into two components.   One of these components, the within-class variation, involved deviations about the category means, whereas the second component involved deviations of the class means about the total or grand mean.   All that we now need to do is to extend these same procedures by breaking the total covariation, or sum of products, into explained and unexplained portions.   Our reasoning will be exactly parallel to that used in connection with sums of squares. Since

$$X_{ij} - \bar{X}.. = (X_{ij} - \bar{X}._j) + (\bar{X}._j - \bar{X}..)$$

and
$$Y_{ij} - \bar{Y}.. = (Y_{ij} - \bar{Y}._j) + (\bar{Y}._j - \bar{Y}..)$$

we may write

$$(X_{ij} - \bar{X}..)(Y_{ij} - \bar{Y}..)$$
$$= [(X_{ij} - \bar{X}._j) + (\bar{X}._j - \bar{X}..)][(Y_{ij} - \bar{Y}._j) + (\bar{Y}._j - \bar{Y}..)]$$

When we sum over all cases and multiply out the factors, we obtain four terms but the middle two will drop out. As a result we may write

$$\sum_i \sum_j (X_{ij} - \bar{X}..)(Y_{ij} - \bar{Y}..) = \sum_i \sum_j (X_{ij} - \bar{X}._j)(Y_{ij} - \bar{Y}._j)$$

Total sum of products   =   within sum of products
(unexplained)

$$+ \sum_i \sum_j (\bar{X}._j - \bar{X}..)(\bar{Y}._j - \bar{Y}..)$$

+ between sum of products
(explained)

Again, it is most convenient to make use of computing formulas for the total and between sums of products, obtaining the within figure by subtraction. These computing formulas turn out to be exactly analogous to those used in getting sums of squares except that a Y value replaces one of the X's so that we get cross products rather than squares. Thus we get

$$\text{Total sum of products} = \sum_i \sum_j X_{ij} Y_{ij} - \frac{\left(\sum_i \sum_j X_{ij}\right)\left(\sum_i \sum_j Y_{ij}\right)}{N} \tag{20.1}$$

$$\text{Between sum of products} = \sum_j \frac{\left(\sum_i X_{ij}\right)\left(\sum_i Y_{ij}\right)}{N_j}$$
$$- \frac{\left(\sum_i \sum_j X_{ij}\right)\left(\sum_i \sum_j Y_{ij}\right)}{N} \tag{20.2}$$

where N_j represents the number of cases in the jth class.

As was true for the sums of squares, the second term in both equations is the same quantity. Notice, also, that in the formula for the between sum of products the quantity in the numerator of the first term simply represents the product of the sum of the X's and the sum of the Y's for each class. The formula tells us to divide this product by the number of cases in the class and then sum over all classes.

There is one important difference between a sum of products and a sum of squares: a sum of products may be negative in value. Thus, the total covariation may be negative but the between value may be positive. This would mean, of course, that when we subtract a positive number from a negative one the resulting within sum of products will be a larger negative number.

Problem. Before going any further it will be helpful to introduce a numerical example and to indicate how the various computations required in analysis of covariance can be carried out in a systematic manner. Table 20.1 shows such computations for the following variables:

Y (dependent variable, interval scale): measure of educational discrimination against Negroes
X (independent variable, interval scale): per cent Negro[1]
A (independent variable, nominal scale): state.

Data were collected for a random sample of 150 Southern counties using the 1950 census. Let us suppose, in this part of the problem, that we are interested in studying the relationship between discrimination scores and per cent Negro, controlling for the state in which the county is located.

At first glance Table 20.1 appears quite formidable, but if we examine it column by column we see that at least the first 13 columns contain nothing really new. Columns 2, 3, 5, 7, 9, and 11 contain the basic data needed for all other computations. Columns 2 to 6 and 7 to 10 are used to obtain the total, between, and within sums of squares for the dependent and independent variables respectively. Using this computing routine, one simply works across the table, obtaining the values for each row by using the formulas as indicated at the top of each column. For example, figures in column 6 representing the sum of squares in Y are obtained by subtracting column 4 from column 5. Therefore, for Florida we have $54,989 = 3,866,409 - 3,811,420$. We thus obtain in column 6 the sum of squares within each state. When these quantities are summed we get the within-class sum of squares so that we can enter this same quantity in the bottom row of column 6. Note that this particular computing routine differs from the one we have previously used in working analysis-of-variance problems in that we have obtained the within-class sum of squares directly, subtracting this value from the total to get the between sum of squares. Thus $1,370,555 = 2,961,762 - 1,591,207$.

[1] In Table 20.1 per cent Negro figures have been multiplied by 10 to avoid decimals.

Table 20.1. Computations for Analysis of Covariance*

Class (1)	N_i (2)	ΣY (3)	$(\Sigma Y)^2/N_i$ (4) = (3)²/(2)	ΣY^2 (5)	Σy^2 (6) = (5) − (4)	ΣX (7)	$(\Sigma X)^2/N_i$ (8) = (7)²/(2)	ΣX^2 (9)	Σx^2 (10) = (9) − (8)
			For computing sums of squares in Y (col. 6)				For computing sums of squares in X (col. 10)		
Florida	11	6,475	3,811,420	3,866,409	54,989	2,683	654,408	744,861	90,453
Alabama	8	4,030	2,030,112	2,168,898	138,786	3,367	1,417,086	1,964,231	547,145
Arkansas	10	4,608	2,123,366	2,223,740	100,374	3,211	1,031,052	1,236,701	205,649
Georgia	33	18,911	10,837,149	11,239,451	402,302	12,707	4,892,965	5,826,629	933,664
Kentucky	9	2,724	824,464	891,102	66,638	695	53,669	63,293	9,624
Louisiana	15	7,476	3,726,038	3,926,182	200,144	5,257	1,842,403	2,025,311	182,908
North Carolina	24	9,281	3,589,040	3,862,309	273,269	7,459	2,318,195	3,266,843	948,648
Mississippi	20	12,206	7,449,322	7,586,664	137,342	10,419	5,427,778	6,043,283	615,505
South Carolina	11	5,967	3,236,826	3,371,315	134,489	4,676	1,987,725	2,367,054	379,329
Tennessee	9	3,260	1,180,844	1,263,718	82,874	1,088	131,527	229,200	97,673
Sums	150	74,938	38,808,581	40,399,788	1,591,207	51,562	19,756,808	23,767,406	4,010,598
Totals	150		37,438,026	40,399,788	2,961,762		17,724,266	23,767,406	6,043,140
Between class (explained by A)					1,370,555				2,032,542
Within class (unexplained by A)					1,591,207				4,010,598

365

* Adapted from [2], Table 74, pp. 486–487, with the kind permission of the publisher.

Table 20.1. Computations for Analysis of Covariance (*Continued*)

Class (1)	For computing covariations (col. 13) ΣXY (11)	$(\Sigma X)(\Sigma Y)/N_j$ (12) = (3)(7)/(2)	Σxy (13) = (11) − (12)	Slopes $b = \Sigma xy/\Sigma x^2$ (14) = (13)/(10)	Explained by X $(\Sigma xy)^2/\Sigma x^2$ (15) = (13)(14)	Unexplained by X $\Sigma y^2 - \dfrac{(\Sigma xy)^2}{\Sigma x^2}$ (16) = (6) − (15)	For computing correlations $r^2 = \dfrac{(\Sigma xy)^2}{\Sigma x^2 \Sigma y^2}$ (17) = (15)/(6)	r (18) = $\sqrt{(17)}$
Florida	1,601,644	1,579,311	22,333	.24690	5,514	49,475	.10027	.317
Alabama	1,894,209	1,696,126	198,083	.36203	71,712	67,074	.51671	.719
Arkansas	1,579,758	1,479,629	100,129	.48689	48,752	51,622	.48570	.697
Georgia	7,765,621	7,281,881	483,740	.51811	250,630	151,672	.62299	.789
Kentucky	217,349	210,353	6,996	.72693	5,086	61,552	.07632	.276
Louisiana	2,700,374	2,620,089	80,285	.43894	35,240	164,904	.17607	.420
North Carolina	3,203,824	2,884,457	319,367	.33665	107,515	165,754	.39344	.627
Mississippi	6,620,545	6,358,716	261,829	.42539	111,379	25,963	.81096	.900
South Carolina	2,737,694	2,536,517	201,177	.53035	106,694	27,795	.79333	.891
Tennessee	464,348	394,098	70,250	.71924	50,527	32,347	.60968	.781
Sums	28,785,366	27,041,177	1,744,189			798,158		
Totals	28,785,366	25,759,688	3,025,678	.50068	1,514,896	1,446,866	.51148	.715
Between class (explained by A)			1,281,489			614,189		
Within class (unexplained by A)			1,744,189	$b_w =$ .43489	758,530	832,677	.47670	.690

366

Table 20.1. Computations for Analysis of Covariance (*Continued*)

For computing adjusted $\bar{Y}$'s (col. 23)

Class (1)	$\bar{X}_{.j} = \Sigma X/N_j$ (19) = (7)/(2)	$x = \bar{X}_{.j} - \bar{X}_{..}$ (20) = (19) − $\bar{X}_{..}$	$b_w x$ (21) = b_w(20)	$\bar{Y}_{.j} = \Sigma Y/N_j$ (22) = (3)/(2)	$\bar{Y}'_{.j} = \bar{Y}_{.j} - b_w x$ (23) = (22) − (21)
Florida	243.909	−99.838	−43.42	588.64	632.06
Alabama	420.875	77.128	33.54	503.75	470.21
Arkansas	321.100	−22.647	−9.85	460.80	470.65
Georgia	385.060	41.313	17.97	573.06	555.09
Kentucky	77.222	−266.525	−115.91	302.67	418.58
Louisiana	350.467	6.720	2.92	498.40	495.48
North Carolina	310.792	−32.955	−14.33	386.71	401.04
Mississippi	520.950	177.203	77.06	610.30	533.24
South Carolina	425.091	81.344	35.38	542.45	507.07
Tennessee	120.889	−222.858	−96.92	362.22	459.14
Sums Totals	$\bar{X}_{..}$ = 343.747			$\bar{Y}_{..}$ = 499.59	

367

In obtaining the total sum of squares we use exactly the same procedure as that used in the case of each state: we subtract column 4 from column 5. In so doing, of course, we are making use of the formula

$$\Sigma y^2 = \Sigma Y^2 - \frac{(\Sigma Y)^2}{N} = 40{,}399{,}788 - \frac{(74{,}938)^2}{150}$$
$$= 40{,}399{,}788 - 37{,}438{,}026 = 2{,}961{,}762$$

Here the N for the totals row is the total number of cases in the sample (150). It will be helpful at this point to work through a sufficient number of the computations in columns 2 to 6 and 7 to 10 so that you understand what is involved and become convinced that the results you obtain by this new method are exactly the same (subject to rounding errors) as those we would have got by the old method.

Columns 11 to 13 are used to break the covariation into component parts in an analogous manner. As indicated above, the formulas are similar to those used for analysis of variance, except that products replace squares, and we therefore obtain column 13 by subtracting 12 from 11 as indicated by the computing formulas. Again, we compute the within sum of products directly and the between value by subtraction. Thus the total covariation is 3,025,678, and the within is 1,744,189, giving 1,281,489 as the between-class covariation. It so happens for these data that all three sums of products, as well as all state values, are positive, but this will not necessarily be the case. We now have performed the basic computations we shall need for our later work, having obtained the total, explained, and unexplained sums for y^2, x^2, and xy. Our attention can now be focused on the various tests and measures needed in carrying out the analysis. The remaining columns in Table 20.1 will be explained as we come to them.

Testing for Interaction. It will be remembered that in two-way analysis of variance the first test we made was for an interaction effect. The reason for making this test first was that if the two independent variables produce different results when acting in combination than would be expected on the basis of their separate effects, then it makes very little sense theoretically to study the effects of one while controlling for the other. In other words, the relationship between one independent variable and the dependent variable differs according to the value of the control variable. If this is the case, the relationship should be studied separately within each of the categories of the control variable. We face a similar problem in analysis of covariance, although instead of thinking in terms of the additivity assumption we shall now find ourselves comparing the slopes of the least-squares equations within each of the categories. Let us first note the parallel between the assumption of additivity and the assumption of equal slopes. Then we shall be in a better position to understand the nature of the test for interaction in analysis of covariance.

In Chap. 16, which covers analysis of variance, we used the following numerical example to illustrate additivity.

	A_1	A_2	A_3
B_1	5	10	20
B_2	10	15	25
B_3	25	30	40

It was noted that it is not necessary to assume equal differences between the scores of B_1 and B_2, on the one hand, and B_2 and B_3 on the other. But we did have to assume that the differences between B_1 and B_2 are

Fig. 20.3. Lines with equal slopes indicating no interaction.

the same for each of the A categories. Now let us suppose that the variable B actually represents an interval-scale variable X which has been categorized. We shall assume that the relationships between X and the dependent variable Y (represented by scores in the body of the table) are linear within each of the categories of A. A little thought will convince you that by properly locating the B categories along the X axis we can translate the additivity property into the statement that the three regression lines all have the same slope. Figure 20.3 indicates this relationship. Thus we see that a test for additivity is directly analogous to a test of the hypothesis that the within-class slopes are equal.

In testing for interaction in two-way analysis of variance, we took the amount of variation in the dependent variable that could not be explained by the two nominal scales when additivity was assumed. This quantity was then broken down into two components: the amount that could be explained by interaction, and the amount still left unexplained by the between-column, between-row, and interaction effects. The ratio of these last two components was used to test for interaction. In analysis of covariance we do exactly the same thing, but as we might expect, our procedure takes a somewhat different form. We have just seen that the assumption of additivity is analogous to the assumption that the population slopes within each of the categories are the same. If there is a significant interaction effect, however, this will mean a different relationship for at least some of the categories. In other words, a given change in X will produce different changes in Y in the various classes of A. If we now take the amount of variation in Y left unexplained by X assuming equal slopes, we can see how much additional variation we can explain through interaction. Then we can test for interaction by comparing the interaction sum of squares with the error term.

How do we determine the amount of variation we can attribute to interaction? In order to answer this question we first must ask ourselves how much variation we could possibly expect to explain using linear models within each of the categories of A. Obviously, the individual least-squares equation for each category gives us the best fit that can be expected of a straight line, and the correlation coefficient computed on the data for that particular category will give a measure of goodness of fit. We therefore can obtain figures for each category representing the amount of the variation in Y that is explained by X, using the straight line which best fits the data for that particular category. When we sum the explained variations for each of the categories we thus obtain the amount of variation actually explained by all of the separate least-squares equations. Similarly, in summing the unexplained sums of squares we obtain the amount of variation in Y which is still left unexplained by these separate least-squares lines.

In Table 20.1 these computations have been carried out in columns 15 and 16. In the case of Florida, for example, the total variation in Y (column 6) is 54,989. Of this quantity, 5,514 is explained by the least-squares equation which best fits the Florida data, and 49,475 is left unexplained. Of the total variation in Y (2,961,762), the quantity 798,158 represents the amount left unexplained by these separate least-squares equations.

We next must ask how much variation is left unexplained when it is assumed that there is no interaction effect. If there is no interaction, then all of the slopes for the categories of A will be equal. Our best estimate of this common slope will be a pooled estimate which is a weighted average of the individual within-class slopes. These slopes have been computed in column 14. The pooled estimate or average within-class slope has also been computed in column 14 by making use of the within-class data from columns 10 and 13. Thus the value .43489 was obtained by dividing 1,744,189 by 4,010,598.

We can now compare the relative explaining abilities of the separate within-class least-squares lines, each with a different slope, and a number of straight lines drawn through the means of each category but all having the same slope, *i.e.*, the average within-class b (see Fig. 20.4). These

Fig. 20.4. Comparison of separate least-squares lines with lines drawn through category means but all having the same slope b_w.

latter parallel lines cannot be expected to explain as much of the total variation as the actual best-fitting lines for each of the categories, but if there is in fact no interaction in the population data, the various regression equations will all have the same slope and we can expect that the least-squares lines will not differ too markedly in slope. In other words, if there is no interaction the series of parallel dashed lines will approximate fairly closely the actual least-squares equations for each category. Since the value of the average within-class slope will then be not too different from that of each of the separate within-class slopes, the dashed lines will have almost as high explanatory power as the solid lines.

Because of sampling fluctuations we can expect some interaction within the sample even though there may be none within the population. The solid and dashed lines will never be identical and therefore the latter lines will always leave somewhat more unexplained variation than the least-squares lines. The question now is whether or not the separate least-squares lines differ sufficiently among themselves, and therefore from the dashed lines, to warrant our concluding that the interaction effect is statistically significant.

In this and other analysis-of-covariance tests we must make a number of assumptions which are essentially those assumptions required by analysis-of-variance and regression analysis. As usual, independent random sampling must be assumed. We must also assume bivariate normality between X and Y within each of the categories of A. Furthermore, we must assume that the variances for both X and Y are the same within all A categories. In the test for interaction our null hypothesis will of course be that each of the category relationships between X and Y involves the same slope β.

In Table 20.2 an F test is made for interaction. We take the amount of variation in Y left unexplained by X and A, assuming no interaction or equal population slopes. This quantity can be found from Table 20.1 by reading across the within-class row until we come to the unexplained

Table 20.2. Analysis-of-variance Test for Interaction

	Sum of squares	Degrees of freedom	Estimate of variance	F
Unexplained by X and A, assuming no interaction	832,677	$N - (k + 1) = 139$		
Explained by interaction	34,519	$k - 1 = 9$	3,835.4	<1.0
Error	798,158	$N - 2k = 130$	6,139.7	

by X column (column 16). Since the figure 832,677 was obtained by using the same set of figures as was the average within-class b, we see that we have essentially assumed equal slopes in computing this unexplained sum of squares. We have also seen that the quantity 798,158 represents the amount of variation left unexplained by the separate least-squares equations. The difference between these two quantities therefore represents the amount of variation that can be attributed to interaction.

In associating degrees of freedom with each of these quantities we count up the number of coefficients that have been estimated in the respective least-squares equations. Looking first at the error term, or the amount left unexplained by the separate least-squares equations, we note that for each of these separate equations we have had to compute two coefficients (a and b). We therefore will lose $2k$ degrees of freedom, where k represents the number of categories of A. Hence the degrees of freedom associated with this term will be $N - 2k$. In making use of the dashed lines, however, we have had to compute only a single slope, the average within-class b. Since each of these lines passes through a different set of sample means, however, we have different a values for each of these lines. We therefore have lost $(k + 1)$ degrees of freedom, and the degrees of freedom associated with this term will be $N - (k + 1)$ or $N - k - 1$.

We can then obtain the degrees of freedom for the interaction term by subtraction, getting

$$(N - k - 1) - (N - 2k) = k - 1$$

or one less than the number of categories. We now compute F in the usual manner and conclude that since $F_{9,130} < 1.0$ we do not have significant interaction.

Since interaction did not turn out to be significant we are justified in throwing the small amount of sample interaction back into the error term, henceforth using the quantity 832,677 as the variation which is unexplained by both X and A. Since we are on the wrong end of the test for interaction, we must of course be somewhat cautious in doing this. With such a large N and small value of F we are undoubtedly safe in ruling out interaction in this particular problem, however.

Had interaction been significant, our next step would be to look for the state or states which are out of line with the rest. This is easily accomplished by looking at the column of b's. If several states are obviously creating the interaction effect and if good theoretical reasons can be suggested why this is the case, it may be possible to exclude these states and repeat the analysis with the remainder. If no states stand out in this manner it may be necessary to proceed by analyzing each state separately. In such an eventuality, valuable theoretical insights might be gained by asking oneself why the relationship between discrimination and per cent Negro should differ from one state to the next.

The Average Within-class Correlation. Having established that there is no significant interaction effect, we are now justified in pooling the individual within-class r's to obtain an average within-class correlation coefficient which will be analogous to the partial correlation coefficient. In other words, since we are justified in assuming a single slope for all the regression equations, we can also assume that the population correlation coefficients will all be the same and that the common value can be estimated by pooling the sample r's for the various classes. The average within-class correlation coefficient, which we can symbolize as $r_{XY \cdot A}$, is computed in the same manner as the average within-class b by using within-class data given in the bottom row of Table 20.1. (See columns 17 and 18.) The square of this coefficient can be interpreted as the proportion of variation in Y which is left unexplained by A but is explained by X. Thus

$$.47670 = (.690)^2 = \frac{758,530}{1,591,207}$$

If you will note the formulas used in computing each of these numbers, you will see that the interpretation follows immediately from these formulas.   As a rough check on one's computations, the average within-class r should turn out to be comparable in magnitude with the various separate within-class r's.   Since it is essentially a weighted average, the states with the largest numbers of counties will have the greatest effect in determining its value.

If we wished a measure analogous to a multiple R, we might take the ratio of the amount of variation explained by *both* X and A to the total sum of squares.   In this problem, for example, we have explained 2,961,762 − 832,677 or 2,129,085.   Therefore we have explained 2,129,085/2,961,762 or 71.9 per cent of the variation.   We must remember, however, that if we wish to form a multiple R by taking the square root of this value, the result will be partially a function of the average number of cases within categories of A (see Sec. 16.4).

We can test for the significance of $r_{XY \cdot A}$ in the usual manner.   First we let the control variable A do all the explaining it can.   We then let X go to work on the variation left unexplained by A, breaking this latter quantity into two components.   The first of these components will be that portion which is explained by X while the other will be the error term which is left unexplained by both X and A (assuming no interaction). We have already seen that the degrees of freedom for the error term will be $N - (k + 1)$.   The degrees of freedom associated with the variation unexplained by A, which is found in the bottom row of column 6, will of course be $N - k$ (see Sec. 16.1).   This leaves 1 degree of freedom associated with the component which is unexplained by A but explained by X.   The results of this test are summarized in Table 20.3.   We thus see that the average within-class correlation is significant at the .001 level.

Table 20.3. Analysis-of-variance Test for Significance of Average Within-classCorrelation ($\rho_{XY \cdot A}$)

	Sum of squares	Degrees of freedom	Estimate of variance	F
Unexplained by A	1,591,207	$N - k = 140$		
Unexplained by A but explained by X	758,530	1	758,530	
Error (assuming no interaction)	832,677	$N - (k + 1) = 139$	5,990.5	126.6

Before we conclude this portion of the chapter in which we have studied the relationship between two interval scales while controlling for the nominal scale, we can draw a comparison with the type of controlling accomplished by partial correlation.   Controlling by means of analysis of covariance obviously involves considerably more work than the use of partial correlation.   As can readily be imagined, extensions involving additional variables will begin to require so many computations that analysis of covariance will generally not be feasible. On the other hand, analysis of covariance supplies us with more information than does partial correlation. Not only may we make a test for interaction, but we can investigate the relationships between X and Y within each of the categories of the control variables, comparing the various values of r and b. In making use of partial correlations, we obtain only the single measure which is comparable to the average within-class correlation, and we cannot make a test for interaction.

We see that analysis of covariance has a number of advantages over analyses using partial correlations, especially in studies where interaction may be expected. Thus in some instances it may be well worth while to convert one of the interval scales into a nominal scale and to proceed with analysis of covariance in preference to partial correlation, even though in so doing we may lose information with respect to the level of measurement.

20.2. Relating Interval and Nominal Scales, Controlling for Interval Scale

In one-way analysis of variance we related an interval scale to a single nominal scale, testing for the significance of the differences among the means of the categories of A. In order to determine the magnitude of the relationship between the two variables, we computed an intraclass correlation coefficient. We also obtained the means of the various categories which could be used for descriptive purposes to indicate the relative scores of one category compared with the others. In two-way analysis of variance we were able to control for a nominal scale and test for interaction. We found ourselves severely limited, however, in that we were required to have equal numbers of cases in each of the subcells. In this section we shall take up situations in which we wish to relate Y and A but where the control variable is an interval scale X. We shall again find that we cannot literally hold the control variable constant. Instead, our method of controlling will involve an adjusting operation.

Suppose that our interest is primarily in discovering the relationship between discrimination rates and subregions of the South, as defined by the various states. Admittedly, states are not the best kinds of units to delineate subregions, but they will serve for illustrative purposes. Obviously, a variable such as per cent Negro needs to be controlled since the various Southern states differ considerably in their minority percentages. Suppose we were to categorize per cent Negro and proceed with separate analyses of variance for each of these categories. Note that we would probably not even attempt two-way analysis of variance because of the necessity of having equal subclasses. But would separate analyses of variance really solve our problem? We would immediately find that when we examined the counties with low minority percentages we would be excluding practically all of the counties in Mississippi and Alabama and including practically all of those in Kentucky and Tennessee. On the other hand, there would be at most one or two counties from these latter states among the counties with high percentages of Negroes. Thus in attempting to control by this method we almost do away with our problem in that only a few of the states will be represented in each of the separate analyses. The effects of subregions or states would be hopelessly confounded with per cent Negro. We cannot literally hold the one variable constant without at the same time decreasing the variability of the other.

Although we cannot actually hold this control variable constant, we can, by using analysis of covariance, make certain adjustments for its effects. Specifically, if we are willing to assume that the regressions of Y on X within each of the categories of A have a common slope which can be estimated by the average within-class b, we can estimate the change in Y produced by a given change in X. In other words, we can make certain predictions about what would happen to the discrimination rates in each state if the minority percentages were to change. In particular, we can ask ourselves what would happen to these rates if the various percentages of Negroes were to be equalized. This sort of adjustment process yields purely hypothetical results, and this fact should be made perfectly clear. We are not getting discrimination rates for the various states with per cent Negro actually held constant; we can only predict what they would be if this were to happen and if the relationships between X and Y were as assumed. Quite conceivably, if Negroes were actually to redistribute themselves more evenly among the Southern states, the particular relationships we found between X and Y would no longer hold. Nevertheless, such an adjustment procedure can often lead to useful insights.

If it can be assumed that there is no interaction effect, we have seen that we can best estimate the common slopes of the within-class regression equations by means of the average within-class b computed in Table 20.1. The adjustment procedure we shall use can now be described. We would like to adjust each of the class means $\bar{Y}_{.j}$ so as to take into consideration the fact that the means in X also differ from state to state. For convenience we shall assume that all of the $\bar{X}_{.j}$'s are adjusted to the grand mean of the X's. This will involve moving the mean in X for each class a distance of $(\bar{X}_{..} - \bar{X}_{.j})$. Figure 20.5 indicates this difference as the length of the base of the triangle. But we know that in order to obtain the amount of change in Y for a given change in X we must multiply the change in X by the average within-class b. Therefore $\bar{Y}_{.j}$ changes by the amount $b_w(\bar{X}_{..} - \bar{X}_{.j})$ where we have used the symbol b_w to represent the average within-class slope. The adjusted value of the means for Y

can now be found by adding this increment to the original mean for Y.
Thus, letting $\bar{Y}'_{\cdot j}$ represent the adjusted value, we get

$$\begin{aligned}
\bar{Y}'_{\cdot j} &= \bar{Y}_{\cdot j} + b_w(\bar{X}_{\cdot\cdot} - \bar{X}_{\cdot j}) \\
&= \bar{Y}_{\cdot j} - b_w(\bar{X}_{\cdot j} - \bar{X}_{\cdot\cdot})
\end{aligned} \tag{20.3}$$

The second of these forms, which just involves reversing the order of $\bar{X}_{\cdot\cdot}$ and $\bar{X}_{\cdot j}$ and changing signs, is the form used in computing the adjusted $\bar{Y}$ in Table 20.1. Notice that the slope in this particular example is positive. Also, the change from $\bar{X}_{\cdot j}$ to $\bar{X}_{\cdot\cdot}$ as shown in Fig. 20.5 is positive.

Fig. 20.5. Geometrical interpretation of the computations for the adjusted Y means.

Exactly the same algebraic results hold in cases where the slope is negative or where the X value is decreased. By now you should be able to convince yourself that this is the case.

Figure 20.6 should help you visualize what we have done in adjusting the mean Y values. We have in effect moved each of the class means parallel to the slope of the average within-class b to a position where all of the $\bar{X}$'s are equal to the grand mean of the X's. The adjusted $\bar{Y}$'s can be found along the vertical dashed line corresponding to the grand mean of the X's. The relative magnitudes of the means in Y may be considerably altered. In Fig. 20.6 the unadjusted $\bar{Y}$ values are such that the mean of A_1 is slightly below that of A_2 which, in turn, is substantially less than that of A_3. Notice that A_1 has a very small $\bar{X}$ value, however. Since the slope is represented as positive, adjusting for X has the effect of increasing the value of Y in the case of A_1. On the other hand, the adjustment process decreases the Y values for both A_2 and A_3 since both of these categories have relatively large X values. As a result, the adjusted $\bar{Y}$ for A_1 is actually larger than that for A_2, and the value for A_3 is much closer to that of A_1.

If you will refer back to Table 20.1, columns 22 and 23, you will note the effect on discrimination rates of adjusting for per cent Negro. Florida, with its relatively low percentage of Negroes, now stands out as having very high adjusted rates, whereas states such as Mississippi and Tennessee have been brought more into line with the remaining states. Note also that the over-all differences among states have been considerably reduced.

It was mentioned earlier in the chapter that analysis of covariance will be useful if scattergrams show that the various class means in X are quite different in value.   This can be seen from Fig. 20.6.   Had the class means

Fig. 20.6. Geometrical interpretation of adjusting Y means by sliding category means parallel to line with slope b_w.

in X been closely bunched around the grand mean, the bases, and therefore the legs, of the triangles would have been quite short.   In other words, adjusting for X would not produce a very marked effect since, in reality, there was very little adjustment actually needed.   Had all the class means in X been exactly equal we would in effect have had a control for X.   It is only when the class means in X are very different that we can expect adjustment to have a noticeable effect.   Put another way, there must be a fairly strong relationship between X and A, the two independent variables.

Something else is also necessary in order for adjustment to be worth while.   Had the average within-class b been very small numerically, it would have taken a very large change in X to produce a slight change in Y.   Thus, if there is little or no relationship between X and Y within classes of A, there will be no point in adjusting for X.   These observations are of course consistent with common sense which tells us that there is not much to be gained in controlling for a variable which is not related to both of the variables in which we are interested. True, if X is related only to the dependent variable it may be controlled as a disturbing influence. We can see from Fig. 20.6, however, that unless there are some variations with respect to X among categories of A there will be little point in adjusting.

In using the average within-class b we have had to assume no interaction effect. Therefore, it will be necessary to carry out the test for interaction as well as the computations for b before going ahead with the adjustment process. If interaction turns out to be significant, the problem is more complicated and beyond the scope of this text. Under some circumstances it may be possible to adjust using the individual within-class slopes. However, the interpretation must be carefully made. Suppose, for example, that the slope for Mississippi turned out to be quite different from that of Tennessee. Could we legitimately use their individual least-squares lines to adjust Y values? This would require the assumption that Mississippi maintains essentially the same patterns of discrimination as it continues to lose Negroes. The fact that other states show different relationships with per cent Negro suggests, however, that this may not be a legitimate assumption. The fact that interaction has been shown to exist should make us cautious in projecting what would happen if the X's actually were changed. On the other hand, if we find essentially the same relationship between per cent Negro and discrimination in each of the states, i.e., no interaction, we are somewhat more confident that adjustment will not lead us too far astray.

We next must raise the question as to the significance of the differences among the adjusted Y means. Differences among the unadjusted means may or may not have been significant, but this does not mean that the same result will hold for the adjusted values. Perhaps adjusting for X has had the effect of moving the Y values closer together. Or perhaps they are now further apart. We have accomplished a descriptive task, that of actually obtaining the adjusted figures so that they may be displayed for comparative purposes. We now must test the null hypothesis that in the population the adjusted Y means are all the same. The assumptions for this test are the usual ones. We must assume independent random samples, normality, and equal variances for the adjusted $\bar{Y}$'s, and we must also make the assumptions required by regression analysis, a bivariate normal distribution of X and Y within each category of A.

Fortunately, we do not have to recompute sums of squares using the adjusted values themselves. We can carry out an analysis-of-variance test using the familiar procedure of first letting the control variable explain all of the variation it can. Since X is now our control variable, we take the amount of variation left unexplained by X as our new total sum of squares.   We then break this quantity into the amount explained by A and the amount left unexplained by both variables.   The degrees of freedom associated with each of these quantities have already been determined.   The results of the F test are summarized in Table 20.4. Thus we see that the adjusted differences, although smaller than the original ones, are significant at the .001 level.   We conclude that, although

Table 20.4. Analysis-of-variance Test for Significance of Differences among Adjusted Means

	Sum of squares	Degrees of freedom	Estimate of variance	F
Unexplained by X	1,446,866	$N - 2 = 148$		
Unexplained by X but explained by A	614,189	$k - 1 = 9$	68,243	11.39
Error (assuming no interaction)	832,677	$N - (k + 1) = 139$	5,990.5	

adjusting for per cent Negro does decrease differences in discrimination rates among states, these differences are not completely wiped out in the process.

Finally, we may wish to compute a partial intraclass correlation between Y and A, controlling for X.   This might be advisable in order to obtain a better indication of the degree of relationship between the two variables than can be indicated by the differences among adjusted means. Simply by looking at these adjusted differences one cannot get a very good idea of their magnitude relative to differences within the categories, and for this reason a partial intraclass correlation may be helpful. Generalizing the notion of intraclass correlation we may write

$$r_{iYA \cdot X} = \frac{V_b - V_e}{V_b + (\bar{n} - 1)V_e}$$

where V_b = between-class estimate (unexplained by X; explained by A)
V_e = error estimate (unexplained by X and A)
$\bar{n}$ = average number of cases per class, as computed in equation 16.12
Here we are interested in the between-class estimate of the variance for the *adjusted* Y's.   Our error estimate takes into consideration that X has already explained all it could of the variation in Y.

Numerically, we thus get

$$\bar{n} = \frac{1}{k-1}\left(\sum_{i=1}^{k} N_i - \frac{\sum_{i=1}^{k} N_i{}^2}{\sum_{i=1}^{k} N_i}\right)$$

$$= \frac{1}{9}\left(150 - \frac{2{,}858}{150}\right)$$

$$= \frac{1}{9}(150 - 19.05) = 14.55$$

and

$$r_{iYA\cdot X} = \frac{68{,}243 - 5{,}990.5}{68{,}243 + 13.55(5{,}990.5)}$$

$$= \frac{62{,}252.5}{149{,}414} = .417$$

20.3. Extensions to Four or More Variables

The addition of a second nominal scale will complicate the analysis of covariance because of the requirement of equal subclasses. Practically speaking, this in effect means that this type of extension will not be feasible except in studies involving experimental designs in which such a control over the number of cases is possible. If we add one or more interval scales, however, the extension is straightforward in principle, although it will introduce a considerable number of additional computations. We shall have to add new columns to the computing table. In particular, there will be a column indicating the amount of variation left unexplained by both interval scales (X and Z) acting simultaneously. We shall thus become involved with multiple least-squares equations for each of the categories of A. In obtaining adjusted Y means, for example, we shall have to adjust for X and Z using both of the partial average within-class b's. Instead of moving category means parallel to a least-squares *line*, we shall now slide them parallel to an average within-class *plane*. In testing for the significance of the adjusted Y's we first let X and Z explain all they can of Y and then let A work on the remainder.

20.4. Other Analysis-of-covariance Techniques

Since we have by no means exhausted the subject of analysis of covariance, you may wish to consult some of the references listed below for other applications and extensions of this general method. In particular, whenever the number of categories in A is quite large, it is sometimes useful to investigate the regression of the category *means* in Y on the *means* in X, thereby in effect considering each category as a case. For example, in the problem we have been considering, we might wish to study the relationship between X and Y using states rather than counties as units, treating the $\bar{X}$'s and $\bar{Y}$'s for each state as single scores. In most problems of interest to sociologists, the number of categories in A will be too small to justify such an analysis, however, and for this reason the topic has not been discussed in the present chapter.

EXERCISES

1. Check as many of the computations in Table 20.1 as is necessary in order for you to understand how these figures were obtained.

2. Take the data for Exercise 1, Chap. 17, and collapse the heterogeneity index into the following categories: 10.0–14.9, 15.0–19.9, 20.0–24.9, 25.0–29.9, and 30.0–49.9. Referring to moral integration as Y, mobility as X, and heterogeneity as A:

    a. Test for interaction.

    b. Obtain $r_{XY \cdot A}$ and test for significance.

    c. Adjust the category means in Y for differences with respect to X.

    d. Test for the significance of differences among the adjusted $\bar{Y}$'s.

    e. Obtain the partial intraclass correlation $r_{iYA \cdot X}$.

REFERENCES

1. Dixon, W. J., and F. J. Massey: *Introduction to Statistical Analysis*, 2d ed., McGraw-Hill Book Company, Inc., New York, 1957, chap. 12.

2. Hagood, M. J., and D. O. Price: *Statistics for Sociologists*, Henry Holt and Company, Inc., New York, 1952, chap. 24.

3. Johnson, P. O.: *Statistical Methods in Research*, Prentice-Hall, Inc., Englewood Cliffs, N.J., 1949, chaps. 10 and 11.

4. McNemar, Q.: *Psychological Statistics*, John Wiley & Sons, Inc., New York, 1955, chap. 17.

5. Walker, H. M., and J. Lev: *Statistical Inference*, Henry Holt and Company, Inc., New York, 1953, chap. 15.

Chapter 21

FACTOR ANALYSIS AND OTHER MULTIVARIATE TECHNIQUES

There are a number of techniques that have been developed for handling problems involving a large number of variables. Multiple regression analysis is one of the most useful of these techniques. Another technique that can be used with interval scales is multiple factor analysis, a procedure developed by Thurstone and others and originally used in psychology to analyze the interrelationships among intelligence or personality tests of various sorts. Basically, factor analysis is a technique which can be used to take a large number of operational indices and reduce these to a smaller number of conceptual variables. The purpose of this chapter is to present a few of the essential ideas of factor analysis without going into computational considerations. Other multivariate procedures will be discussed even more briefly in order to indicate some of the other possibilities that are available.

21.1. Multiple Factor Analysis

Underlying the use of factor analysis is the notion that if we have a large number of indices or variables which are intercorrelated, these interrelationships may be due to the presence of one or more underlying variables or *factors* which are related to the indices to varying degrees. In the simplest case, there may be only one underlying variable which is imperfectly measured by each of the indices used. Those indices which are most highly correlated with the underlying factor, i.e., those which are the best measures of this factor, should in such a case be most highly related to the other indices. In other words, the imperfect correlations among indices may be accounted for by their varying associations with the underlying factor. By examining the intercorrelations among indices we may be able to make inferences as to the correlations of each index with the common factor if this factor could actually be measured.

If there are several underlying factors, any given index may be correlated with more than one factor. Thus an index may be conceived as having several components, one associated with the first factor, another with the second, and so forth. In other words, the index may be measuring several factors simultaneously, although it may be much more highly correlated with one than with the others. One of the goals of factor analysis is to estimate the correlations of each index with all of the underlying factors and, in so doing, to gain insights as to what these factors may be. Factor analysis may also be used to test hypotheses concerning the nature of such underlying factors.

Notice that we are making use of one particular way of conceptualizing the problem of interrelating theory and research. We conceive of underlying variables which "really exist" but which can be only imperfectly measured by indices. One of the problems posed in every factor analysis is the theoretical one of identifying these underlying variables. In some cases it may make sense theoretically to think in terms of such underlying factors. Perhaps the main value of factor analysis is that it enables one to replace a large number of indices which may have very little theoretical meaning with a much smaller number of conceptual variables which may make very good sense theoretically. It is very possible, however, to end up with a set of factors which have very little theoretical meaning. We then have merely replaced a large number of clear-cut operational indices by a smaller number of theoretically meaningless factors.

Factor analysis will therefore be of relatively little value unless the factors obtained can be identified. But how does one go about identifying the factors he obtains? Here we run into certain difficulties. Usually, although not always, the various operational indices will be clustered in the sense that within any given cluster of indices there will be high intercorrelations whereas correlations between clusters will be relatively low. If this is the case, we may make the theoretical assumption that the high intercorrelations within each cluster are due to the presence of a single factor representing that cluster. We then may try to associate a second factor with another cluster, and so on until all clusters have been identified. By examining the nature of the indices in each cluster we may be in a position to identify what they all have in common. This common element among all the indices of the cluster is, presumably, the factor associated with the cluster and can be named accordingly.

Unfortunately, the procedures used in obtaining or "extracting" the underlying factors do not immediately yield such pure or readily interpretable factors. The first factors to be extracted always turn out to be uncorrelated with each other. Since those factor-analysis techniques in common use all assume linear relationships among indices, this means that the uncorrelated factors will be independent of each other.   Such independent factors are referred to as *orthogonal factors*, since uncorrelated factors can be represented geometrically as perpendicular or orthogonal axes.   (See Fig. 21.1.)   It is possible to represent the correlation between any two variables in terms of the angle between them, with the angle between two highly correlated variables being very small.   As the correlation approaches zero, the angle between the two lines will approach 90 degrees.   A cluster of highly intercorrelated indices can thus be represented as a cluster of lines.   Strictly speaking, it would require a k-dimensional space to represent a cluster of k items if all possible intercorrelations were to be represented accurately.   For visual purposes a two-dimensional diagram will usually be sufficient, however.

Fig. 21.1. Geometrical interpretation of intercorrelations, showing clustering effect and oblique factors fitting the clusters.

In Fig. 21.1 there are two distinct clusters.   Since the angle between the two clusters is not 90 degrees, we see that the clusters themselves are intercorrelated, making it impossible to fit both clusters with perpendicular or orthogonal factors.   It is because of this fact that factors must be "rotated."   Under most schemes of rotation, it is possible to end up with nonperpendicular or "oblique" factors which fit the clusters more perfectly.   These rotated factors may in fact turn out to be uncorrelated, but usually this will not be the case.   The aim of rotation is to obtain a set of factors which has the property that any given factor will be fairly highly correlated with some of the indices but uncorrelated with the rest. Each factor can then be identified with one of the clusters of indices, thereby reducing the effective number of variables to the number of factors used.

In very brief outline this is what we accomplish with factor analysis. Although it will not be possible here to take up the actual computations used in obtaining the original orthogonal factors or the rotated factors, we can indicate what they involve.   Since factor analysis is basically a technique for analyzing the interrelationships among the various indices, we start with the matrix of intercorrelations among indices.   A matrix is simply a rectangular arrangement of scores. The matrix of correlations indicates the correlations of each index with every other index (see Table 21.1). These are the basic data used in factor analysis. If the data are taken from a sample, there will inevitably be certain sampling errors involved in these correlation coefficients. Since factor analysis is ordinarily used as a descriptive technique rather than a test of statistical hypotheses, it is essential that the sample be quite large so that sampling errors are minimal. If the sample r's were to vary considerably from one sample to the next, the factors obtained would have even greater instability and the resulting analysis might be highly misleading. Factor analysis is, therefore, a technique that can only be used with large samples.[1]

In extracting the factors from the correlation matrix one must go through a process referred to as matrix inversion. Unless one is familiar with matrix algebra, this procedure will inevitably involve "cookbook" operations which will not be clearly understood. Factors will be computed or extracted in the order of their ability to explain the variation in the indices used. It is, therefore, relatively easy to determine when to stop extracting factors. If, say, the fourth factor explains only a very small proportion of the total variation in the indices, the fifth and subsequent factors will explain even less.

We then proceed to rotate these factors to obtain factors which are more easily interpreted. One criterion for rotation is Thurstone's "simple structure" criterion which involves finding factors which are highly correlated with given clusters of variables but which are uncorrelated with those indices belonging to the other clusters. The term *factor loading* is used to refer to the correlation between an index and a given factor. We can also compute the proportion of the total variation in each index explained by all of the factors used. This squared multiple correlation between the index (taken as the dependent variable) and the several factors is referred to as the *communality* of the index.

Let us now illustrate the use of factor analysis by means of a sociological example taken from Bell's study of census tracts in the San Francisco Bay region [1]. Bell used seven indices designed to measure different characteristics of the area. The results are summarized in Table 21.1. In order to determine whether or not the clustering effect among these indices would warrant the use of a smaller number of conceptual variables, Bell extracted three orthogonal factors, as indicated in Table 21.2. Notice that although one can get some idea of the clustering effect from Table 21.1, the pattern is by no means obvious.

[1] In situations in which N is relatively small but where a very large number of indices have been used, it is possible to make use of what has been termed "inverted" factor analysis. See [7]. Usually, however, factor analysis requires large samples.

Nor is the picture much more clear in Table 21.2, in which are given the correlations of the several indices with each of three factors. For example, we see that factor I (unnamed) is highly related to five of the indices and weakly related to the remaining two. Factor II is positively

Table 21.1. Correlation Matrix

Measures	(1) Occ.	(2) Educ.	(3) Rent	(4) Fert.	(5) WLF	(6) SFDU	(7) SEG
(1) Occupation	....	.780	.775	.678	.482	.190	.135
(2) Education	.780	......	.796	.490	.126	−.255	.488
(3) Rent (−)	.775	.796	......	.555	.260	−.051	.360
(4) Fertility	.678	.490	.555	....	.759	.476	.205
(5) Women in the labor force (−)	.482	.126	.260	.759	......	.753	−.066
(6) Single family dwelling units	.190	−.255	−.051	.476	.753	......	−.248
(7) Relative number of persons in subordinate ethnic groups	.135	.488	.360	.205	−.066	−.248	

SOURCE: W. Bell [1], Table 6, p. 50, with the kind permission of the author and publisher.

Table 21.2. Orthogonal Matrix

Measures	Factors			Communalities h^2
	I	II	III	
(1) Occupation	.844	.185	−.319	.848
(2) Education	.711	.659	.053	.943
(3) Rent (−)	.771	.457	−.179	.835
(4) Fertility	.866	−.256	.114	.828
(5) WLF (−)	.679	−.650	−.073	.889
(6) SFDU	.357	−.744	−.175	.712
(7) SEG	.301	.394	.426	.427

SOURCE: W. Bell [1], Table 7, p. 50, with the kind permission of the author and publisher.

related to some indices but negatively to others. The communalities h^2 indicate the proportion of variation in each index explained by the three factors. Thus, since the factors in Table 21.2 are uncorrelated, the communality for the first index (.848) is obtained by squaring each of the three correlations in the top row and then adding. We see that the three orthogonal factors explain a very high percentage of the variation in all but the last index, but since we cannot identify the factors involved this fact is of little theoretical significance.

Bell then proceeded to rotate in order to obtain a new set of factors which are more easily identified (see Table 21.3). Notice that the first of these rotated factors is highly related to the first three indices but unrelated to the rest. The second factor is related to the following three indices but not to the remainder, while the third is related to the last index but very weakly related to the others. We are now faced with the theoretical problem of interpreting these factors. Examining the nature of the first three indices, as contrasted with the others, Bell argued that

Table 21.3. Rotated Matrix

Measures	Factors*		
	I′	II′	III′
(1) Occupation	.635	.070	−.178
(2) Education	.467	−.105	.209
(3) Rent (−)	.602	−.071	−.028
(4) Fertility	.097	.630	.215
(5) WLF (−)	.031	.711	−.029
(6) SFDU	−.031	.573	−.183
(7) SEG	−.098	.106	.496

* I′ = economic status, II′ = family status, III′ = ethnic status.

SOURCE: W. Bell [1], Table 9, p. 50, with the kind permission of the author and publisher.

since each of these indices more or less directly involved economic status, the first factor could be identified as such. The following three indices seemed to have in common a focus on family patterns, and therefore factor II′ was conceptualized as "family status." The final index apparently formed a cluster to itself, being not too highly related to the remaining indices. Bell therefore identified factor III′ as "ethnic status."[2]

In the above example, we see how seven indices have been essentially reduced to three conceptual variables. The primary value of this kind of use of factor analysis seems to be in the contribution it may make to conceptual clarification. In areas of research where there is apparently no end to the number of indices which may be computed, but where the theory underlying use of these indices is either not in existence or badly in need of clarification, factor analysis may prove to be a very useful exploratory device. In other instances, especially where it is difficult to identify the final factors even after rotation has been accomplished, factor analysis may not be worth the effort involved. Like other

[2] Actually, Bell did not identify these factors in ex post facto fashion as implied here. They were hypothesized as a result of a previous study.

statistical techniques, it should be used as a tool which may possibly contribute to the clarification of theory, but it cannot be expected to serve as a substitute for sound theoretical thinking.

Factor analysis may also be used in a purely practical manner as a criterion for the construction of indices (see [4]). Suppose, for example, that one wishes to establish a general index of social class or discrimination. He may have half a dozen or more separate indices all designed to measure the "same" underlying variable. Rather than relating each of these separate indices to other variables, he may wish to combine them in some manner to obtain a better single index of this underlying variable. Quite commonly, arbitrary weightings are used in order to accomplish this. Sometimes equal weights are given to all indices. On other occasions, a researcher may use his own judgment as to which index is most satisfactory, giving this index more weight than the others.

If factor analysis is used in assigning weights, we first determine whether or not a single factor should be used to account for the intercorrelations among indices. If the second and subsequent factors can be shown to explain very little of the common variance among the indices, it can be reasoned that the intercorrelations among these indices are due to the presence of a single factor, presumably the factor being measured by the indices. The indices can then be weighted according to their correlations or loadings with this factor, with those indices having the highest loadings receiving the greatest weight. Indices are thus in effect weighted according to the strength of their intercorrelations with the other indices rather than arbitrarily. The weighting criterion used is therefore a function of the internal consistency among indices.

21.2. Other Multivariate Techniques

One of the major advantages of interval scales over either nominal or ordinal scales is that as yet no techniques have been developed in the case of the latter scales which are comparable to regression analysis or analysis of covariance. It is, of course, possible to control simultaneously for several variables by looking separately at the various subcategories of control variables, but a very large number of cases will be required if this is to be done satisfactorily. We have seen that partial correlations can be computed using Kendall's tau. It has been indicated in Sec. 15.4 that partial coefficients can also be computed for contingency tables by obtaining a weighted average of the coefficients computed for the various categories of the control variables.

It is also possible to compute multiple coefficients in the case of nominal scales by relating the dependent variable to a single independent variable consisting of all combinations of categories of the independent variables.

Thus, if variables A and B are the independent variables, we could take as categories of a single independent variable the subcategories A_1B_1, A_1B_2, A_2B_1, A_2B_2, A_3B_1, etc. If we then compute a measure of association, such as V or τ_b, between this combination variable and a dependent variable C, we have in effect a multiple correlation coefficient. For example, Goodman and Kruskal's τ_c could be interpreted as the proportional reduction in the number of errors in C when information about A and B is used. To the writer's knowledge, there have as yet been developed no really satisfactory measures of multiple rank-order correlation, nor are there any nonparametric rank-order techniques comparable to analysis of covariance.

Certain procedures comparable to factor analysis have been developed for use with nominal or ordinal scales, but these techniques are so new that they have seldom, if ever, been used in the sociological literature. Latent structure analysis is a multivariate technique developed by Lazarsfeld and others and is theoretically a generalization of factor analysis for the case of nominal scales (see [5]). By postulating the existence of one or more underlying factors or dimensions, as well as a given number of categories or "latent classes" for each dimension, one can account for certain interrelationships among nominal scales in much the same manner as can be done by means of factor analysis. In most of the applications of latent structure analysis published by the Lazarsfeld group, the nominal scales have been dichotomized items taken from attitude questionnaires, and the technique has been used to sort persons into categories along a single dimension according to their response patterns. When more than one dimension is postulated and when nominal scales with more than two categories are used, the computations apparently become quite involved, so that for all practical purposes the method is of limited use at the present time. It is hoped, however, that as computing techniques become perfected and simplified, latent structure analysis will come to fill an important gap in the body of available techniques. Also of potential value are some nonmetric factor-analysis techniques being developed by Coombs and his associates (see [3]).

There is no doubt that once such procedures have been developed and simplified to the point where they can be used and understood by the average practitioner, we shall have much more powerful tools for investigating the interrelationships among a large number of variables. As is true in the case of factor analysis, however, we can expect these techniques to require large samples. Apparently there is no computationally simple procedure as yet developed which can handle large numbers of variables while simultaneously requiring only moderate-sized samples. Perhaps no such technique can ever be developed. If this turns out to be the case, the implications for social research are profound.

GLOSSARY

Communalities
Correlation matrix
Factor loading
Oblique factors
Orthogonal factors

REFERENCES

1. Bell, W.: "Economic, Family, and Ethnic Status: An Empirical Test," *American Sociological Review*, vol. 20, pp. 45–52, February, 1955.

2. Cattell, R. B.: *Factor Analysis: An Introduction and Manual for the Psychologist and Social Scientist*, Harper & Brothers, New York, 1952.

3. Coombs, C. H., and R. C. Kao: *Nonmetric Factor Analysis*, Engineering Research Institute, University of Michigan, Ann Arbor, Mich., 1955.

4. Hagood, M. J., and D. O. Price: *Statistics for Sociologists*, Henry Holt and Company, Inc., New York, 1952, chap. 26.

5. Lazarsfeld, P.: "The Logical and Mathematical Foundation of Latent Structure Analysis," in S. A. Stouffer et al., *Measurement and Prediction*, Princeton University Press, Princeton, N.J., 1950, pp. 362–412.

6. Peters, C. C., and W. R. Van Voorhis: *Statistical Procedures and Their Mathematical Bases*, McGraw-Hill Book Company, Inc., New York, 1940, chap. 9.

7. Stephenson, W.: "The Inverted Factor Technique," *British Journal of Psychology*, vol. 26, pp. 344–361, 1936.

8. Thurstone, L. L.: *Multiple-factor Analysis: A Development and Expansion of the Vectors of Mind*, University of Chicago Press, Chicago, 1947.

Chapter 22

SAMPLING

All the tests we have considered, as well as the procedures used for obtaining confidence intervals, have required the assumption of random sampling. In fact, you may have formed the impression that random sampling is the only respectable kind of sampling used by the statistician. This is far from the case. There are four basic types of probability sampling which will be discussed in this chapter: random sampling, systematic sampling, stratified sampling, and cluster sampling. As we shall see, it is possible to make use of statistical inference with each of these four types of probability samples, although it is unfortunately true that at the present time we are quite restricted as to the number of different types of tests that can be used with nonrandom probability samples. Especially in the case of cluster samples, our formulas also become much more complicated. In a general text such as this, it will therefore be impossible to do much more than to indicate some general considerations of strategy in choosing the type of sampling which will be most appropriate in a given situation.

We have indicated that there are four basic types of probability sampling, one of which is random sampling. What, then, is a probability sample? The distinguishing characteristic of a probability sample is that every individual must have a *known* probability of being included in the sample. In a random sample we have seen that all combinations of individuals have an equal chance of appearing. In making statistical inferences it is not absolutely necessary that all probabilities be equal, since, if the probability of selection is known, it will be possible to adjust for unequal probabilities by a weighting procedure of some kind. It is essential, however, that probabilities be known in order to arrive at the proper weights. If probabilities are unknown, it will be impossible to make legitimate use of statistical inference. With nonprobability sampling we may actually obtain a very representative sample, but we shall not be in a position to evaluate the risks of error involved. After describing and comparing each of the four types of probability sampling, we shall discuss briefly certain instances where nonprobability samples are likely to be obtained.

22.1. Simple Random Sampling

It has been emphasized that in random sampling not only must each individual have an equal chance of being selected but that all combinations must be equally probable. We have also indicated that it is usually more convenient to sample without replacement. Sampling specialists usually refer to such a sample as a "simple random sample." Notice that on each successive draw the probability of an individual's being selected is slightly increased because of the fact that there will be fewer and fewer individuals left unselected from the population. If, on any given draw, the probabilities of all remaining individuals being selected are equal regardless of the individuals previously selected, then we have a simple random sample. In effect, we have independence from one draw to the next except for the fact that no individual can be selected twice.

By what mechanical procedures are random samples selected? It is sometimes erroneously thought that almost any "hit or miss" method of sampling will yield a random sample. This is far from the case. Such methods almost invariably lead to a biased sample because of the human element involved. In order to assure ourselves that all individuals, including those who are atypical or difficult to locate, do in fact have an equal chance of appearing, we must ordinarily go to great lengths to draw our sample. First, we must be sure that each individual in the population is listed once and only once. We can then associate a number with each position on the list and make use of some mechanical procedure, such as that used in a bingo game, to assure equal probabilities of selection. Let us first examine certain problems that may be encountered in the listing process itself.

It might be thought that obtaining a list is usually a simple matter. In most practical research problems this is not the case. Often, there are no lists at all. For example, there is no list of residents of the United States or the state of Michigan. There will almost certainly be no list of Negroes or Japanese living in a given community. If no list exists, it may be extremely expensive to compile one. If this is the case, other methods of probability sampling may be preferable to simple random sampling. Lists may exist, but they may be out of date. Some individuals may not have been included while others on the list may no longer be members of the population concerned. City directories, which at first thought appear to be the ideal source for one who wishes to draw a random sample of residents, may be so out of date by the time they are published as to be next to useless. Those individuals who have recently arrived will be excluded from the list and therefore will have no chance of being selected in the sample. To the degree that such persons differ from the rest of the population with respect to whatever characteristics are being studied, the researcher will obtain a biased sample and misleading results. Other lists, such as telephone directories or motor-vehicle registration lists, may be biased in that lower-income groups are especially likely to be underrepresented. It is safe to say, therefore, that no matter how accurate a list appears to be, you should always carefully investigate its adequacy. A poor list can be worse than none at all if it leads to an unusually biased sample.

What can we do if the list is inadequate? If the list is complete but involves duplications, the problem is relatively simple provided, of course, that the duplications are readily spotted. For example, if the list consists of all children at a particular school and we wish to select a random sample of *parents*, we would undoubtedly discover that some parents had more than one child attending school. Therefore if we gave each *child's* card an equal chance of being selected, certain parents would have a better chance than others of being included. In order to remedy this situation we could simply remove the cards of all but one sibling, or we could select a parent only if his oldest child's card were chosen, rejecting him if any of his other children's cards have been included.

It should be noted that if Jones's second or third child were selected and we therefore did not include Jones in the sample, it would not be legitimate to substitute for Jones the parent whose child appeared next to Jones's on the list. If this were done, persons with cards next to parents with more than one child would have a higher probability of being selected. The correct procedure would be to omit Jones and go on to the next card selected by probability methods. Another alternative which is theoretically possible but which may create additional problems for analysis would be to include Jones if any of his children's cards are selected but to give him relatively less weight in the analysis. Thus, if he has three children and therefore three times the ordinary probability of selection, his scores would be given one-third the weight of the parent with only one child.

In most problems it is more likely that the list will be incomplete or that it will include names of individuals who are no longer members of the population. Here it will again be possible to purify the list until it is correct. If this is not feasible, it may be desirable to redefine the population slightly to conform to the list. Suppose a list of employees is known to be complete and accurate as of the first of the year. Rather than obtain the names of all persons hired since that date, it may be possible to confine one's attention to employees who were with the company prior to this time and who are presently employed there.   Any persons included in the sample but found to have left the company can then be ignored.   Notice, however, that the population studied would not be *all* present employees, and any reader should be made well aware of this fact.

Having obtained an accurate list, it is a relatively simple matter to draw a random sample.   Theoretically, a number of mechanical devices could be used to assure equal probabilities of selection.   One could use a well-shuffled deck of cards or draw numbers from a hat.   Perhaps a round cage containing balls with numbers on them would give more reliable results because of the tendency of cards or slips of paper to stick together when shuffled or mixed.   Actually, the researcher need not go through such an involved process since tables of random numbers have already been constructed for this purpose.   Such tables were constructed by using mechanical devices such as indicated above.   For example, one could place an equal number of balls with the digits 0, 1, 2, . . . , 9 in a basket and proceed to select balls, each time replacing and shuffling thoroughly. The resulting digits could then be used to form a table of random numbers such as that given in Table B of Appendix 2.

In using a table of random numbers it makes no difference whether we go down columns or across rows, nor does it matter which column or row we start with—as long as our decision is made prior to examining the data.   To illustrate the use of a table of random numbers, let us suppose that one wishes to draw a sample of size 100 from a population consisting of 736 individuals.   Since the number 736 consists of three digits, we shall find it convenient to select three adjacent columns (any three), selecting another three columns when we come to the bottom of the page. Suppose, for example, that we decide to use the first three columns of the first page of Table B.   As the first case in the sample, we select the first number between 001 and 736 which appears.   This number is 100. In other words, the one hundredth individual will be in the sample.   We proceed down columns 1 to 3, obtaining the numbers 375 and 084.   We then come to the number 990.   This would correspond to the 990th individual in the population, but since there is no such individual we move on to the next number which is 128.

After a while, we begin to run into numbers which have already been selected.   Since we are sampling without replacement, we must omit these repetitions until we have finally selected 100 cases.   This is all there is to it.   The reason that the process is so simple and that arbitrary decisions can be made as to the use of columns or rows is, of course, that the numbers appearing in the table are completely random.   As a matter of fact, it is almost impossible to use such a table incorrectly unless columns (or rows) are repeated or unless one cheats by deciding he wants the 219th case in the sample and deliberately looks for a column containing this number.

Correction for Sampling without Replacement. It was mentioned in Chap. 9, which was on probability, that when we sample without replacement we violate the assumption of independence and that, strictly speaking, we therefore must modify our formulas to take this fact into consideration. Usually the problem is not a serious one since the sample selected is a small fraction of the population, and therefore the chances of any given individual's being selected two or more times is rather slight. If the sample size is as much as one-fifth the size of the population, however, it may be desirable to introduce correction factors whenever these factors are known. Unfortunately, exact correction factors are known only in the simplest kinds of problems. This fact is seldom a disturbing one, however, since, if we were going to select a sample which is one-third or one-half the size of the population, we would probably be in a position to select the entire population anyway. The use of a correction factor for formulas involving the standard error of the mean will be discussed below. In more complicated cases you should refer to a standard text on sampling, although you will probably not find any discussion of correction factors for the various nonparametric tests, in such texts. Such tests, however, are most applicable for small samples where the replacement problem is of minor importance.

The formula we should actually use for the standard error of the mean if we have sampled without replacement is

$$\sigma_{\bar{x}} = \sqrt{1 - f}\, \frac{\sigma}{\sqrt{N}} \qquad (22.1)$$

where f represents the "sampling fraction" or the ratio of the number of cases in the sample to the size of the population. If we refer to the sample size as N and the population size as M, we may rewrite the correction factor as

$$\sqrt{1 - \frac{N}{M}}$$

It can immediately be seen that if the sample size is relatively small as compared with M, the value of the correction factor becomes approximately unity and there is little or no point in using it. Thus, if a sample of 500 is selected from a population of 10,000, the sampling fraction is $\frac{1}{20}$ and the value of the correction factor becomes .975. Notice that since the correction factor must be less than 1 for finite populations, the corrected value of the standard error will always be less than the uncorrected figure.   Thus, if we desire a small standard error, as is usually the case, we shall be on the conservative side if we do not make use of the correction.   Unless the sampling fraction is of the order of one-fifth or more, we seldom bother to use it.

This same correction factor can be used in other formulas involving standard errors of means or proportions.   Thus, if an estimate is to be used, we would use the formula

$$\hat{\sigma}_{\bar{x}} = \sqrt{1 - f}\left(\frac{\hat{\sigma}}{\sqrt{N}}\right) = \sqrt{1 - f}\left(\frac{s}{\sqrt{N - 1}}\right) \qquad (22.2)$$

In a difference-of-means test there would be two sampling fractions, and the basic formula for the estimate of the standard error of the difference of means would be

$$\hat{\sigma}_{\bar{x}_1 - \bar{x}_2} = \sqrt{(1 - f_1)\frac{\hat{\sigma}_1{}^2}{N_1} + (1 - f_2)\frac{\hat{\sigma}_2{}^2}{N_2}} \qquad (22.3)$$

22.2. Systematic Sampling

Another type of sampling used quite frequently is likely to be confused with simple random sampling and, in fact, is often used interchangeably with simple random sampling.   In systematic sampling, instead of using a table of random numbers we simply go down a list taking every kth individual, starting with a randomly selected case among the first k individuals.   Thus, if we wanted to select a sample of 90 persons from a list of 1,800, we would take every twentieth in the list.   Our first choice, however, must be determined by some random process such as the use of a table of random numbers.   Suppose the eleventh person were selected. The sample would then consist of individuals numbered 11, 31, 51, 71, 91, ...

Systematic sampling is obviously much simpler than random sampling whenever a list is extremely long or whenever a large sample is to be drawn.   If a telephone directory or city directory could legitimately be used, we can imagine the difficulty in locating the 512th, 1,078th, and 15,324th individuals.   If the ordering used in compiling the list can be considered to be essentially random with respect to the variables being measured, a systematic sample will be equivalent to a simple random sample.   For example, most lists are given in alphabetical order.   Surnames, of course, are not random.   A husband and wife listed separately would have practically no chance of appearing together in the sample unless their name were an extremely common one.   Certain ethnic groups may have an undue proportion of names beginning with the same letter (O'Brien, O'Neil, etc.).   Actually, in the case of alphabetical lists we have something approximating a stratified sample (see below) in which ethnic groups may have a tendency to be grouped together. Taking every kth individual is thus likely to give a proper representation of each group. In practice, since alphabetical ordering is essentially irrelevant to most variables studied, we are usually safe in considering a systematic sample as equivalent to a simple random sample. Special formulas have been developed, however, which make use of somewhat different assumptions. In most cases they will hardly be worth the extra trouble.

There are two types of situations in which systematic sampling may cause serious biases. Fortunately, neither occurs very frequently in sociological problems. *First*, the individuals may have been ordered so that a trend occurs. If persons have been listed according to office, prestige, or seniority, the position of the random start may affect the results. Suppose, for example, that the sampling fraction is $\frac{1}{30}$. Two persons may draw systematic samples with very different random starts. A random start of two would yield a considerably higher average score (if individuals were ranked from high to low) than a start of 27 since each individual in the first sample will be 25 ranks ahead of the comparable person in the second sample. If a trend of this sort is noticed, the list may have to be shuffled somewhat or a "middle start" used (e.g., start with the fifteenth or sixteenth individual).

The *second* type of situation to be avoided is that in which the list has some periodic or cyclical characteristic which corresponds to the sampling fraction. For example, in a housing development or apartment house every eighth dwelling unit may be a corner unit. If it is somewhat larger than the others its occupants can be expected to differ as well. If the sampling fraction also happens to be $\frac{1}{8}$, one could obtain a sample with either all corner units or no corner units depending on the random start. To avoid this pitfall, one could change the sampling fraction slightly to $\frac{1}{7}$ or $\frac{1}{9}$, or he could make use of several different random starts. After selecting ten households, he could pick another random number and go to ten more residences, draw a third number, and so on.

Systematic sampling, in combination with other designs, is often used in social surveys because of its simplicity. An untrained interviewer can much more easily be told to go to every third house in a block than to use a table of random numbers. As with simple random sampling, however, the listing must be complete and accurate. If the interviewer were to miss the smaller apartments or certain residences in back alleys, serious errors could result. It is important to realize that in all types of probability sampling there must be both some element of randomization and some sort of a complete listing. As we shall see presently, however, the nature of the required lists may differ from one design to the next, some being much simpler to obtain than others. It will always be necessary for the researcher to examine his list carefully and to know how it has been constructed and the nature of its defects.

22.3. Stratified Sampling

While the differences between simple random and systematic sampling are usually relatively minor in terms of cost saving or problems of analysis, the remaining two basic types of sampling differ in certain fundamental respects from the preceding two already discussed. As we shall see, both stratified and cluster sampling can be used, under certain circumstances, to improve the efficiency of the sampling design. In other words, they may be designed to yield greater accuracy for the same cost or, if you prefer, to involve less cost for the same accuracy. It will also be found that both of these designs require different formulas from any we have previously used.

In a stratified sample we first divide all individuals into groups or categories and then select independent samples within each group or stratum. It is important that the strata be defined in such a way that each individual appears in one and only one stratum. In the simplest and most frequently used types of stratified sampling, we take either a simple random sample or a systematic sample within each stratum. The sampling fractions for each stratum may be equal, in which case we speak of *proportional* stratified sampling, or we may have *disproportional* stratified sampling.

One reason that we often stratify a sample is that different sampling methods or lists may have been used for each stratum. For example, the strata may consist of separate factories, schools, or dormitories, each of which was studied at a different time and by different persons. It might have been completely unfeasible to combine the lists for all strata and then to select a single random sample. Another important reason for stratifying rather than taking a random sample is to reduce the number of cases required in order to achieve a given degree of accuracy. To the degree that the strata are homogeneous with respect to the variables being studied, we can improve the efficiency of the design. By discussing proportional and disproportional stratified sampling, we shall see more specifically some of the advantages of stratified sampling over simple random sampling.

Proportional Stratified Sampling. Proportional stratified sampling is often used to assure a more representative sample than might be expected under simple random or systematic sampling. Suppose, for example, that it is known that there are 600 Protestants, 300 Catholics, and 100 Jews in a given population. If a random sample of size 100 were drawn, we would certainly not expect to get exactly 60 Protestants, 30 Catholics, and 10 Jews. The proportion of Jews, especially, might be relatively either too large or too small. Now suppose we were interested in studying some variable, such as church attendance, which is closely related to denomination. Suppose, also, that we wished to estimate the mean number of times persons in the population attended church. It is easy to see intuitively that a proportional stratified sample in which the sampling fractions for all three strata were $\frac{1}{10}$ (i.e., consisting of 60 Protestants, 30 Catholics, and 10 Jews) would ordinarily yield more reliable results than a simple random sample.

We have here, in effect, a problem analogous to analysis of variance. In a random sample there are two sources of variation. There may be sampling errors *within* each stratum and there may be errors *between* strata with respect to the relative numbers selected. Not only might we select very atypical Jews or Catholics but also might select too many or too few of each type. In stratified sampling we have eliminated this type of between-stratum variation and are left only with the within variation. If the strata were completely homogeneous, proportional stratified sampling would always yield exactly correct results whereas simple random sampling would not. On the other hand, if the strata were as heterogeneous as would be expected by chance we would gain nothing by stratifying. In other words, if the differences between groups are small as compared with the within differences, stratification is of no help. Thus the gain from stratifying is roughly proportional to the intraclass correlation between the two variables. If the criterion for stratifying is highly related to the variable studied, the gain may therefore be considerable. In gaining control over the number of cases in each stratum, something that was not possible in random sampling, we can assure ourselves of more accuracy for a given size sample.

You should not come to expect too much of proportional stratified sampling. If the size of the sample is relatively large, we expect, of course, that chance factors alone will assure us of approximately the correct proportions from each of the strata. Since problems of analysis are not made too complex by proportional stratified sampling, there is little to lose by stratifying, however. It is usually neither essential nor feasible to hunt around to obtain a single "best" criterion for stratifying. To obtain a proportional stratified sample the sizes of the population strata must be known, and it will, of course, only be possible to stratify according to variables for which information is given from the listing at the time the sample is drawn. This often means that one is confined to such simple variables as sex, age, occupation, or area of residence. Several of these variables may even be used in combination, if so desired, although it will seldom be advantageous to stratify by more than two or three variables simultaneously. Since stratification is such a simple procedure, however, its possibilities should always be explored.

Disproportional Stratified Sampling. In disproportional stratified sampling we make use of different sampling fractions to manipulate the number of cases selected in order to improve still further the efficiency of the design. There are several types of situations in which this type of sampling is desirable. Often our interest may center primarily on the separate subpopulations represented by the strata rather than on the entire population. Suppose, for example, that we wished to *compare* the three major religious groups with respect to their attendance. Obviously, both simple random sampling and proportional stratified sampling would give us too few Jews in the sample to make meaningful comparisons. We might therefore decide to select equal numbers from each group, thereby giving each Jewish person a probability of selection equal to three times that of each Catholic and six times that of any given Protestant. If we were to select 50 from each group, the respective sampling fractions would thus be $\frac{1}{12}$, $\frac{1}{6}$, and $\frac{1}{2}$. If we then wished to generalize to the entire population in order to estimate the mean attendance figure, we would have to weight the means of the three strata to compensate for the fact that Jews have been oversampled. This weighting procedure will be described below.

Even if our goal is to generalize to the entire population rather than to compare different subpopulations, it may still be desirable to make use of disproportional stratified sampling if either (1) the standard deviations within the separate strata differ considerably among themselves or (2) the cost of gathering data varies substantially from stratum to stratum. There will always be some *optimum allocation* for which the sampling design will have maximum efficiency. In other words, there will be a certain set of sampling fractions which will yield the smallest sampling error for a given cost. We can obtain such an optimum allocation if we *make the sampling fraction for each stratum directly proportional to the standard deviation within the stratum and inversely proportional to the square root of the cost of each case within the stratum.* Let us see intuitively why this is the case, looking first at the question of the standard deviations.

If one particular stratum is unusually homogeneous with respect to the variable being studied, it will be unnecessary to select a very large sample from this stratum in order to obtain a given degree of accuracy. On the other hand, it will be advisable to take a much larger sample from a very heterogeneous stratum. Since our over-all accuracy will be determined primarily by the degree of accuracy in the weakest link in the chain, so to speak, it is important that we do not have one or two strata with large sampling errors. This is especially true if these strata happen to be large ones. It would be pointless to have perfect accuracy in several of the smaller strata but a very large sampling error in another stratum. Therefore, if we take relatively more cases from the heterogeneous strata and fewer from the homogeneous ones, we can get by with fewer cases. As it turns out mathematically, the desired sampling fractions are actually proportional to the relative standard deviations rather than the variances.

A word of caution is necessary at this point. A particular stratum may be very homogeneous with respect to one variable being studied and yet heterogeneous with respect to another. Since a research project usually involves a study of more than one variable, it therefore may be extremely difficult to find allocations which are optimal, or nearly optimal, for more than one variable. In fact, a design which is very efficient for one variable may be extremely inefficient for another. Therefore, it is best to consult a sampling specialist and to be well aware of the important variables before using disproportional allocation. When in doubt, proportional allocation would be much safer.

Thus far, cost considerations have never been considered because of the fact that we have been implicitly assuming equal costs for gathering data on all individuals. Suppose, however, that this is not the case and that certain strata involve higher costs than others. Various administrators, for example, may permit different data-collecting techniques, or perhaps the physical layouts in the different strata are such that more time is consumed interviewing in one stratum than in the rest. Other factors being equal, it would obviously be less expensive to select a relatively larger number of cases from the cheapest strata. It can be shown mathematically that optimum allocation will be attained if sampling fractions are taken inversely proportional to the square root of the cost factors.

Notice that in the special case where all costs are equal and where all within-stratum standard deviations are equal, the sampling fractions will also be equal and we have the situation in which proportional stratification gives us optimum allocation. In general, it is usually wise to follow the rule of using proportional stratification unless cost differentials are very great or unless stratum standard deviations are substantially different. As will be seen below, the use of disproportional sampling tends to complicate problems of analysis and should therefore not be used unless it is clearly to one's advantage to do so.

We have not as yet faced up to an extremely important question. How can we make use of cost calculations and the relative standard deviations when these are unknown at the time the sample is drawn? The obvious answer is that they have to be estimated, just as we had to make enlightened guesses as to the values of certain parameters before we could estimate the size of the sample we would need. We must realize, however, that the kinds of estimates we need are not the kinds of estimates we make from sample statistics. Of course, it would be possible to do a pilot study in order to obtain such estimates, but unless the study is to be an extremely large and expensive one, such an outlay of money will probably not be feasible. Our estimates must therefore be based on the experience of experts or on the results of previous studies. The situation is not quite as bad as it sounds, however, since it is usually possible to obtain very good approximations to optimum allocation with very crude guesses as to costs and standard deviations. In other words, if there is reason to suspect large differences among strata with respect to either of these factors, an enlightened guess is likely to yield a design which is almost as efficient as would be obtained with exact values.

Computations with Stratified Samples. When computing estimates of means and estimating standard errors from stratified samples, we must compute values separately for each of the strata and then weight them according to the relative size of the stratum in the population. If we let W_i indicate the weight of the ith stratum in the population and if we set $\Sigma W_i = 1$, thereby reducing the weights to proportions, we can write the formula for estimating the population mean as

$$\bar{X} = \sum_{i=1}^{k} W_i \bar{X}_i$$

where the $\bar{X}_i$ are the sample means for each of the k strata. This formula is as we would expect. It simply says that if one stratum is three times as large as a second, its mean should receive three times as much weight.

If *proportional* stratified sampling has been used and if we let N_i and M_i, respectively, indicate the sizes of the sample and population for the ith stratum, then by definition all N_i/M_i will be equal to N/M. But since for the ith stratum

$$\bar{X}_i = \frac{\sum_{j=1}^{N_i} X_{ij}}{N_i}$$

and also

$$W_i = \frac{M_i}{M} = \frac{N_i}{N}$$

we have

$$\bar{X} = \sum_{i=1}^{k} \frac{N_i}{N} \frac{\sum_{j=1}^{N_i} X_{ij}}{N_i} = \frac{1}{N} \sum_{i=1}^{k} \sum_{j=1}^{N_i} X_{ij}$$

This double summation simply means that we have summed all of the X's. Since we then divide this sum by the total number of cases to get $\bar{X}$, we thus see that in the case of proportional stratified sampling we could have obtained the estimate of μ exactly as we did in the case of simple random samples. For this reason we refer to proportional stratification as being "self-weighting." In other words, each stratum has received its proper weight. If stratification has been disproportional, we must multiply each $\bar{X}_i$ by the weight of that stratum *in the population*.

In estimating the standard error of the mean, our computations cannot be worked out so easily. We must first estimate the standard error for each stratum and then pool the results as was done in the difference-of-means test and in analysis of variance. It will be remembered that instead of summing standard deviations, we worked with the variances and sums of squares. We also have to square the weights W_i. The formula for the estimated *variance* of the mean using stratified sampling can thus be written

$$\hat{\sigma}_{\bar{X}}{}^2 = \Sigma W_i{}^2 \hat{\sigma}_{\bar{X}_i}{}^2$$

where $\hat{\sigma}_{\bar{X}_i}{}^2$ indicates an estimate of the variance of the mean within the ith stratum. We can obtain the estimated standard error of the mean by taking the square root of the above expression and can then compute the t statistic as before.

Suppose, for example, that there are three counties and that data for the counties can be summarized as in Table 22.1. Notice that we have

Table 22.1. Data for Computing Parameter Estimates from Stratified Samples

	County			Total
	1	2	3	
Size of county (M_i)	10,000	15,000	25,000	50,000 ($= M$)
Weight (W_i)	.20	.30	.50	1.00
Size of sample (N_i)	50	50	50	150 ($= N$)
Sample mean ($\bar{X}_i$)	3,100	4,300	3,800	
Sample standard deviation (s_i)	500	400	300	

obtained a disproportionate sample since unequal sampling fractions have been used. Let us assume that simple random sampling was used within each stratum and that samples were independently drawn. The estimated standard errors, ignoring the factor $1 - f$, are

County 1: $\dfrac{s_1}{\sqrt{N_1 - 1}} = \dfrac{500}{\sqrt{49}} = 71.4$

County 2: $\dfrac{s_2}{\sqrt{N_2 - 1}} = \dfrac{400}{\sqrt{49}} = 57.1$

County 3: $\dfrac{s_3}{\sqrt{N_3 - 1}} = \dfrac{300}{\sqrt{49}} = 42.9$

The estimated mean and variance will therefore be

$$\bar{X} = .20(3,100) + .30(4,300) + .50(3,800) = 3,810$$

and
$$\hat{\sigma}_{\bar{X}}^2 = (.20)^2(71.4)^2 + (.30)^2(57.1)^2 + (.50)^2(42.9)^2$$
$$= 957.5$$

Although computations for means and proportions are straightforward in the case of stratified samples, it should be recognized that one cannot legitimately use the various nonparametric tests, tests for the significance of correlation, analysis of covariance, etc., without substantial modification. Unfortunately, you will generally not find discussions of these problems in textbooks on sampling. We know how to handle complicated statistical problems if we can assume the simplest kind of sampling, random sampling. With the more complicated sampling designs we can handle the simplest of statistical problems such as estimating means or proportions, computing confidence intervals for means and proportions, and making tests of differences of means. There is a gap, however, when it comes to more sophisticated statistical techniques with complicated sample designs. It is hoped that this gap can be filled in the near future.

22.4. Cluster Sampling

In stratified sampling we divided our population into groups which we called strata and we sampled from *every* stratum. Sometimes it is advantageous to divide the population into a large number of groups, called clusters, and to sample *among* the clusters. For example, we might divide a city into several hundred census tracts and then select 40 tracts for our sample. Such a sampling design is referred to as cluster sampling and is frequently used in social surveys in order to cut down on the cost of gathering data. As we shall see presently, the aim in cluster sampling is to select clusters which are as *heterogeneous* as possible but which are small enough to cut down on such expenses as travel costs involved in interviewing.

In cluster sampling we do not sample our elements directly. Instead, we sample clusters or groups of elements. In the simplest of cluster designs we might use random selection among clusters and then select every individual within those clusters included in the sample of clusters. Such a design is often referred to as a single-stage cluster design since sampling occurs only once in the process. In multistage sampling, on the other hand, the design may be much more complicated. We might first take a simple random sample of census tracts within the city. Then within each tract we might take a simple random sample of blocks (smaller clusters). Finally, the interviewer might be instructed to select every third dwelling unit within those blocks included and to interview every second adult within each of these households. Thus, sampling procedures may enter the selection process at a number of points. It is essential in probability sampling, of course, that there be some element of randomness in the procedure. Sampling fractions may be computed which produce unbiased samples so that every individual in the population has an equal chance of appearing in the sample. It will not be possible to ensure independence of selection by this method, however. Persons within the same cluster will generally have a better chance of appearing together in the same sample than members of different clusters. In fact, the whole purpose of cluster sampling is to ensure that this will occur.

It will be instructive to compare cluster sampling with both simple random sampling and stratified sampling. In order to simplify the argument, let us suppose that we are using a single-stage cluster design in which clusters are selected randomly and then every individual within the sampled clusters is used in the total sample. How does cluster sampling differ from stratified sampling? Notice that although both involve dividing the population into groups, they in a sense involve opposite sampling operations. In stratified sampling we *sample individuals* within every stratum. We are therefore sure that every stratum is represented by a certain number of cases. Our sampling errors involve variability *within* the strata. We therefore want the strata to be as homogeneous as possible and as different as possible from each other.

In (single-stage) cluster sampling, on the other hand, we have no source of sampling error within a cluster because every case is being used. Since we are only taking a sample of clusters our error now involves variability *between* the clusters. If the cluster means differ considerably as compared to the variability within clusters, we run the risk of obtaining some very unusual clusters in our sample of clusters. If this should occur, and if the clusters are homogeneous, our sampling error could be considerable. But if the clusters are heterogeneous as compared with differences among clusters, we can get by with relatively few large clusters. Suppose, in the extreme, that every cluster were heterogeneous and that, by comparison, differences among cluster means were insignificant. We could then simply select one very large cluster and obtain an excellent sample. However, if the clusters were completely homogeneous we would need only one case in each cluster. We thus attempt to obtain homogeneous strata but heterogeneous clusters, the reason for the variance in strategy being the difference in the point at which the sample is drawn.

Let us now compare cluster sampling with simple random sampling. In practically all examples you will encounter, cluster samples will be *less efficient* (i.e., will yield greater sampling errors) than simple random samples *of the same size*. As we shall see shortly, however, it may *cost* considerably less to obtain cluster samples. Our problem will be essentially that of balancing cost and efficiency. How, then, do we compare the relative efficiencies of the two designs? Efficiency is most conveniently measured in terms of the size of the standard error of the estimate, a small standard error indicating high efficiency. As we have seen, it is desirable to obtain clusters which are as heterogeneous as possible. This intuitive notion can be translated into a formula involving the intraclass correlation coefficient. It can be shown that the ratio of the variances of the estimates of μ for cluster and for simple random samples is approximately

$$\frac{\sigma_{\bar{X}_C}{}^2}{\sigma_{\bar{X}_R}{}^2} = 1 + \rho_i(\bar{N} - 1)$$

where $\sigma_{\bar{X}_C}{}^2$ and $\sigma_{\bar{X}_R}{}^2$ represent the variances of the means for cluster and simple random samples, respectively, ρ_i represents the population intraclass correlation, and N is the mean number of cases in each of the clusters.

Notice that the ratio of variances will ordinarily be greater than unity, indicating larger variances (and hence standard errors) for cluster sampling. The expression will be greater than unity unless either $\bar{N} = 1$ or $\rho_i \leq 0$. Obviously, if $\bar{N} = 1$ the cluster sample reduces to the special case of a random sample since each "cluster" consists of a single case. Intraclass correlation is, of course, a measure of homogeneity. If the cluster is more homogeneous than would be expected by chance, ρ_i will be greater than zero, and the more homogeneous the cluster, the larger the value of ρ_i. Conceivably, ρ_i can be negative. But this would require that the cluster be more heterogeneous than would be expected by chance. As it turns out, the kinds of clusters which we ordinarily select for practical purposes will nearly always be at least as homogeneous as expected by chance.

We see that if $\rho_i > 0$, the larger the number of cases $\bar{N}$ in the cluster, the greater the ratio of variances and therefore the lower the relative efficiency of the cluster design. This can be seen intuitively. If a cluster is quite homogeneous we do not need very many cases to obtain an accurate estimate of its mean. We might very well have taken a small sample from within the cluster and used the money saved to study additional clusters. There are thus two factors which determine the relative efficiency of the cluster design: the degree of homogeneity within the clusters and the size of the cluster itself. We want homogeneous clusters to be small; if they are heterogeneous we can afford to take more cases within each cluster without seriously impairing the efficiency.

As we have already indicated, cluster sampling is usually more economical than simple random sampling. Suppose, for example, that one wished to obtain a nationwide sample to study voting or fertility behavior. In the first place, no list of adults would be available. The cost of compiling such a list would be prohibitive. Lists of counties are available, however. It would certainly be much less expensive to draw a random (or systematic or stratified) sample of counties and then to work only within those counties actually selected. Even within each county a simple random sample would probably not be feasible. There is another obvious cost-saving factor. It will be much less expensive to send interviewers into, say, 50 counties than to scatter them all over the countryside. In a simple random sample, there might be only ten persons selected in the state of Montana. Imagine sending an interviewer all over the state to collect data on these persons! With cluster sampling, local interviewers can be efficiently trained, and each can obtain a relatively large number of interviews without incurring huge travel expenses. Cluster samplings taken on state, county, or city levels would all have the same advantages, although to a lesser degree to be sure.

There are a number of costs involved in any sample survey. It is these costs, not the number of cases, which set the limits to the study. There are certain fixed costs which will be independent of the sample design and the number of cases selected. For our purposes, these can be ignored since they can simply be subtracted from the total funds available. Then there will be costs involved in actually listing the units to be sampled. As we have seen, cluster sampling often reduces listing costs considerably. Certain costs will be directly proportional to the number of cases ultimately selected. The salary paid to the interviewer while he is actually talking to the respondent, costs of coding the data, and certain computational costs fall into this category.

Other costs may be proportional to the number of *clusters* selected, however. Most travel costs, including costs of call-backs, are of this variety. It will be more economical to send an individual into a given county for several days and then into a second county than to have him travel all over the state only to find that certain respondents are not home the first time he calls. Generally speaking, whenever travel costs and other costs which depend on the number of *clusters* selected are quite large as compared with costs which vary directly with the number of cases, cluster sampling will be more economical than simple random sampling. For example, in a survey of a large area involving very short interviews, cluster sampling may be appropriate. If interviews last for several hours or more, simple random sampling may be more sensible provided listing costs are not prohibitive.

Thus, when deciding which design to use, one must balance cost considerations against the efficiency of the design. Whichever method will yield a smaller standard error for a given cost should be used.   Since it is not necessary to take every individual within sampled clusters, a multistage sample may provide a satisfactory compromise.   We then have the complicated problem of selecting an optimum design in which we must determine the number of stages in which sampling is to be used, the number of clusters to be used, and the number of cases to be selected from within each cluster.   The problem is further complicated by the fact that most studies will undoubtedly involve not one but a number of variables and that the clusters will not be of the same size.   Lest there be any doubt in your mind at this point, it is therefore always wise to consult a sampling specialist before making a decision as to design. Careful planning not only can be economical but also can result in fewer problems when it comes to analysis of the data.

Before closing this section on cluster sampling, it is again necessary to inject a word of caution.   Formulas found in this text cannot be used with cluster sampling.   As has been pointed out, errors introduced by using simple random sampling formulas for data collected from cluster samples can be extremely serious.   These errors are not of the order of magnitude of errors introduced by using the normal table instead of the t table.   They may be much greater.   Instead of having significance at the .05 level, the true level (as obtained by correct cluster sample formulas) may be as high as .50 (see [3]).   If we wish to reject a null hypothesis, we shall seldom if ever be on the conservative side using random sampling formulas for clustered data.   It will be remembered that cluster samples are less efficient than simple random samples of the same size.   Therefore, simple random sample formulas will *underestimate* the true standard errors.   Put differently, a cluster sample of a given size may be equivalent in terms of efficiency to a much smaller random sample.   A cluster sample of size 800 may be equivalent in efficiency to a simple random sample of 500.   If simple random sample formulas are used with an N of 800, therefore, we are more likely to obtain significance than if the correct procedures were used.

One should thus be extremely cautious in analyzing data from clustered samples.   He should not make use of statistics such as chi square unless the sampling specialist can help him introduce appropriate correction factors.   The problem is not quite so serious with stratified samples because, if anything, stratified samples are more efficient than simple random samples.   A stratified sample of a given size may be equivalent in efficiency to a somewhat larger random sample, and the researcher will generally be on the conservative side in rejecting a null hypothesis. This is not always the case, however, and proper caution should therefore be exercised.

22.5. Nonprobability Sampling

We turn, briefly, to certain situations in which nonprobability sampling has been used.   The major disadvantage of nonprobability sampling is that we can obtain no valid estimate of our risks of error.   Therefore, statistical inference is not legitimate and should not be used.   This does not mean that nonprobability sampling is never appropriate.   In exploratory studies, the main goal of which is to obtain valuable insights which ultimately may lead to testable hypotheses, probability sampling either may be too expensive or lead to fewer such insights.   One may wish to interview persons who are in especially good positions to supply information, for example.   Or he may wish to interview extreme cases, those which will provide him with most striking differences.   If this is done, of course, he has no legitimate right to test for the significance of differences among extremes unless he is attempting to generalize to a population made up entirely of such persons.   The fact that you can undoubtedly think of studies in which statistical tests have been made on such extreme cases does not mean that such a procedure is legitimate. This is not to deny, however, that useful insights may be obtained by such a comparison.

Nonprobability methods are sometimes used when the purpose is to make generalizations about a population sampled.   Such methods invariably either make use of the interviewer's judgment as to the individuals to be included or permit an individual sampled to be selected out of the study on some nonrandom basis.

Quota samples often used in public opinion surveys seem, on the surface, to be similar to stratified samples.   An interviewer is given certain "quotas" he must fill.   He must have so many females over 40, so many persons with an income of less than $3,000, or a certain percentage of Catholics.   But it is left up to his discretion *which* females over 40 or which Catholics to interview.   Being only human, he is likely to select those persons who are most conveniently located.   If he goes to their home, he may select only those persons who are at home at the time. Even if he is consciously aware of such a selective tendency it will be difficult for him to correct for it exactly.   An extremely conscientious interviewer might even oversample persons who are seldom at home or lower-class individuals who might be missed by other interviewers. Perhaps a well-trained person may become quite expert in the use of his judgment.   But it will be difficult if not impossible to tell.   If any group which is either under- or oversampled happens to differ markedly from others with respect to the variable being studied, the sample may be seriously biased.   What is more, we have no way of estimating just how biased it may be.   The famous example of the *Literary Digest* poll, in which such a biased sample was obtained in predicting election results, is an example of a nonprobability sample and what can happen when one attempts to generalize on the basis of such results.

Whenever lists are incomplete or whenever a large percentage of persons must be considered as nonrespondents, we have in effect another example of nonprobability sampling. If one receives a 50 per cent return on a mailed questionnaire, serious biases can be introduced owing to the fact that nonrespondents may differ significantly from those who returned the questionnaire. Thus, even though pains may have been taken initially to obtain a probability sample, certain individuals actually have no probability of being included in the ultimate sample because they have selected themselves out by refusing to answer. It is for this reason that it is of utmost importance to follow up a mailed questionnaire with one or more postcards in order to obtain a higher percentage return. Likewise, the interviewer must learn to be persistent and must expect to make several call-backs in order to get a sufficient return. Obviously, a substantial bias cannot be compensated for by a large sample.

22.6. Nonsampling Errors and Sample Size

Even if one has been extremely careful to design a study which meets all of the requirements of good sampling, there will always be certain nonsampling errors involved. Probability theory enables us to evaluate the risks of sampling errors, i.e., those errors introduced by virtue of the fact that samples vary from one to the next. Nonsampling errors, on the other hand, are errors of measurement. In a study involving an interview or questionnaire there will always be response errors. In some cases, such as women's ages, for example, there may be a consistency of errors leading to a definite bias. In other examples, response errors may be more or less random. An interviewer's own biases may color his results.

In this text we cannot go into a detailed discussion of the kinds of nonsampling errors possible, nor is this necessary since this question has been treated more than adequately in a number of sources. One extremely important point is worth mentioning, however. There is nothing to be gained in reducing sampling errors below a certain point as compared with nonsampling errors. If these two types of errors can be assumed to be independent of each other, we can diagram the situation as in Fig. 22.1. The total error is thus a function of two independent sources of error and cannot be substantially reduced unless both types are simultaneously controlled. If nonsampling mistakes such as response or interviewing errors are large, there is no point in taking a huge sample in order to reduce the standard error of the estimate since the total error will be primarily determined by the length of the base of the triangle. Likewise, if one is willing to go to great pains to reduce nonsampling errors to a minimum, it will be foolish for him to make use of a small sample, thereby having a large sampling error. A proper balance between sampling and nonsampling errors should therefore be maintained. Research accuracy limits effective sample size and vice versa. Unfortunately, nonsampling

Fig. 22.1. Relationship between total error and sampling and nonsampling errors.

errors are usually difficult to estimate. If errors can be estimated, however, the most effective total design would be one for which both legs of the triangle are equal. It is well to keep this fact in mind.

GLOSSARY

Cluster sample
Sampling fraction
Simple random sample
Stratified sample
Systematic sample

REFERENCES

1. Cochran, W. G.: *Sampling Techniques,* John Wiley & Sons, Inc., New York, 1953.

2. Hansen, M. H., W. N. Hurwitz, and W. G. Madow: *Sample Survey Methods and Theory,* vol. 1, John Wiley & Sons, Inc., New York, 1953.

3. Kish, L.: "Confidence Intervals for Clustered Samples," *American Sociological Review,* vol. 22, pp. 154–165, April, 1957.

4. ———: "Selection of the Sample," in L. Festinger and D. Katz (eds.), *Research Methods in the Behavioral Sciences,* The Dryden Press, New York, 1953, chap. 5.

5. McCarthy, P. J.: *Introduction to Statistical Reasoning,* McGraw-Hill Book Company, Inc., New York, 1957, chaps. 6 and 10.

Chapter 23

CONCLUSIONS

We have covered a fairly broad range of statistical techniques, and while there are many other topics which are beyond the scope of this text, you should have a reasonably clear conception of the kind of tasks statistics can and cannot perform. It is hoped, of course, that any previous misconceptions you may have had about the field have disappeared and that you now perceive statistics neither as a subject which should be avoided at all costs nor as a tool which in itself assures the inevitable development of a scientific discipline. We have seen that statistics cannot serve as a substitute for sound theory, nor can it be used to solve the difficult problems of measurement presently confronting the social sciences. On the other hand, we have seen that such multivariate techniques as multiple and partial correlation, analysis of covariance, and factor analysis can be used for exploratory purposes in order to help locate the important variables, permit indirect causal inferences, make hypothetical adjustments to take into consideration the effects of uncontrolled variables, or even as an aid to conceptual clarification. Although we should be on guard against expecting too much of this relatively new and rapidly developing discipline, we may look forward to some exciting new developments in the not-too-distant future. For this reason, if for no other, it is hoped that you will endeavor to look into topics other than those covered in this text and that you will be alert for new possible applications of statistics to your own field.

Although it is impossible to summarize briefly all of the tests and other procedures discussed in the preceding chapters, we can indicate once more the general kinds of procedures we have covered. We shall then turn to a consideration of one's over-all strategy in deciding what technique to use in any given problem.

We have, first of all, certain descriptive measures which include not only such quantities as percentages, means, and standard deviations but also the various measures of association between two or more variables.

Multiple factor analysis belongs under the heading of descriptive statistics since, although interest may ultimately center on generalizing to a population on the basis of sample results, we can as yet make no statements of inference concerning the sampling fluctuations of factor loadings.

The value of inductive statistics, the second major category we used in delimiting the field of statistics, lies in the fact that we are able to make use of probability theory to make rational decisions concerning the nature of the population on the basis of limited sample information. The major portion of this book has been concerned with the testing of hypotheses, most of which have taken the form of null hypotheses predicting no relationship between two variables. We have seen that although the usual reason for establishing confidence intervals is to estimate population parameters, the basic logic underlying tests of hypotheses and interval estimation is essentially the same. For example, we found that confidence intervals can be used to test a whole range of hypotheses simultaneously.

An important question that you have undoubtedly been raising for quite some time concerns the problem of deciding which among a large number of possible techniques will be most appropriate for a given application. There is, of course, no simple answer to such a general question, since every problem will be unique in some aspects and since there may be several satisfactory procedures, no one of which is clearly superior to the others. Perhaps the best that can be done here is to list some general canons of strategy that one should follow in narrowing down his range of choice. Having thought his problem through and arrived at some tentative decisions, one should always consult a statistician where feasible unless the problem is a straightforward one. This, incidentally, should be considered the most important canon of strategy; if followed, it can save considerable grief later on.

Listed below are three general steps that should be carried out in the planning of any statistical project. Ideally, they should be considered more or less simultaneously since the decisions made in connection with any one step may affect those for the others. It will be impossible in any realistic problem to make all such decisions prior to the collection of data. The more the major problems can be anticipated and intelligent decisions made at an early stage, however, the more likely the research design will be a good one.

1. Anticipating Results. Before proceeding very far with a research project it is always a good idea to try to predict what the results will look like when the study is completed. For example, one may construct dummy tables using hypothetical data which are as realistic as possible. How will such tables have to be modified when certain controls are introduced? About how many cases will be needed to obtain significance with results such as these? What measures, if any, will be needed? How will items be scored? Which variables should be related first? By attempting to answer questions such as these, with hypothetical data in front of him to make it easier to visualize the form of his results, a researcher can acquire valuable insights about how he will analyze his data to obtain the kinds of information he desires. By setting up dummy tables, for example, he may discover that his questions must be asked and scored in one manner rather than another, and he can design his research instrument accordingly. If considerations of analysis are postponed until after the data have been collected, he may find that he lacks just that piece of information required in one of his tests. Or he may find that one of his procedures requires an ordinal scale which might have been obtained had his questions been asked in a different manner.

2. Choosing a Sample Design. If the problem of sample selection is at all complicated, a sampling specialist should be consulted at an early stage in the development of the project. Not only must one consider such factors as the number of cases sampled, the availability of lists, and cost considerations, but he should also anticipate the kind of analysis he wishes to perform. For example, if he wishes to use analysis of covariance or certain nonparametric procedures on a given subsample, he may wish to avoid cluster-sample designs even at a slight cost in sampling efficiency. To the extent that he can inform the sampling specialist of his tentative plans for analysis, it may be possible to work out certain modifications in the sampling design which make for the most effective possible compromise.

3. Selecting among Alternative Procedures for Analysis. One of the first decisions with respect to analysis will involve the general kind of procedures to be used: significance tests, confidence intervals, measures of association, regression equations, etc. Assuming that his interest is focused on the relationships among several variables, there is a definite sequence one will probably wish to follow. *First*, he will want to test for the significance of a relationship to see whether or not a relationship (however slight) may be assumed to exist. If he has established the existence of a relationship, he has at least discovered that there is one which may be worth explaining. *Second*, if a relationship has been found to exist, he will then want to ask how strong it is. Some measure of degree of relationship can be used to answer this question. He will also probably want to ask the theoretical question, "How *important* is this relationship, given the fact that it is at least moderately strong?" *Third*, if the relationship is at least moderately strong and if an interval-scale level of measurement has been attained, it may be desirable to obtain a prediction equation describing the nature of the relationship between the variables concerned. We thus have three levels of analysis, each designed to answer a different question. Significance tests provide answers to the weakest of these questions and cannot be used directly to make inferences about the strength of relationship.

Having decided upon the general class of procedure to be used, and having also decided which variables are to be interrelated and which controlled, it will then be necessary to select among the various available tests and measures.   In selecting among measures, one considers the level of measurement attained for each of the variables being interrelated and then examines the properties of the various measures available.   In choosing between alternative tests, one is confronted with a somewhat more complicated problem.   We first determine the level of measurement attained for each of the variables used.   This will ordinarily narrow down the range of alternative procedures and sometimes will almost automatically point to a particular technique.   For example, if there are two interval scales and one nominal, analysis of covariance would come to mind.   With one interval and one nominal we would think of analysis of variance.

After deciding upon the level of measurement, we then examine the assumptions required by each of the remaining alternative tests.   When choosing among these tests we consider the degree to which these assumptions may be violated, balancing against this criterion the power of the test.   If two tests are almost equally powerful, we would ordinarily choose the one involving weaker assumptions.   This may involve dropping back to a lower level of measurement, with a loss of certain information.   The choice of test or measure may also be influenced by other considerations such as the degree of sophistication expected of the reader. If a large number of different variables are to be related, it may be necessary to make use of the same procedure in each case for the sake of comparability or readability.

There are thus no hard and fast rules that can be used to provide "cookbook" answers to the important question of which procedure to use.   It will often be almost impossible to evaluate the degree to which certain assumptions are being violated, nor will exact power functions be known.   It would therefore be extremely misleading if you were left with the impression that the application of statistics to specific research problems involves a routine procedure of locating the "correct" test or measure.   It is for this reason that it is much more important to obtain a good grasp of the fundamentals of statistical inference, together with some understanding of the assumptions underlying each test, than to master a wide range of techniques in the hope that one of them will apply to any particular problem at hand.

An effort has been made to help you develop a strict statistical conscience in avoiding the use of techniques requiring dubious assumptions. On the other hand, you should try not to permit an overly strict conscience to restrict the use of certain powerful techniques such as analysis of covariance or regression analysis to situations in which you are almost certain the assumptions have been met. Especially in instances where comparable nonparametric techniques are not available and where the aims of the research are exploratory in nature, valuable insights may be gained through the use of these methods even though results must be interpreted with caution. Statistics is one among a number of tools used by the social scientist. Like all tools, if used skillfully and sensibly statistics can be of considerable value to the practitioner; if misused, it may lead to conclusions which are highly misleading.

Appendix 1

REVIEW OF ALGEBRAIC OPERATIONS

Since most students will have forgotten much of what they learned in elementary algebra, a brief review of some of the basic algebraic operations may be helpful. Some of these rules will be stated below in very concise form. If a more extensive review is needed, you should consult an algebra text.

One of the basic things to remember about arithmetic and algebraic manipulations is that the *order* in which the operation is carried out is of extreme importance. Generally speaking, whenever there is a fairly complicated expression one works from the inside out. The following rules should be more or less committed to memory.

1. *Expanding a Squared Sum or Difference*

$$(a + b)^2 = a^2 + 2ab + b^2 \neq a^2 + b^2$$
$$(a - b)^2 = a^2 - 2ab + b^2 \neq a^2 - b^2$$

The converse holds when dealing with square roots

$$\sqrt{a^2 + 2ab + b^2} = \sqrt{(a + b)^2} = a + b$$

It is definitely *not true* that

$$\sqrt{a^2 + b^2} = a + b$$

2. *Dividing by a Sum or Difference.* Although it is true that

$$\frac{a + b}{c} = \frac{a}{c} + \frac{b}{c}$$

we cannot so readily simplify the expressions

$$\frac{a}{b + c} \quad \text{or} \quad \frac{a}{b - c}$$

For example,
$$\frac{a}{b + c} \neq \frac{a}{b} + \frac{a}{c}$$

3. *Dividing by a Fraction.* If the denominator is itself a fraction, we can place the denominator of the denominator in the numerator as follows:

$$\frac{a}{b/c} = a\frac{c}{b} = \frac{ac}{b}$$

Likewise,
$$\frac{a/b}{c/d} = \frac{a}{b}\frac{d}{c} = \frac{ad}{bc}$$

and
$$\frac{a}{b/(c + d)} = a\frac{c + d}{b} = \frac{a(c + d)}{b}$$

4. *Multiplication of Powers.* If we have the product of a number raised to the power a and the *same number* raised to the power b, we may *add* exponents. Thus

$$X^a X^b = X^{a+b} \quad \text{and} \quad X^3 X^2 = X^5$$
But $\quad X^a + X^b \neq X^{a+b} \quad$ and $\quad X^3 + X^2 = X^2(X + 1) \neq X^5$

Similarly, we subtract exponents when dividing

$$\frac{X^a}{X^b} = X^{a-b} \quad \text{and} \quad \frac{X^3}{X^2} = X^1 = X$$
In particular, $\quad \dfrac{X^a}{X^a} = X^{a-a} = X^0 = 1$

Thus, any real number (other than 0) when raised to the 0 power is 1.

5. *Negative Exponents.* A number raised to a negative power may be written as the reciprocal of that number raised to the same positive power. Thus

$$X^{-a} = \frac{1}{X^a} \quad \text{and} \quad X^{-2} = \frac{1}{X^2}$$

6. *Removing or Adding Parentheses.* Here we follow the rule of working from the inside out. A negative sign before a parenthesis means that each term within the parentheses must have its sign changed if the parentheses are removed. Thus

$$-[a - (b - c)] = -[a - b + c] = -a + b - c$$
and
$$\begin{aligned} a - [b - (c - d)^2] &= a - [b - (c^2 - 2cd + d^2)] \\ &= a - [b - c^2 + 2cd - d^2] \\ &= a - b + c^2 - 2cd + d^2 \end{aligned}$$

Similarly, we must change all signs of quantities placed inside any parentheses we may introduce if the parentheses are preceded by a negative sign. Thus

$$a - b - c = a - (b + c)$$
$$\text{and} \quad a - b + c - d = (a - b) + (c - d) = -(b - a) - (d - c)$$

Use of Summation Signs. In statistics it is frequently necessary to make use of formulas involving sums of numerous quantities. As a shorthand substitute for writing out each of these sums at length, we make use of the Greek letter Σ (capital sigma) to indicate a summation. As a general rule, whenever this symbol appears it means that all quantities appearing to the right of it should be summed. Rather than using completely different letters for each quantity being summed (e.g., $a, b, c, d, e, f, \ldots$), we ordinarily make use of a single letter (usually X, Y, or Z), together with a subscript i, j, or k which can take on any numerical values we please. Usually, although not always, the first score will be symbolized by X_1, the second by X_2, and so forth. We then make use of Σ as follows:

$$\sum_{i=1}^{N} X_i = X_1 + X_2 + X_3 + \cdots + X_N$$

The notations above and below Σ are used to indicate that i takes on the successive values 1, 2, 3, up to N. Similarly, we might write

$$\sum_{i=3}^{8} X_i = X_3 + X_4 + X_5 + X_6 + X_7 + X_8$$

In this latter case, we have been instructed to add the scores of the third through the eighth observations.

If we follow the usual rules of algebra, we may derive certain rules which must apply to summations. Most of these rules will be stated with little or no explanation, since many obviously follow from the definition of Σ and very simple rules of algebra.

1. $$\sum_{i=1}^{N} X_i^2 = X_1^2 + X_2^2 + X_3^2 + \cdots + X_N^2$$

2. $$\sum_{i=1}^{N} X_i Y_i = X_1 Y_1 + X_2 Y_2 + X_3 Y_3 + \cdots + X_N Y_N$$

3. $$\sum_{i=1}^{N} (X_i + Y_i) = (X_1 + Y_1) + (X_2 + Y_2) + \cdots + (X_N + Y_N)$$
$$= (X_1 + X_2 + \cdots + X_N)$$
$$+ (Y_1 + Y_2 + \cdots + Y_N)$$
$$= \sum_{i=1}^{N} X_i + \sum_{i=1}^{N} Y_i$$

4. $\displaystyle\sum_{i=1}^{N} (X_i - Y_i) = \sum_{i=1}^{N} X_i - \sum_{i=1}^{N} Y_i$ (see 3)

5. $\displaystyle\sum_{i=1}^{N} (X_i + Y_i)^2 = \sum_{i=1}^{N} (X_i^2 + 2X_iY_i + Y_i^2)$

$$= \sum_{i=1}^{N} X_i^2 + \sum_{i=1}^{N} 2X_iY_i + \sum_{i=1}^{N} Y_i^2$$

$$\neq \sum_{i=1}^{N} X_i^2 + \sum_{i=1}^{N} Y_i^2$$

Note: The factor 2 can be taken out of the second term, giving $2 \displaystyle\sum_{i=1}^{N} X_iY_i$ (see 6)

6. If k is a constant

$$\sum_{i=1}^{N} kX_i = kX_1 + kX_2 + \cdots + kX_N$$

$$= k(X_1 + X_2 + \cdots + X_N) = k \sum_{i=1}^{N} X_i$$

7. $\displaystyle\left(\sum_{i=1}^{N} X_i \right)^2 = (X_1 + X_2 + \cdots + X_N)^2$

$$= X_1^2 + X_2^2 + \cdots + X_N^2 + 2X_1X_2$$
$$+ 2X_1X_3 + \cdots + 2X_{N-1}X_N$$
$$\neq X_1^2 + X_2^2 + \cdots + X_N^2$$

In other words, we must distinguish between

$$\sum_{i=1}^{N} X_i^2 \quad \text{and} \quad \left(\sum_{i=1}^{N} X_i \right)^2$$

We may also sometimes find it convenient to express a sum in terms of a double summation over two indices i and j. Each quantity to be summed can be written with a double subscript (ij). The quantity $\displaystyle\sum_{i=1}^{N} \sum_{j=1}^{M} X_{ij}$ means that we first sum the second subscript j from 1 to M, and then, working outwards, we sum i from 1 to N. Thus

$$\sum_{i=1}^{N} \sum_{j=1}^{M} X_{ij} = \sum_{i=1}^{N} (X_{i1} + X_{i2} + X_{i3} + \cdots + X_{iM})$$

$$= (X_{11} + X_{12} + \cdots + X_{1M}) + (X_{21} + X_{22} + \cdots + X_{2M})$$
$$+ \cdots + (X_{N1} + X_{N2} + \cdots + X_{NM})$$

Similarly,

$$\sum_{i=1}^{N} \left(\sum_{j=1}^{M} X_{ij} \right)^2 = \sum_{i=1}^{N} (X_{i1} + X_{i2} + \cdots + X_{iM})^2$$

Working with Very Large or Very Small Numbers. In working with very large or small numbers, especially when taking squares or square roots, it is often convenient to make use of powers of 10. Since $10^1 = 10$, $10^2 = 100$, $10^3 = 1,000$ and so forth, by counting the number of places to either the right or left of the decimal we can write any figure as a number between 0 and 10 times a certain power of 10. Thus

$$13 = 1.3(10) = 1.3 \times 10^1$$
$$138 = 1.38(100) = 1.38 \times 10^2$$
$$1,382 = 1.382(1,000) = 1.382 \times 10^3$$
$$1,382,461 = 1.382461 \times 10^6$$
$$.13 = \frac{1.3}{10} = 1.3 \times 10^{-1}$$
$$.013 = \frac{1.3}{100} = \frac{1.3}{10^2} = 1.3 \times 10^{-2}$$
$$.00013 = \frac{1.3}{10,000} = 1.3 \times 10^{-4}$$

If we wish to square the quantity 1,382, we get

$$1,382^2 = (1.382 \times 10^3)^2 = 1.382^2 \times 10^6$$
$$= 1.9099 \times 1,000,000 = 1,909,900$$

It is thus much easier to keep track of the decimal point.

In taking square roots it is simplest to make use of even powers of ten.

Since $\sqrt{100} = \sqrt{10^2} = 10$ and $\sqrt{10,000} = \sqrt{10^4} = 10^2 = 100$
and, in general, $\sqrt{10^{2k}} = 10^k$
whereas

$$\sqrt{1,000} = \sqrt{10^3} = 10\sqrt{10} \quad \text{and} \quad \sqrt{100,000} = \sqrt{10^5} = 100\sqrt{10}$$

we see that it is always possible to take even powers of 10 out from under the radical, although this is not possible with odd powers. When taking a square root, therefore, we can count the number of *pairs* of digits to the right or left of the decimal and can express the original quantity as a number between 1 and 100 times an even power of 10.

Thus $\sqrt{20,681,461,385} = \sqrt{2.068 \times 10^{10}} = 10^5 \sqrt{2.068}$

and $\sqrt{151,456,008,351.75} = \sqrt{15.146 \times 10^{10}} = 10^5 \sqrt{15.146}$

Also $\sqrt{.000003571} = \sqrt{3.571 \times 10^{-6}} = 10^{-3} \sqrt{3.571} = \dfrac{\sqrt{3.571}}{1,000}$

Appendix 2

TABLES

Table A. Table of Squares and Square Roots

Number	Square	Square root	Number	Square	Square root
1	1	1.0000	31	9 61	5.5678
2	4	1.4142	32	10 24	5.6569
3	9	1.7321	33	10 89	5.7446
4	16	2.0000	34	11 56	5.8310
5	25	2.2361	35	12 25	5.9161
6	36	2.4495	36	12 96	6.0000
7	49	2.6458	37	13 69	6.0828
8	64	2.8284	38	14 44	6.1644
9	81	3.0000	39	15 21	6.2450
10	1 00	3.1623	40	16 00	6.3246
11	1 21	3.3166	41	16 81	6.4031
12	1 44	3.4641	42	17 64	6.4807
13	1 69	3.6056	43	18 49	6.5574
14	1 96	3.7417	44	19 36	6.6332
15	2 25	3.8730	45	20 25	6.7082
16	2 56	4.0000	46	21 16	6.7823
17	2 89	4.1231	47	22 09	6.8557
18	3 24	4.2426	48	23 04	6.9282
19	3 61	4.3589	49	24 01	7.0000
20	4 00	4.4721	50	25 00	7.0711
21	4 41	4.5826	51	26 01	7.1414
22	4 84	4.6904	52	27 04	7.2111
23	5 29	4.7958	53	28 09	7.2801
24	5 76	4.8990	54	29 16	7.3485
25	6 25	5.0000	55	30 25	7.4162
26	6 76	5.0990	56	31 36	7.4833
27	7 29	5.1962	57	32 49	7.5498
28	7 84	5.2915	58	33 64	7.6158
29	8 41	5.3852	59	34 81	7.6811
30	9 00	5.4772	60	36 00	7.7460

SOURCE: H. Sorenson, *Statistics for Students of Psychology and Education*, McGraw-Hill Book Company, Inc., New York, 1936, table 72, pp. 347–359, with the kind permission of the author.

Table A, Table of Squares and Square Roots (*Continued*)

Number	Square	Square root	Number	Square	Square root
61	37 21	7.8102	101	1 02 01	10.0499
62	38 44	7.8740	102	1 04 04	10.0995
63	39 69	7.9373	103	1 06 09	10.1489
64	40 96	8.0000	104	1 08 16	10.1980
65	42 25	8.0623	105	1 10 25	10.2470
66	43 56	8.1240	106	1 12 36	10.2956
67	44 89	8.1854	107	1 14 49	10.3441
68	46 24	8.2462	108	1 16 64	10.3923
69	47 61	8.3066	109	1 18 81	10.4403
70	49 00	8.3666	110	1 21 00	10.4881
71	50 41	8.4261	111	1 23 21	10.5357
72	51 84	8.4853	112	1 25 44	10.5830
73	53 29	8.5440	113	1 27 69	10.6301
74	54 76	8.6023	114	1 29 96	10.6771
75	56 25	8.6603	115	1 32 25	10.7238
76	57 76	8.7178	116	1 34 56	10.7703
77	59 29	8.7750	117	1 36 89	10.8167
78	60 84	8.8318	118	1 39 24	10.8628
79	62 41	8.8882	119	1 41 61	10.9087
80	64 00	8.9443	120	1 44 00	10.9545
81	65 61	9.0000	121	1 46 41	11.0000
82	67 24	9.0554	122	1 48 84	11.0454
83	68 89	9.1104	123	1 51 29	11.0905
84	70 56	9.1652	124	1 53 76	11.1355
85	72 25	9.2195	125	1 56 25	11.1803
86	73 96	9.2736	126	1 58 76	11.2250
87	75 69	9.3274	127	1 61 29	11.2694
88	77 44	9.3808	128	1 63 84	11.3137
89	79 21	9.4340	129	1 66 41	11.3578
90	81 00	9.4868	130	1 69 00	11.4018
91	82 81	9.5394	131	1 71 61	11.4455
92	84 64	9.5917	132	1 74 24	11.4891
93	86 49	9.6437	133	1 76 89	11.5326
94	88 36	9.6954	134	1 79 56	11.5758
95	90 25	9.7468	135	1 82 25	11.6190
96	92 16	9.7980	136	1 84 96	11.6619
97	94 09	9.8489	137	1 87 69	11.7047
98	96 04	9.8995	138	1 90 44	11.7473
99	98 01	9.9499	139	1 93 21	11.7898
100	1 00 00	10.0000	140	1 96 00	11.8322

Table A. Table of Squares and Square Roots (*Continued*)

Number	Square	Square root	Number	Square	Square root
141	1 98 81	11.8743	181	3 27 61	13.4536
142	2 01 64	11.9164	182	3 31.24	13.4907
143	2 04 49	11.9583	183	3 34 89	13.5277
144	2 07 36	12.0000	184	3 38 56	13.5647
145	2 10 25	12.0416	185	3 42 25	13.6015
146	2 13 16	12.0830	186	3 45 96	13.6382
147	2 16 09	12.1244	187	3 49 69	13.6748
148	2 19 04	12.1655	188	3 53.44	13.7113
149	2 22 01	12.2066	189	3 57.21	13.7477
150	2 25 00	12.2474	190	3 61 00	13.7840
151	2 28 01	12.2882	191	3 64 81	13.8203
152	2 31 04	12.3288	192	3 68 64	13.8564
153	2 34 09	12.3693	193	3 72 49	13.8924
154	2 37 16	12.4097	194	3 76 36	13.9284
155	2 40 25	12.4499	195	3 80 25	13.9642
156	2 43 36	12.4900	196	3 84 16	14.0000
157	2 46 49	12.5300	197	3 88 09	14.0357
158	2 49 64	12.5698	198	3 92 04	14.0712
159	2 52 81	12.6095	199	3 96 01	14.1067
160	2 56 00	12.6491	200	4 00 00	14.1421
161	2 59 21	12.6886	201	4 04 01	14.1774
162	2 62 44	12.7279	202	4 08 04	14.2127
163	2 65 69	12.7671	203	4 12 09	14.2478
164	2 68 96	12.8062	204	4 16 16	14.2829
165	2 72 25	12.8452	205	4 20 25	14.3178
166	2 75 56	12.8841	206	4 24 36	14.3527
167	2 78 89	12.9228	207	4 28 49	14.3875
168	2 82 24	12.9615	208	4 32 64	14.4222
169	2 85 61	13.0000	209	4 36 81	14.4568
170	2 89 00	13.0384	210	4 41 00	14.4914
171	2 92 41	13.0767	211	4 45 21	14.5258
172	2 95 84	13.1149	212	4 49 44	14.5602
173	2 99 29	13.1529	213	4 53 69	14.5945
174	3 02 76	13.1909	214	4 57 96	14.6287
175	3 06 25	13.2288	215	4 62 25	14.6629
176	3 09 76	13.2665	216	4 66 56	14.6969
177	3 13 29	13.3041	217	4 70 89	14.7309
178	3 16 84	13.3417	218	4 75 24	14.7648
179	3 20 41	13.3791	219	4 79 61	14.7986
180	3 24 00	13.4164	220	4 84 00	14.8324

Table A. Table of Squares and Square Roots (*Continued*)

Number	Square	Square root	Number	Square	Square root
221	4 88 41	14.8661	261	6 81 21	16.1555
222	4 92 84	14.8997	262	6 86 44	16.1864
223	4 97 29	14.9332	263	6 91 69	16.2173
224	5 01 76	14.9666	264	6 96 96	16.2481
225	5 06 25	15.0000	265	7 02 25	16.2788
226	5 10 76	15.0333	266	7 07 56	16.3095
227	5 15 29	15.0665	267	7 12 89	16.3401
228	5 19 84	15.0997	268	7 18 24	16.3707
229	5 24 41	15.1327	269	7 23 61	16.4012
230	5 29 00	15.1658	270	7 29 00	16.4317
231	5 33 61	15.1987	271	7 34 41	16.4621
232	5 38 24	15.2315	272	7 39 84	16.4924
233	5 42 89	15.2643	273	7 45 29	16.5227
234	5 47 56	15.2971	274	7 50 76	16.5529
235	5 52 25	15.3297	275	7 56 25	16.5831
236	5 56 96	15.3623	276	7 61 76	16.6132
237	5 61 69	15.3948	277	7 67 29	16.6433
238	5 66 44	15.4272	278	7 72 84	16.6733
239	5 71 21	15.4596	279	7 78 41	16.7033
240	5 76 00	15.4919	280	7 84 00	16.7332
241	5 80 81	15.5242	281	7 89 61	16.7631
242	5 85 64	15.5563	282	7 95 24	16.7929
243	5 90 49	15.5885	283	8 00 89	16.8226
244	5 95 36	15.6205	284	8 06 56	16.8523
245	6 00 25	15.6525	285	8 12 25	16.8819
246	6 05 16	15.6844	286	8 17 96	16.9115
247	6 10 09	15.7162	287	8 23 69	16.9411
248	6 15 04	15.7480	288	8 29 44	16.9706
259	6 20 01	15.7797	289	8 35 21	17.0000
250	6 25 00	15.8114	290	8 41 00	17.0294
251	6 30 01	15.8430	291	8 46 81	17.0587
252	6 35 04	15.8745	292	8 52 64	17.0880
253	6 40 09	15.9060	293	8 58 49	17.1172
254	6 45 16	15.9374	294	8 64 36	17.1464
255	6 50 25	15.9687	295	8 70 25	17.1756
256	6 55 36	16.0000	296	8 76 16	17.2047
257	6 60 49	16.0312	297	8 82 09	17.2337
258	6 65 64	16.0624	298	8 88 04	17.2627
259	6 70 81	16.0935	299	8 94 01	17.2916
260	6 76 00	16.1245	300	9 00 00	17.3205

Table A. Table of Squares and Square Roots (*Continued*)

Number	Square	Square root	Number	Square	Square root
301	9 06 01	17.3494	341	11 62 81	18.4662
302	9 12 04	17.3781	342	11 69 64	18.4932
303	9 18 09	17.4069	343	11 76 49	18.5203
304	9 24 16	17.4356	344	11 83 36	18.5472
305	9 30 25	17.4642	345	11 90 25	18.5742
306	9 36 36	17.4929	346	11 97 16	18.6011
307	9 42 49	17.5214	347	12 04 09	18.6279
308	9 48 64	17.5499	348	12 11 04	18.6548
309	9 54 81	17.5784	349	12 18 01	18.6815
310	9 61 00	17.6068	350	12 25 00	18.7083
311	9 67 21	17.6352	351	12 32 01	18.7350
312	9 73 44	17.6635	352	12 39 04	18.7617
313	9 79 69	17.6918	353	12 46 09	18.7883
314	9 85 96	17.7200	354	12 53 16	18.8149
315	9 92 25	17.7482	355	12 60 25	18.8414
316	9 98 56	17.7764	356	12 67 36	18.8680
317	10 04 89	17.8045	357	12 74 49	18.8944
318	10 11 24	17.8326	358	12 81 64	18.9209
319	10 17 61	17.8606	359	12 88 81	18.9473
320	10 24 00	17.8885	360	12 96 00	18.9737
321	10 30 41	17.9165	361	13 03 21	19.0000
322	10 36 84	17.9444	362	13 10 44	19.0263
323	10 43 29	17.9722	363	13 17 69	19.0526
324	10 49 76	18.0000	364	13 24 96	19.0788
325	10 56 25	18.0278	365	13 32 25	19.1050
326	10 62 76	18.0555	366	13 39 56	19.1311
327	10 69 29	18.0831	367	13 46 89	19.1572
328	10 75 84	18.1108	368	13 54 24	19.1833
329	10 82 41	18.1384	369	13 61 61	19.2094
330	10 89 00	18.1659	370	13 69 00	19.2354
331	10 95 61	18.1934	371	13 76 41	19.2614
332	11 02 24	18.2209	372	13 83 84	19.2873
333	11 08 89	18.2483	373	13 91 29	19.3132
334	11 15 56	18.2757	374	13 98 76	19.3391
335	11 22 25	18.3030	375	14 06 25	19.3649
336	11 28 96	18.3303	376	14 13 76	19.3907
337	11 35 69	18.3576	377	14 21 29	19.4165
338	11 42 44	18.3848	378	14 28 84	19.4422
339	11 49 21	18.4120	379	14 36 41	19.4679
340	11 56 00	18.4391	380	14 44 00	19.4936

Table A. Table of Squares and Square Roots (*Continued*)

Number	Square	Square root	Number	Square	Square root
541	29 26 81	23.2594	581	33 75 61	24.1039
542	29 37 64	23.2809	582	33 87 24	24.1247
543	29 48 49	23.3024	583	33 98 89	24.1454
544	29 59 36	23.3238	584	34 10 56	24.1661
545	29 70 25	23.3452	585	34 22 25	24.1868
546	29 81 16	23.3666	586	34 33 96	24.2074
547	29 92 09	23.3880	587	34 45 69	24.2281
548	30 03 04	23.4094	588	34 57 44	24.2487
549	30 14 01	23.4307	589	34 69 21	24.2693
550	30 25 00	23.4521	590	34 81 00	24.2899
551	30 36 01	23.4734	591	34 92 81	24.3105
552	30 47 04	23.4947	592	35 04 64	24.3311
553	30 58 09	23.5160	593	35 16 49	24.3516
554	30 69 16	23.5372	594	35 28 36	24.3721
555	30 80 25	23.5584	595	35 40 25	24.3926
556	30 91 36	23.5797	596	35 52 16	24.4131
557	31 02 49	23.6008	597	35 64 09	24.4336
558	31 13 64	23.6220	598	35 76 04	24.4540
559	31 24 81	23.6432	599	35 88 01	24.4745
560	31 36 00	23.6643	600	36 00 00	24.4949
561	31 47 21	23.6854	601	36 12 01	24.5153
562	31 58 44	23.7065	602	36 24 04	24.5357
563	31 69 69	23.7276	603	36 36 09	24.5561
564	31 80 96	23.7487	604	36 48 16	24.5764
565	31 92 25	23.7697	605	36 60 25	24.5967
566	32 03 56	23.7908	606	36 72 36	24.6171
567	32 14 89	23.8118	607	36 84 49	24.6374
568	32 26 24	23.8328	608	36 96 64	24.6577
569	32 37 61	23.8537	609	37 08 81	24.6779
570	32 49 00	23.8747	610	37 21 00	24.6982
571	32 60 41	23.8956	611	37 33 21	24.7184
572	32 71 84	23.9165	612	37 45 44	24.7385
573	32 83 29	23.9374	613	37 57 69	24.7588
574	32 94 76	23.9583	614	37 69 96	24.7790
575	33 06 25	23.9792	615	37 82 25	24.7992
576	33 17 76	24.0000	616	37 94 56	24.8193
577	33 29 29	24.0208	617	38 06 89	24.8395
578	33 40 84	24.0416	618	38 19 24	24.8596
579	33 52 41	24.0624	619	38 31 61	24.8797
580	33 64 00	24.0832	620	38 44 00	24.8998

Table A. Table of Squares and Square Roots (*Continued*)

Number	Square	Square root	Number	Square	Square root
621	38 56 41	24.9199	661	43 69 21	25.7099
622	38 68 84	24.9399	662	43 82 44	25.7294
623	38 81 29	24.9600	663	43 95 69	25.7488
624	38 93 76	24.9800	664	44 08 96	25.7682
625	39 06 25	25.0000	665	44 22 25	25.7876
626	39 18 76	25.0200	666	44 35 56	25.8070
627	39 31 29	25.0400	667	44 48 89	25.8263
628	39 43 84	25.0599	668	44 62 24	25.8457
629	39 56 41	25.0799	669	44 75 61	25.8650
630	39 69 00	25.0998	670	44 89 00	25.8844
631	39 81 61	25.1197	671	45 02 41	25.9037
632	39 94 24	25.1396	672	45 15 84	25.9230
633	40 06 89	25.1595	673	45 29 29	25.9422
634	40 19 56	25.1794	674	45 42 76	25.9615
635	40 32 25	25.1992	675	45 56 25	25.9808
636	40 44 96	25.2190	676	45 69 76	26.0000
637	40 57 69	25.2389	677	45 83 29	26.0192
638	40 70 44	25.2587	678	45 96 84	26.0384
639	40 83 21	25.2784	679	46 10 41	26.0576
640	40 96 00	25.2982	680	46 24 00	26.0768
641	41 08 81	25.3180	681	46 37 61	26.0960
642	41 21 64	25.3377	682	46 51 24	26.1151
643	41 34 49	25.3574	683	46 64 89	26.1343
644	41 47 36	25.3772	684	46 78 56	26.1534
645	41 60 25	25.3969	685	46 92 25	26.1725
646	41 73 16	25.4165	686	47 05 96	26.1916
647	41 86 09	25.4362	687	47 19 69	26.2107
648	41 99 04	25.4558	688	47 33 44	26.2298
649	42 12 01	25.4755	689	47 47 21	26.2488
650	42 25 00	25.4951	690	47 61 00	26.2679
651	42 38 01	25.5147	691	47 74 81	26.2869
652	42 51 04	25.5343	692	47 88 64	26.3059
653	42 64 09	25.5539	693	48 02 49	26.3249
654	42 77 16	25.5734	694	48 16 36	26.3439
655	42 90 25	25.5930	695	48 30 25	26.3629
656	43 03 36	25.6125	696	48 44 16	26.3818
657	43 16 49	25.6320	697	48 58 09	26.4008
658	43 29 64	25.6515	698	48 72 04	26.4197
659	43 42 81	25.6710	699	48 86 01	26.4386
660	43 56 00	25.6905	700	49 00 00	26.4575

Table A. Table of Squares and Square Roots (*Continued*)

Number	Square	Square root	Number	Square	Square root
701	49 14 01	26.4764	741	54 90 81	27.2213
702	49 28 04	26.4953	742	55 05 64	27.2397
703	49 42 09	26.5141	743	55 20 49	27.2580
704	49 56 16	26.5330	744	55 35 36	27.2764
705	49 70 25	26.5518	745	55 50 25	27.2947
706	49 84 36	26.5707	746	55 65 16	27.3130
707	49 98 49	26.5895	747	55 80 09	27.3313
708	50 12 64	26.6083	748	55 95 04	27.3496
709	50 26 81	26.6271	749	56 10 01	27.3679
710	50 41 00	26.6458	750	56 25 00	27.3861
711	50 55 21	26.6646	751	56 40 01	27.4044
712	50 69 44	26.6833	752	56 55 04	27.4226
713	50 83 69	26.7021	753	56 70 09	27.4408
714	50 97 96	26.7208	754	56 85 16	27.4591
715	51 12 25	26.7395	755	57 00 25	27.4773
716	51 26 56	26.7582	756	57 15 36	27.4955
717	51 40 89	26.7769	757	57 30 49	27.5136
718	51 55 24	26.7955	758	57 45 64	27.5318
719	51 69 61	26.8142	759	57 60 81	27.5500
720	51 84 00	26.8328	760	57 76 00	27.5681
721	51 98 41	26.8514	761	57 91 21	27.5862
722	52 12 84	26.8701	762	58 06 44	27.6043
723	52 27 29	26.8887	763	58 21 69	27.6225
724	52 41 76	26.9072	764	58 36 96	27.6405
725	52 56 25	26.9258	765	58 52 25	27.6586
726	52 70 76	26.9444	766	58 67 56	27.6767
727	52 85 29	26.9629	767	58 82 89	27.6948
728	52 99 84	26.9815	768	58 98 24	27.7128
729	53 14 41	27.0000	769	59 13 61	27.7308
730	53 29 00	27.0185	770	59 29 00	27.7489
731	53 43 61	27.0370	771	59 44 41	27.7669
732	53 58 24	27.0555	772	59 59 84	27.7849
733	53 72 89	27.0740	773	59 75 29	27.8029
734	53 87 56	27.0924	774	59 90 76	27.8209
735	54 02 25	27.1109	775	60 06 25	27.8388
736	54 16 96	27.1293	776	60 21 76	27.8568
737	54 31 69	27.1477	777	60 37 29	27.8747
738	54 46 44	27.1662	778	60 52 84	27.8927
739	54 61 27	27.1846	779	60 68 41	27.9106
740	54 76 00	27.2029	780	60 84 00	27.9285

Table A. Table of Squares and Square Roots (*Continued*)

Number	Square	Square root	Number	Square	Square root
781	60 99 61	27.9464	821	67 40 41	28.6531
782	61 15 24	27.9643	822	67 56 84	28.6705
783	61 30 89	27.9821	823	67 73 29	28.6880
784	61 46 56	28.0000	824	67 89 76	28.7054
785	61 62 25	28.0179	825	68 06 25	28.7228
786	61 77 96	28.0357	826	68 22 76	28.7402
787	61 93 69	28.0535	827	68 39 29	28.7576
788	62 09 44	28.0713	828	68 55 84	28.7750
789	62 25 21	28.0891	829	68 72 41	28.7924
790	62 41 00	28.1069	830	68 89 00	28.8097
791	62 56 81	28.1247	831	69 05 61	28.8271
792	62 72 64	28.1425	832	69 22 24	28.8444
793	62 88 49	28.1603	833	69 38 89	28.8617
794	63 04 36	28.1780	834	69 55 56	28.8791
795	63 20 25	28.1957	835	69 72 25	28.8964
796	63 36 16	28.2135	836	69 88 96	28.9137
797	63 52 09	28.2312	837	70 05 69	28.9310
798	63 68 04	28.2489	838	70 22 44	28.9482
799	63 84 01	28.2666	839	70 39 21	28.9655
800	64 00 00	28.2843	840	70 56 00	28.9828
801	64 16 01	28.3019	841	70 72 81	29.0000
802	64 32 04	28.3196	842	70 89 64	29.0172
803	64 48 09	28.3373	843	71 06 49	29.0345
804	64 64 16	28.3549	844	71 23 36	29.0517
805	64 80 25	28.3725	845	71 40 25	29.0689
806	64 96 36	28.3901	846	71 57 16	29.0861
807	65 12 49	28.4077	847	71 74 09	29.1033
808	65 28 64	28.4253	848	71 91 04	29.1204
809	65 44 81	28.4429	849	72 08 01	29.1376
810	65 61 00	28.4605	850	72 25 00	29.1548
811	65 77 21	28.4781	851	72 42 01	29.1719
812	65 93 44	28.4956	852	72 59 04	29.1890
813	66 09 69	28.5132	853	72 76 09	29.2062
814	66 25 96	28.5307	854	72 93 16	29.2233
815	66 42 25	28.5482	855	73 10 25	29.2404
816	66 58 56	28.5657	856	73 27 36	29.2575
817	66 74 89	28.5832	857	73 44 49	29.2746
818	66 91 24	28.6007	858	73 61 64	29.2916
819	67 07 61	28.6082	859	73 78 81	29.3087
820	67 24 00	28.6356	860	73 96 00	29.3258

Table A. Table of Squares and Square Roots (*Continued*)

Number	Square	Square root	Number	Square	Square root
861	74 13 21	29.3428	901	81 18 01	30.0167
862	74 30 44	29.3598	902	81 36 04	30.0333
863	74 47 69	29.3769	903	81 54 09	30.0500
864	74 64 96	29.3939	904	81 72 16	30.0666
865	74 82 25	29.4109	905	81 90 25	30.0832
866	74 99 56	29.4279	906	82 08 36	30.0998
867	75 16 89	29.4449	907	82 26 49	30.1164
868	75 34 24	29.4618	908	82 44 64	30.1330
869	75 51 61	29.4788	909	82 62 81	30.1496
870	75 69 00	29.4958	910	82 81 00	30.1662
871	75 86 41	29.5127	911	82 99 21	30.1828
872	76 03 84	29.5296	912	83 17 44	30.1993
873	76 21 29	29.5466	913	83 35 69	30.2159
874	76 38 76	29.5635	914	83 53 96	30.2324
875	76 56 25	29.5804	915	83 72 25	30.2490
876	76 73 76	29.5973	916	83 90 56	30.2655
877	76 91 29	29.6142	917	84 08 89	30.2820
878	77 08 84	29.6311	918	84 27 24	30.2985
879	77 26 41	29.6479	919	84 45 61	30.3150
880	77 44 00	29.6648	920	84 64 00	30.3315
881	77 61 61	29.6816	921	84 82 41	30.3480
882	77 79 24	29.6985	922	85 00 84	30.3645
883	77 96 89	29.7153	923	85 19 29	30.3809
884	78 14 56	29.7321	924	85 37 76	30.3974
885	78 32 25	29.7489	925	85 56 25	30.4138
886	78 49 96	29.7658	926	85 74 76	30.4302
887	78 67 69	29.7825	927	85 93 29	30.4467
888	78 85 44	29.7993	928	86 11 84	30.4631
889	79 03 21	29.8161	929	86 30 41	30.4795
890	79 21 00	29.8329	930	86 49 00	30.4959
891	79 38 81	29.8496	931	86 67 61	30.5123
892	79 56 64	29.8664	932	86 86 24	30.5287
893	79 74 49	29.8831	933	87 04 89	30.5450
894	79 92 36	29.8998	934	87 23 56	30.5614
895	80 10 25	29.9166	935	87 42 25	30.5778
896	80 28 16	29.9333	936	87 60 96	30.5941
897	80 46 09	29.9500	937	87 79 69	30.6105
898	80 64 04	29.9666	938	87 98 44	30.6268
899	80 82 01	29.9833	939	88 17 21	30.6431
900	81 00 00	30.0000	940	88 36 00	30.6594

Table A. Table of Squares and Square Roots (*Continued*)

Number	Square	Square root	Number	Square	Square root
941	88 54 81	30.6757	971	94 28 41	31.1609
942	88 73 64	30.6920	972	94 47 84	31.1769
943	88 92 49	30.7083	973	94 67 29	31.1929
944	89 11 36	30.7246	974	94 86 76	31.2090
945	89 30 25	30.7409	975	95 06 25	31.2250
946	89 49 16	30.7571	976	95 25 76	31.2410
947	89 68 09	30.7734	977	95 45 29	31.2570
948	89 87 04	30.7896	978	95 64 84	31.2730
949	90 06 01	30.8058	979	95 84 41	31.2890
950	90 25 00	30.8221	980	96 04 00	31.3050
951	90 44 01	30.8383	981	96 23 61	31.3209
952	90 63 04	30.8545	982	96 43 24	31.3369
953	90 82 09	30.8707	983	96 62 89	31.3528
954	91 01 16	30.8869	984	96 82 56	31.3688
955	91 20 25	30.9031	985	97 02 25	31.3847
956	91 39 36	30.9192	986	97 21 96	31.4006
957	91 58 49	30.9354	987	97 41 69	31.4166
958	91 77 64	30.9516	988	97 61 44	31.4325
959	91 96 81	30.9677	989	97 81 21	31.4484
960	92 16 00	30.9839	990	98 01 00	31.4643
961	92 35 21	31.0000	991	98 20 81	31.4802
962	92 54 44	31.0161	992	98 40 64	31.4960
963	92 73 69	31.0322	993	98 60 49	31.5119
964	92 92 96	31.0483	994	98 80 36	31.5278
965	93 12 25	31.0644	995	99 00 25	31.5436
966	93 31 56	31.0805	996	99 20 16	31.5595
967	93 50 89	31.0966	997	99 40 09	31.5753
968	93 70 24	31.1127	998	99 60 04	31.5911
969	93 89 61	31.1288	999	99 80 01	31.6070
970	94 09 00	31.1448	1000	100 00 00	31.6228

Table B. Random Numbers

```
10 00 73 25 33    76 52 01 35 86    34 67 35 48 76    80 95 90 91 17    39 29 27 49 45
37 54 20 48 05    64 89 47 42 96    24 80 52 40 37    20 63 61 04 02    00 82 29 16 65
08 42 26 89 53    19 64 50 93 03    23 20 90 25 60    15 95 33 47 64    35 08 03 36 06
99 01 90 25 29    09 37 67 07 15    38 31 13 11 65    88 67 67 43 97    04 43 62 76 59
12 80 79 99 70    80 15 73 61 47    64 03 23 66 53    98 95 11 68 77    12 17 17 68 33

66 06 57 47 17    34 07 27 68 50    36 69 73 61 70    65 81 33 98 85    11 19 92 91 70
31 06 01 08 05    45 57 18 24 06    35 30 34 26 14    86 79 90 74 39    23 40 30 97 32
85 26 97 76 02    02 05 16 56 92    68 66 57 48 18    73 05 38 52 47    18 62 38 85 79
63 57 33 21 35    05 32 54 70 48    90 55 35 75 48    28 46 82 87 09    83 49 12 56 24
73 79 64 57 53    03 52 96 47 78    35 80 83 42 82    60 93 52 03 44    35 27 38 84 35

98 52 01 77 67    14 90 56 86 07    22 10 94 05 58    60 97 09 34 33    50 50 07 39 98
11 80 50 54 31    39 80 82 77 32    50 72 56 82 48    29 40 52 42 01    52 77 56 78 51
83 45 29 96 34    06 28 89 80 83    13 74 67 00 78    18 47 54 06 10    68 71 17 78 17
88 68 54 02 00    86 50 75 84 01    36 76 66 79 51    90 36 47 64 93    29 60 91 10 62
99 59 46 73 48    87 51 76 49 69    91 82 60 89 28    93 78 56 13 68    23 47 83 41 13

65 48 11 76 74    17 46 85 00 50    58 04 77 69 74    73 03 95 71 86    40 21 81 65 44
80 12 43 56 35    17 72 70 80 15    45 31 82 23 74    21 11 57 82 53    14 38 55 37 63
74 35 09 98 17    77 40 27 72 14    43 23 60 02 10    45 52 16 42 37    96 28 60 26 55
69 91 62 68 03    66 25 22 91 48    36 93 68 72 03    76 62 11 39 90    94 40 05 64 18
09 89 32 05 05    14 22 56 85 14    46 42 75 67 88    96 29 77 88 22    54 38 21 45 98

91 49 91 45 23    68 47 92 76 86    46 16 28 35 54    94 75 08 99 23    37 08 92 00 48
80 33 69 45 98    26 94 03 68 58    70 29 73 41 35    53 14 03 33 40    42 05 08 23 41
44 10 48 19 49    85 15 74 79 54    32 97 92 65 75    57 60 04 08 81    22 22 20 64 13
12 55 07 37 42    11 10 00 20 40    12 86 07 46 97    96 64 48 94 39    28 70 72 58 15
63 60 64 93 29    16 50 53 44 84    40 21 95 25 63    43 65 17 70 82    07 20 73 17 90

61 19 69 04 46    26 45 74 77 74    51 92 43 37 29    65 39 45 95 93    42 58 26 05 27
15 47 44 52 66    95 27 07 99 53    59 36 78 38 48    82 39 61 01 18    33 21 15 94 66
94 55 72 85 73    67 89 75 43 87    54 62 24 44 31    91 19 04 25 92    92 92 74 59 73
42 48 11 62 13    97 34 40 87 21    16 86 84 87 67    03 07 11 20 59    25 70 14 66 70
23 52 37 83 17    73 20 88 98 37    68 93 59 14 16    26 25 22 96 63    05 52 28 25 62

04 49 35 24 94    75 24 63 38 24    45 86 25 10 25    61 96 27 93 35    65 33 71 24 72
00 54 99 76 54    64 05 18 81 59    96 11 96 38 96    54 69 28 23 91    23 28 72 95 29
35 96 31 53 07    26 89 80 93 54    33 35 13 54 62    77 97 45 00 24    90 10 33 93 33
59 80 80 83 91    45 42 72 68 42    83 60 94 97 00    13 02 12 48 92    78 56 52 01 06
46 05 88 52 36    01 39 09 22 86    77 28 14 40 77    93 91 08 36 47    70 61 74 29 41

32 17 90 05 97    87 37 92 52 41    05 56 70 70 07    86 74 31 71 57    85 39 41 18 38
69 23 46 14 06    20 11 74 52 04    15 95 66 00 00    18 74 39 24 23    97 11 89 63 38
19 56 54 14 30    01 75 87 53 79    40 41 92 15 85    66 67 43 68 06    84 96 28 52 07
45 15 51 49 38    19 47 60 72 46    43 66 79 45 43    59 04 79 00 33    20 82 66 95 41
94 86 43 19 94    36 16 81 08 51    34 88 88 15 53    01 54 03 54 56    05 01 45 11 76
```

SOURCE: The RAND Corporation, *A Million Random Digits*, Free Press, Glencoe, Ill., 1955, pp. 1–3, with the kind permission of the publisher.

Table B. Random Numbers (*Continued*)

```
98 08 62 48 26    45 24 02 84 04    44 99 90 88 96    39 09 47 34 07    35 44 13 18 80
33 18 51 62 32    41 94 15 09 49    89 43 54 85 81    88 69 54 19 94    37 54 87 30 43
80 95 10 04 06    96 38 27 07 74    20 15 12 33 87    25 01 62 52 98    94 62 46 11 71
79 75 24 91 40    71 96 12 82 96    69 86 10 25 91    74 85 22 05 39    00 38 75 95 79
18 63 33 25 37    98 14 50 65 71    31 01 02 46 74    05 45 56 14 27    77 93 89 19 36

74 02 94 39 02    77 55 73 22 70    97 79 01 71 19    52 52 75 80 21    80 81 45 17 48
54 17 84 56 11    80 99 33 71 43    05 33 51 29 69    56 12 71 92 55    36 04 09 03 24
11 66 44 98 83    52 07 98 48 27    59 38 17 15 39    09 97 33 34 40    88 46 12 33 56
48 32 47 79 28    31 24 96 47 10    02 29 53 68 70    32 30 75 75 46    15 02 00 99 94
69 07 49 41 38    87 63 79 19 76    35 58 40 44 01    10 51 82 16 15    01 84 87 69 38

09 18 82 00 97    32 82 53 95 27    04 22 08 63 04    83 38 98 73 74    64 27 85 80 44
90 04 58 54 97    51 98 15 06 54    94 93 88 19 97    91 87 07 61 50    68 47 66 46 59
73 18 95 02 07    47 67 72 52 69    62 29 06 44 64    27 12 46 70 18    41 36 18 27 60
75 76 87 64 90    20 97 18 17 49    90 42 91 22 72    95 37 50 58 71    93 82 34 31 78
54 01 64 40 56    66 28 13 10 03    00 68 22 73 98    20 71 45 32 95    07 70 61 78 13

08 35 86 99 10    78 54 24 27 85    13 66 15 88 73    04 61 89 75 53    31 22 30 84 20
28 30 60 32 64    81 33 31 05 91    40 51 00 78 93    32 60 46 04 75    94 11 90 18 40
53 84 08 62 33    81 59 41 36 28    51 21 59 02 90    28 46 66 87 95    77 76 22 07 91
91 75 75 37 41    61 61 36 22 69    50 26 39 02 12    55 78 17 65 14    83 48 34 70 55
89 41 59 26 94    00 39 75 83 91    12 60 71 76 46    48 94 97 23 06    94 54 13 74 08

77 51 30 38 20    86 83 42 99 01    68 41 48 27 74    51 90 81 39 80    72 89 35 55 07
19 50 23 71 74    69 97 92 02 88    55 21 02 97 73    74 28 77 52 51    65 34 46 74 15
21 81 85 93 13    93 27 88 17 57    05 68 67 31 56    07 08 28 50 46    31 85 33 84 52
51 47 46 64 99    68 10 72 36 21    94 04 99 13 45    42 83 60 91 91    08 00 74 54 49
99 55 96 83 31    62 53 52 41 70    69 77 71 28 30    74 81 97 81 42    43 86 07 28 34

33 71 34 80 07    93 58 47 28 69    51 92 66 47 21    58 30 32 98 22    93 17 49 39 72
85 27 48 68 93    11 30 32 92 70    28 83 43 41 37    73 51 59 04 00    71 14 84 36 43
84 13 38 96 40    44 03 55 21 66    73 85 27 00 91    61 22 26 05 61    62 32 71 84 23
56 73 21 62 34    17 39 59 61 31    10 12 39 16 22    85 49 65 75 60    81 60 41 88 80
65 13 85 68 06    87 64 88 52 61    34 31 36 58 61    45 87 52 10 69    85 64 44 72 77

38 00 10 21 76    81 71 91 17 11    71 60 29 29 37    74 21 96 40 49    65 58 44 96 98
37 40 29 63 97    01 30 47 75 86    56 27 11 00 86    47 32 46 26 05    40 03 03 74 38
97 12 54 03 48    87 08 33 14 17    21 81 53 92 50    75 23 76 20 47    15 50 12 95 78
21 82 64 11 34    47 14 33 40 72    64 63 88 59 02    49 13 90 64 41    03 85 65 45 52
73 13 54 27 42    95 71 90 90 35    85 79 47 42 96    08 78 98 81 56    64 69 11 92 02

07 63 87 79 29    03 06 11 80 72    96 20 74 41 56    23 82 19 95 38    04 71 36 69 94
60 52 88 34 41    07 95 41 98 14    59 17 52 06 95    05 53 35 21 39    61 21 20 64 55
83 59 63 56 55    06 95 89 29 83    05 12 80 97 19    77 43 35 37 83    92 30 15 04 98
10 85 06 27 46    99 59 91 05 07    13 49 90 63 19    53 07 57 18 39    06 41 01 93 62
39 82 09 89 52    43 62 26 31 47    64 42 18 08 14    43 80 00 93 51    31 02 47 31 67
```

Table B. Random Numbers (*Continued*)

59 58 00 64 78	75 56 97 88 00	88 83 55 44 86	23 76 80 61 56	04 11 10 84 08
38 50 80 73 41	23 79 34 87 63	90 82 29 70 22	17 71 90 42 07	95 95 44 99 53
30 69 27 06 68	94 68 81 61 27	56 19 68 00 91	82 06 76 34 00	05 46 26 92 00
65 44 39 56 59	18 28 82 74 37	49 63 22 40 41	08 33 76 56 76	96 29 99 08 36
27 26 75 02 64	13 19 27 22 94	07 47 74 46 06	17 98 54 89 11	97 34 13 03 58
91 30 70 69 91	19 07 22 42 10	36 69 95 37 28	28 82 53 57 93	28 97 66 62 52
68 43 49 46 88	84 47 31 36 22	62 12 69 84 08	12 84 38 25 90	09 81 59 31 46
48 90 81 58 77	54 74 52 45 91	35 70 00 47 54	83 82 45 26 92	54 13 05 51 60
06 91 34 51 97	42 67 27 86 01	11 88 30 95 28	63 01 19 89 01	14 97 44 03 44
10 45 51 60 19	14 21 03 37 12	91 34 23 78 21	88 32 58 08 51	43 66 77 08 83
12 88 39 73 43	65 02 76 11 84	04 28 50 13 92	17 97 41 50 77	90 71 22 67 69
21 77 83 09 76	38 80 73 69 61	31 64 94 20 96	63 28 10 20 23	08 81 64 74 49
19 52 35 95 15	65 12 25 96 59	86 28 36 82 58	69 57 21 37 98	16 43 59 15 29
67 24 55 26 70	35 58 31 65 63	79 24 68 66 86	76 46 33 42 22	26 65 59 08 02
60 58 44 73 77	07 50 03 79 92	45 13 42 65 29	26 76 08 36 37	41 32 64 43 44
53 85 34 13 77	36 06 69 48 50	58 83 87 38 59	49 36 47 33 31	96 24 04 36 42
24 63 73 87 36	74 38 48 93 42	52 62 30 79 92	12 36 91 86 01	03 74 28 38 73
83 08 01 24 51	38 99 22 28 15	07 75 95 17 77	97 37 72 75 85	51 97 23 78 67
16 44 42 43 34	36 15 19 90 73	27 49 37 09 39	85 13 03 25 52	54 84 65 47 59
60 79 01 81 57	57 17 86 57 62	11 16 17 85 76	45 81 95 29 79	65 13 00 48 60
03 99 11 04 61	93 71 61 68 94	66 08 32 46 53	84 60 95 82 32	88 61 81 91 61
38 55 59 55 54	32 88 65 97 80	08 35 56 08 60	29 73 54 77 62	71 29 92 38 53
17 54 67 37 04	92 05 24 62 15	55 12 12 92 81	59 07 60 79 36	27 95 45 89 09
32 64 35 28 61	95 81 90 68 31	00 91 19 89 36	76 35 59 37 79	80 86 30 05 14
69 57 26 87 77	39 51 03 59 05	14 06 04 06 19	29 54 96 96 16	33 56 46 07 80
24 12 26 65 91	27 69 90 64 94	14 84 54 66 72	61 95 87 71 00	90 89 97 57 54
61 19 63 02 31	92 96 26 17 73	41 83 95 53 82	17 26 77 09 43	78 03 87 02 67
30 53 22 17 04	10 27 41 22 02	39 68 52 33 09	10 06 16 88 29	55 98 66 64 85
03 78 89 75 99	75 86 72 07 17	74 41 65 31 66	35 20 83 33 74	87 53 90 88 23
48 22 86 33 79	85 78 34 76 19	53 15 26 74 33	35 66 35 29 72	16 81 86 03 11
60 36 59 46 53	35 07 53 39 49	42 61 42 92 97	01 91 82 83 16	98 95 37 32 31
83 79 94 24 02	56 62 33 44 42	34 99 44 13 74	70 07 11 47 36	09 95 81 80 65
32 96 00 74 05	36 40 98 32 32	99 38 54 16 00	11 13 30 75 86	15 91 70 62 53
19 32 25 38 45	57 62 05 26 06	66 49 76 86 46	78 13 86 65 59	19 64 09 94 13
11 22 09 47 47	07 39 93 74 08	48 50 92 39 29	27 48 24 54 76	85 24 43 51 59
31 75 15 72 60	68 98 00 53 39	15 47 04 83 55	88 65 12 25 96	03 15 21 92 21
88 49 29 93 82	14 45 40 45 04	20 09 49 89 77	74 84 39 34 13	22 10 97 85 08
30 93 44 77 44	07 48 18 38 28	73 78 80 65 33	28 59 72 04 05	94 20 52 03 80
22 88 84 88 93	27 49 99 87 48	60 53 04 51 28	74 02 28 46 17	82 03 71 02 68
78 21 21 69 93	35 90 29 13 86	44 37 21 54 86	65 74 11 40 14	87 48 13 72 20

Table B. Random Numbers (*Continued*)

```
41 84 98 45 47    46 85 05 23 26    34 67 75 83 00    74 91 06 43 45    19 32 58 15 49
46 35 23 30 49    69 24 89 34 60    45 30 50 75 21    61 31 83 18 55    14 41 37 09 51
11 08 79 62 94    14 01 33 17 92    59 74 76 72 77    76 50 33 45 13    39 66 37 75 44
52 70 10 83 37    56 30 38 73 15    16 52 06 96 76    11 65 49 98 93    02 18 16 81 61
57 27 53 68 98    81 30 44 85 85    68 65 22 73 76    92 85 25 58 66    88 44 80 35 84

20 85 77 31 56    70 28 42 43 26    79 37 59 52 20    01 15 96 32 67    10 62 24 83 91
15 63 38 49 24    90 41 59 36 14    33 52 12 66 65    55 82 34 76 41    86 22 53 17 04
92 69 44 82 97    39 90 40 21 15    59 58 94 90 67    66 82 14 15 75    49 76 70 40 37
77 61 31 90 19    88 15 20 00 80    20 55 49 14 09    96 27 74 82 57    50 81 69 76 16
38 68 83 24 86    45 13 46 35 45    59 40 47 20 59    43 94 75 16 80    43 85 25 96 93

25 16 30 18 89    70 01 41 50 21    41 29 06 73 12    71 85 71 59 57    68 97 11 14 03
65 25 10 76 29    37 23 93 32 95    05 87 00 11 19    92 78 42 63 40    18 47 76 56 22
36 81 54 36 25    18 63 73 75 09    82 44 49 90 05    04 92 17 37 01    14 70 79 39 97
64 39 71 16 92    05 32 78 21 62    20 24 78 17 59    45 19 72 53 32    83 74 52 25 67
04 51 52 56 24    95 09 66 79 46    48 46 08 55 58    15 19 11 87 82    16 93 03 33 61

83 76 16 08 73    43 25 38 41 45    60 83 32 59 83    01 29 14 13 49    20 36 80 71 26
14 38 70 63 45    80 85 40 92 79    43 52 90 63 18    38 38 47 47 61    41 19 63 74 80
51 32 19 22 46    80 08 87 70 74    88 72 25 67 36    66 16 44 94 31    66 91 93 16 78
72 47 20 00 08    80 89 01 80 02    94 81 33 19 00    54 15 58 34 36    35 35 25 41 31
05 46 65 53 06    93 12 81 84 64    74 45 79 05 61    72 84 81 18 34    79 98 26 84 16

39 52 87 24 84    82 47 42 55 93    48 54 53 52 47    18 61 91 36 74    18 61 11 92 41
81 61 61 87 11    53 34 24 42 76    75 12 21 17 24    74 62 77 37 07    58 31 91 59 97
07 58 61 61 20    82 64 12 28 20    92 90 41 31 41    32 39 21 97 63    61 19 96 79 40
90 76 70 42 35    13 57 41 72 00    69 90 26 37 42    78 46 42 25 01    18 62 79 08 72
40 18 82 81 93    29 59 38 86 27    94 97 21 15 98    62 09 53 67 87    00 44 15 89 97

34 41 48 21 57    86 88 75 50 87    19 15 20 00 23    12 30 28 07 83    32 62 46 86 91
63 43 97 53 63    44 98 91 68 22    36 02 40 09 67    76 37 84 16 05    65 96 17 34 88
67 04 90 90 70    93 39 94 55 47    94 45 87 42 84    05 04 14 98 07    20 28 83 40 60
79 49 50 41 46    52 16 29 02 86    54 15 83 42 43    46 97 83 54 82    59 36 29 59 38
91 70 43 05 52    04 73 72 10 31    75 05 19 30 29    47 66 56 43 82    99 78 29 34 78
```